RANDY STERTMEYER

Chrome Plated Years

First published by ImPress Self-Publishing Services 2020

First edition

ISBN: 978-1-945493-41-6

Cover art by Daniel Traynor

This book was professionally typeset on Reedsy.
Find out more at reedsy.com

In Memory of

Harold Herbert Henry Joseph Stertmeyer,

Paula Charlotta Theobald Stertmeyer

Winifred Susan Theobald Sutton

and

Lois Joyce Theobald Anderson

For

Scott

Allison

Tori

Tayler

Ashley

McKenzie

Ella

Maddie

Ian

Brandon

Danielle

...and

especially **Xavier**

and

Those Yet to Come

Esse Quam Videri

(To be, rather than to seem to be)

The William Woodward High Scholl Motto

Introduction

This whole process began on cocktail napkins and borrowed sheets of paper in bars and restaurants more than thirty years ago, as I traveled North America and Europe on business. Part modern-day Willie Loman (sad, but determined) with, maybe, a hint of Gordon Gecko (sadly ego-driven), a smidge of Ricky Roma (fun loving) and a jigger of Jerry McGuire (human) thrown in, I spent most of that time pitching building materials from insulation, to roofing, to Italian ceramic tile and natural stone, and finally to hardwood flooring. Sounds boring, I know. But it wasn't.

The process of this largely unchosen career proved fortuitous, fortunate, flukish and even serendipitous, as I often found myself alone at wonderful places like Gallagher's or the Monkey Bar in New York, or at the Cape Cod Room in Chicago and sometimes at the iconic Polo Lounge at the Beverly Hills Hotel in LA. No complaints, with venues like that at my disposal. And each of those, like so many others I enjoyed, were great spots to people-watch and find inspiration for detailing my own stories. Fairly quickly, the cocktail napkins were replaced by a long line of journals. And the more notes I registered in these little leather-bound beauties, the more I realized that the best route for me was to speak specifically to the joy and the strife I had experienced growing up. It also became clear that this was best done in a series of short stories rather than trying to write a novel or a personal and mundane piece of non-fiction.

The operative words in the sub-title I have chosen are "Almost True." While each story is based upon a real, actual event in my life, a few names have been changed to protect both the innocent as well as the guilty. And, while I have been blessed (and sometimes cursed) with an exceptional memory, we all know that events and their details begin to blur very quickly. So, yes, I have filled in the color to the point that I can fairly call these stories "Personal Historical Fiction."

I should also note that this is not my attempt to become another Bill Bryson or Bill Geist. Rather, it is to leave behind something for my children, grandchildren and generations of my family not yet born. We all get a short period of time in which to exist. It is fascinating how little we know about our own ancestors. My goal is to leave to my future generations a bit more than was left to me. There are many people who willingly or unwillingly contributed to my effort. Memories of special family members must be acknowledged to include my Mother and Father, Paula and Harold Stertmeyer, my two Aunts, Winifred Sutton and Lois Anderson, my cousins Paul and Rick Anderson, and my third cousin Jay Pittroff, who was my good pal in the 1940s and early 1950s. So many friends have inspired the tales I tell here. Many will recognize themselves by name, others, maybe by innuendo. Those who must be thanked are first and foremost my two *brothers from other mothers* (a saying that gets worn out today, but is true of these two) Fred Zigler and the late Sandy Schwartz. Thanks also to Neil van Outer, Chris Gobble, Billy Tate, Ed Wikas, Walt Bohl, Carl Schiele, Mike Cohen, Jerry Ivins, Jim Cloughessy and Pat Boyd.

And a tip of the old chapeau to two men that helped to guide me when I most needed guidance, Bob Von Holle and Walter "Bip" Bohl.

I must make a note of gratitude to my old *Woodward High School Tall Tales and Blasts from the Past Lunch Group* who keeps the memories alive and well, each time we share a Skyline chili. Special appreciation goes out to Stuart Hodesh, the Chairman of the Board of that group, for keeping it going over so many years.

Sincere, thanks to my friend, neighbor and a former English teacher, Barb Filipiak, for her proofing and editing skills. Of course, I must acknowledge the incredible filial piety shown to me by my children Allison and Scott. There is no greater gift.

And the ultimate thanks to my cheerleader and proficient proofreader;

my wife Peggy. She has endured so much with such grace. She is the real hero in our family.

I have dug very deeply. The process of excavation has taken many joyful hours... years actually. While these are my novellistes, I say merci beaucoup to so many for being part of my story.

As T.S. Elliot wrote in his poem "Little Gidding":

We shall not cease from exploration, and the end of all our exploring will be to arrive where we started and know the place for the first time.

Rainbow Connection

Why are there so many songs about rainbows?
And what's on the other side?
...What's so amazing?
That keeps us star gazing?
And what do we think we might see?
...All of us under its spell,
We know that it's probably magic.
Someday we'll find it,
The rainbow connection,
The lovers, the dreamers and me.

From *Rainbow Connection*
By Kenny Asher and Paul Williams

Magical Time

I truly entered the world at a magical moment. At least it was magical if you were born as I – a healthy male, Caucasian, middle-class, Midwestern American.

The year 1942 fell into a short period that has never had a true generational designation… well we have been called the *Silent Generation* (whatever the hell that means). But, the group before us was the *Depression Generation,* later to be called the *Greatest Generation* by Tom Brokaw. And a mere four years after I was born came the *Baby Boom Generation.* But, what of us who showed up between the mid 1930s and 1946? Maybe we should be known as the *Just-Before Generation.* After all, a large majority of us were conceived *just before* our fathers went off to war.

I firmly believe that if you were to pick a time to appear on the scene, it is hard to imagine choosing a better moment than what fate dealt me. My good fortune to grow up at the time I did was the pot of gold at the end of the rainbow.

So, what exactly was the significance of this award-winning date? From both a personal and historic perspective I would offer the following facts about December 10, 1942.

It was one year and three days after the Japanese attack on Pearl Harbor and sixty-one years before our second *Baby-Boomer* President sent American troops into Iraq over something that did not exist.

It was four days after my father's thirty-third birthday, twenty-seven years before my first child was born and fifty-two years before my first grandchild entered a much different world. And, it was a single day after football great, Dick Butkus was born, and four years to the day, before the passing of the great American storyteller Damon Runyon.

It was seventy-eight years after the *Emancipation Proclamation*, twelve years before *Brown vs. the Board of Education* and almost a full 66 years before Barrack Obama was elected as the 44th President of the United States. Also, of real significance, it was 73 years after the Cincinnati Red Stockings became the first professional baseball team and five years before Jackie Robinson broke the *color barrier* to become the first African-American major league baseball player.

The year of my birth came 38 years after the birth of the Ford Motor Company and 58 years before Japan became the world's largest producer of automobiles. It was 39 years after the Wright Brothers of Dayton, Ohio broke the chains of gravity with the first powered flight at Kitty Hawk, North Carolina. It was 5 years before Chuck Yeager, in the X-1, broke the sound barrier and 27 years before Apollo 11 broke the *surly bonds of earth* on its way to the first moon landing.

The day I was born was 36 years to the day from when Theodore Roosevelt became the first American to be awarded the Nobel Peace Prize and five years to the day after my great-grandfather and former Roosevelt Rough Rider, Jake Loewenstine, passed away. Martin Luther King was awarded the Nobel Peace Prize on my 22nd birthday.

1942 was exactly 100 years after New York City began public streetcar service and 9 years before the city of Cincinnati retired their public streetcars in favor of buses.

It was only 46 years after a young Italian named Guglielmo Marconi secured the first patent in radiotelegraphy and exactly 20 years after David Sarnoff and his Radio Corporation of America (RCA) introduced the first Radiola console that sold for $75 each. Shortly after, Cincinnatian, Powell Crosley was advertising his Ace Type 3C Consolette, proving radio was no longer an experiment, but, rather, an electronic wonder transmitting news, music and entertainment into the homes of America.

And only 4 years after my birth the first experimental broadcast was transmitted by W8XCT in Cincinnati on something called television. Less than two years later on February 9, 1948, WLW-TV channel 4, became the first commercial television station in Cincinnati. Twenty months later a small 13" screen Philco showed up at our house.

I was born 150 years after the New York Stock Exchange was founded under a tree on what is now Wall Street and thirteen years after the famous Stock Market Crash that led to the Great Depression.

You would have to go back twelve centuries to the Tang dynasty in China to find the invention of gun powder, but it was only a short three years after my birth that Harry Truman deemed it necessary to drop the first atom bomb on Japan. The League of Nations was founded 22 years before and the United Nations three years after I debuted. On my sixth birthday the United Nations adopted its Universal Declaration on Human Rights (sixteen years before the United States passed our first Civil Rights Bill).

Thirty years before I came on the scene Roald Amundsen and his expedition just beat Robert F. Scott, to become the first humans to set foot at the South Pole (Scott perished on the return trip) and it was nine years after my birth that Sir Edmund Hillary became the first to scale Mt Everest.

As to the year of 1942 – well there was a war going on. Thanks to the war, New Year's Day saw the Rose Bowl moved to Duke Stadium in North Carolina due to the enforced curtailment of public gatherings on the west coast. Also, in January, Nazi officials held the Wannsee Conference in Berlin at which Adolf Eichmann was given responsibility for the *Final Solution* that called for the extermination of all Jews. And on the 17th day of 1942, "The Greatest" Mohammad Ali, or Casius Clay as he was originally named, was born just 100 miles south of Cincinnati, in Louisville, Kentucky.

Elmer's Tune by the Glenn Miller Orchestra topped the charts as the year began. Miller continued to dominate later in the year with *A String of Pearls* and *Moonlight Cocktail* while winning the first ever Gold Record *for Chattanooga Choo Choo.*

President Roosevelt ordered General MacArthur to leave the Bataan Peninsula leading MacArthur to proclaim, "I shall return!" In March the

Stage Door Canteen opened in New York as a club for servicemen.

RCA introduced the push-button Victrola that combined a radio with a retractable record turntable that accommodated eight 78 RPM records. My Aunt Lois was one of their first customers. In May the song everyone was singing was *Tangerine* as recorded by Helen O'Conner, Bob Eberly and the Tommy Dorsey Orchestra.

In the Pacific theater significant battles were fought in the Coral Sea, at Midway and later at Guadalcanal, helping to turn the tide of the war in the favor of the U.S.

On Broadway the Rodgers and Hammerstein musical *Oklahoma* opened while in movie theaters the big hits of the year included *Yankee Doodle Dandy, Mrs. Minerva, The Pride of the Yankees (the Lou Gehrig Story), Wake Island, For Me and My Gal, Now Voyager, Gentleman Jim,* and, of course, *Casablanca.*

And in the movie *Holiday Inn* Bing Crosby sat down at a baby grand piano by a warm, crackling fireplace and said to Marjorie Reynolds, "I wrote special music for each of the holidays, and this sort of gives me the chance to keep a little promise I made to myself. This is the song I was going to sing at the Inn tonight."

With that, he sang a little ditty that would change the sound of Christmas forever. Innocently and unceremoniously, the Irving Berlin masterpiece, *White Christmas* was born. Another, if less significant, Christmas classic, *Happy Holidays,* was also written for the movie.

Bursting onto the national scene for the first time were a skinny kid from Hoboken, New Jersey named Frank Sinatra with his first hit, *Night and Day,* and a new cartoon hero named "Mighty Mouse".

Sadly, in Boston, a fire at the famous Cocoanut Grove Supper Club claimed 492 lives. On a positive note, at Rutgers University streptomycin was isolated leading to a cure for tuberculosis. At a modified squash court at the University of Chicago Enrico Fermi and his team achieved the first controlled self-containing nuclear reaction within the top secret "Manhattan Project".

In sports Byron Nelson defeated Ben Hogan in an 18-hole play-off to claim the Masters Golf Tournament. First prize was worth $1,500. In horseracing a chestnut colt named "Shut Out" with Cincinnatian Eddie Arcaro aboard, won the Kentucky derby, while "Alsab" took the Preakness Stakes. "Shut Out" came back to win the Belmont Stakes. The Indianapolis 500 race was cancelled due to rationing restrictions. The St. Louis Cardinals won the World Series, Sugar Ray Robinson won his 34th straight prizefight, and in the 10th NFL Championship game the Washington Redskins upset the Chicago Bears 14-6.

As to the cost of things in 1942, a stamp for a first-class letter cost 3 cents, a loaf of bread cost 9 cents and new Ford automobile had a sticker price of $850. The average price of a new home stood at $3,825.

As war raged around the world, in the United States life went on, if not as usual, still not so bad. By the end of the War more than 56 million people had died. Of that total only a half million Americans lost their lives almost all of whom were military personnel. A terrible toll to be sure, but it pales in comparison to the loss in the USSR, for example, where 13,600,000 soldiers and 7,700,000 civilians died. Americans pulled together like never before and great sacrifices were made. Yet, not for a moment did the hopes and dreams of most Americans falter.

And, I would be totally remiss, as I wax sentimental about my good fortune, not to point out that the United States, the beacon of freedom for the rest of the world, was riddled with prejudices that deprived African Americans, women, Japanese Americans, Native Americans and many other groups, of the benefits I would enjoy over the next twenty years. More than seventy-five years after the Civil War the level of hatred and prejudice toward African-American citizens, in particular, ran deep in the American psyche.

Prejudice was still legislated in the Deep South and more than implied in the rest of the country. The proper designation of "Negro" at the time was, more often than not, replaced with the word "nigger". I am ashamed to admit that in my early years this term was uttered, though infrequently, from time to time, in my own home.

It was not unusual to hear the words *Jap, Kraut, Mick, Guiney, Wop,*

Kike, Boot-head and Red Skin, bandied about by educated and otherwise sophisticated members of the *Greatest Generation.* And there was a plethora of terms supporting the fact that women were second-class citizens. Most of the bars in Cincinnati had a Lady's entrance, indicating that women were not welcome up front at the bar, but only in the back room where less serious frolicking occurred.

Yet, in 1942, the true promise of the American dream certainly did exist; just much more so for a white boy like me.

I once heard it said that the stories we tell become our new reality. And, I suppose, to a large extent, this is true. My journey through the 40's, 50's and into the 60's is something I look back on now with gratitude and fondness. For me it surly was a magical time. These stories are a humble attempt to capture the reality of those years.

... And, as F. Scott Fitzgerald once said, "What people are ashamed of usually makes a good story.

1942

Wait a minute!
What if he is a girl?
What would I do with her?

From *Soliloquy from Carrousel*
By Richard Rodgers and Oscar Hammerstein II

A GIRL?

I believe that it is fair to say that Paula Charlotta Theobald Stertmeyer and I did not get off to a good start.

You see, according to her doctor and his simple mathematical equation, I was scheduled to exit her womb on Thanksgiving Day, 1942. And, although years later I would be referred to as a *turkey* many times, the only thing that appeared on the last Thursday of November 1942 was the more traditional version. This was fine with my father, Harold Herbert Henry Joseph Stertmeyer, whose personal target date was his birthday, December 6th. I was a no-show that day also.

On Monday the 7th day of December, the first anniversary of the bombing of Pearl Harbor, I remained reluctant to vacate the warmth and security my mother had provided now for more than nine months. Inducing labor was not a popular option in 1942. So poor Paula Stertmeyer, who once believed she could endure anything to have a baby girl, was becoming impatient.

Finally, two weeks to the day after I was billed to debut, I knocked on the door marked *exit*. This first labor pain occurred around 4:30 AM in the small bedroom of the Stertmeyers' rented walk-up apartment at 425 E. 5th Street in Newport, Kentucky. It was just a twinge, but it was enough to awaken Paula, and she knew I was announcing my readiness to enter the world. One thing was certain in her mind. Her baby girl would not be born in Kentucky. She and Harold would be heading *across the river* to Cincinnati, or as my Aunt Win liked to say, *back to civilization* (the Civil War had been over less than eighty years).

The next little shot of pain did not occur until almost 5:00 AM. By that time, she had packed her *grip* while hurriedly prodding Harold Herbert Henry Joseph into one of his banker suits. Over the next hour, they would make the trek to her parents' home in the Walnut Hills suburb of Cincinnati. Bundled against the December chill, they walked two blocks to the bus stop on Washington Avenue and caught the Green Line bus that crossed the Central Bridge over the grey Ohio River and deposited them at the Dixie Terminal Building in downtown Cincinnati. They then walked a block north to Government Square, where they boarded the number 7 streetcar that would eventually drop them in front of Dow Drugs near the corner of Hewitt and Woodburn Avenues. The marquee on the Ritz Theater across the street from the car-stop listed a double-feature of *Rings on Her Fingers* with Gene Tierney and *Captains of the Clouds*, staring James Cagney in some new thing called *Technicolor*.

They stepped down from the streetcar and walked the final two-and-one-half blocks that placed them at the door of my soon-to-be grandparents, Lou and Cosey Theobald. Paula's two sisters Winifred and Lois along with their husbands also lived in the tiny two-story house.

As the Stertmeyers entered the house where Paula and her two sisters had been raised, her forth and most substantial labor pain struck. Within seconds the whole family was engulfed in a flurry of excitement and concern. Gathered around the kitchen table with Harold and Paula were the fore-mentioned Lou, Cosey, and Winifred as well as her husband Bill Sutton. Having been aroused by all of the fuss, the baby of the family, Lois and her husband Private First-Class Joe Anderson emerged from their bedroom behind the upstairs kitchen. The newlyweds forced their way into what space remained around the porcelain topped table.

Winnie struck a Cat's Eye wooden match against the edge of the matchbox hanging over the gas range igniting the front right burner. Cosey placed the coffee pot over the fire. With the gurgle of percolating coffee in the background they began to strategize. Cosey being the only person seated at the planning table with any real practical experience in such matters took charge.

"How far apart are the pains?" she asked.

"She's only had four," Harold said. Then seeing his wife take in a large gulp of air without exhaling, changed his answer. "Make that five," he corrected.

"When did they start?" Cosey inquired.

Now able to speak, Paula replied, "About 4:30."

Well, this is your first baby. As I've told you all along, it's going to take a while."

Paula digested this fact and began to wonder if this baby thing was such a good idea. She was two months past her thirty-fifth birthday. She and Harold had been *trying* for over five years when they learned that I had been conceived. She had been ecstatic with the good news. Now the thrill of the upcoming event was rapidly turning to fear.

As Bill Sutton poured coffee, pain number six hit with a vengeance. They were not supposed to be so severe so soon.

"Should we go to the hospital?" Harold asked.

"No, no, not yet," said Cosey. "It's almost seven. I guess it would be OK to run down the street and asked Doctor Gillespie to come up for a look."

Fortunately, although Dr. Gillespie's office was more than five miles away at 2367 Auburn Ave., he lived just around the corner on Hewitt Ave.

Bill, not thrilled with all of the commotion, promoted himself from coffee pourer to doctor retriever. He bolted to the closet, threw on his overcoat, collar upturned, and his new navy-blue Royal Stetson fedora hat with the brim pulled down over his left eye, and headed for the side door. This brought a smile to the face of everyone but the mother-to-be.

It was decided that Harold should go on to work at the bank. Bethesda Hospital was only a five-minute streetcar ride up the hill from town. They would call him when the doctor said it was time.

As he wrapped his gray silk muffler around his neck he said, "We still haven't decided on a boy's name."

"We don't need one," snapped Paula. "Her name is going to be Sandra and that's that. You can just go ahead and get some of those *It's-a- Girl* cigars."

Harold shrugged as he kissed his wife on the cheek. "Call me when you head to the hospital," he said.

As he opened the door, he discovered a light snow had begun to fall. As he waded through some of the lingering fallen autumn leaves on the Spokane Avenue sidewalk, he saw Bill Sutton and Doctor William Gillespie headed toward him.

"Where are you headed?" queried the doctor. "No stomach for labor pains?"

"No, they chased me out," Harold responded. "Mom Theobald said it would be a while."

"Well, she's probably right," said the doctor. "They tell me, I'm supposed to deliver a girl."

"There's an extra sawbuck in it for you if you can sneak a boy passed her," Harold joked.

"If I was able to do that, it would be worth more than ten dollars. I'm afraid you'll have to settle on whatever fate has in store."

"A healthy mother and baby will suit us all just fine," Harold said. "I guess I'll see ya both at Bethesda Hospital. Do good work Doc."

"I always do," Gillespie cracked.

With that Harold was off to work. He sat on the streetcar reflecting on how his life was about to change. Bringing a child into a world immersed in war and economic woes had caused him some worries. He still was awaiting word from the Merchant Marines regarding his application for Officer's Training School. Having been rejected by the Army and Navy because of his age, he was one of the few able-bodied men still working at the bank. His last hope to serve rested with the Merchant Marines.

An elderly man reached over him to pull the cord that signaled the streetcar operator that he wanted to get off at the next stop, bringing Harold back to reality. He noticed that he was just two stops from Government Square, where he would get off. The snow was now falling much harder.

From the day Paula had told him she was expecting their first child, he was filled with the certainty that it would be a boy. This was not something his wife cared to discuss, so he had kept this feeling to himself.

For Christ sakes, he thought, we don't even have a boy's name picked out. As he passed the Franklin Book Store on Fifth Street he gazed in the window, his eyes drawn to a thick book titled *Lee, Grant & Sherman,* by Alfred H. Burne. Having grown up in Kentucky, Robert E. Lee was one of his real heroes.

Suddenly it hit him. That's it, he thought. We'll name him Lee. When she doesn't get her girl, she won't care what we call him. "Lee Stertmeyer," he softly mumbled to himself.

As he came to the Walnut Street entrance to the Fifth Third Bank, he bolstered his determination by repeating the name over and over, "Lee Stertmeyer."

Across the street from the bank entrance sat the Straus Tobacco Shop with the required wooden Indian poised at the door. Harold gazed at the tobacco store and smiled, wondering *blue for Lee or pink for Sandra? We'll see.*

He then quickly entered the bank where he had worked since the end of his junior year in high school. He had started as a runner, carrying bags of stocks and documents from bank to bank or bank to brokerage house. That was how he got his nickname, *Scratch.* Essentially, as a runner he carried money, or *scratch* as it was known, for the bank. He never returned to school. Fifth Third had survived the Crash of 1929, and Harold was grateful to have the security of a job that had allowed him to grow with only an eleventh-grade education. And it was at the bank where he had met his future wife, Paula Theobald, eight years earlier.

Meanwhile back on Spokane Avenue, Dr. Gillespie was on the case. After the requisite questions and a quick check of Paula's pulse and blood pressure he suggested they do further analysis in the bedroom behind the kitchen.

"Would you mind joining us Cosey?" he asked, establishing the proper etiquette for an examination of that type.

Shortly thereafter, they all exited the small bedroom, Cosey announcing that they were off to the hospital. Dr. Gillespie was confident that it would be a while, but felt Paula would be more comfortable in the delivery area of Bethesda Hospital.

Fortunate that Bill Sutton worked at Gilbert Avenue Pontiac near Peoples Corner, and, therefore, drove the only car in the family, a used 1936 Packard, it was determined that he would drive Paula, Cosey and his wife Winifred to the hospital. The newly married Lois and Joe Anderson would go on to work downtown, he as an Army recruiter and her as a bookkeeper at Brighton Screw Company, manufactures of a wide variety of, guess what - screws. They struck quite a picture of supreme happiness in their respective outfits. Married less than six weeks, they stared incessantly at each other while spouting a considerable amount of romantic gibberish.

The big black Packard arrived at the Reading Road entrance to Bethesda Hospital at 10:15. By then Paula was not faring well. She had lost all enthusiasm for the baby thing and was starting to rethink the marriage thing. Her gentile manner that normally limited her to exclaim things such as *darn, heck* and *son-of-a-gun* was quickly evolving to the earthier proclamation, "*damn*, this hurts like *hell.* How come that *son-of-a-bitch* I'm married to doesn't have to go through this?"

The nurses got Paula dressed in a hospital gown and into a hand-cranked bed. The towel they gave her to bite on when the pains came provided little comfort. Once in bed, her mother Cosey positioned herself in a chair on one side of the bed while her sister Winnie, who had called in sick for the first time ever at her job at Western Union Telegraph, took a spot on the other side of the bed.

For Paula, the next ten hours were filled with increasingly frequent and excruciating labor pains to which she reacted by towel biting, cursing, moaning and screaming. Meanwhile, Harold had spent a fairly routine day in the Coupon Department on the second floor of the bank, where he co-mingled with Cincinnati's affluent and their investments. In contrast with the pure torture his wife was experiencing, Harold calmly whiled the hours with work and the joy of the growing number of his co-workers who had heard the news and had stopped by to wish their buddy Scratch well.

Winnie called him at around two o'clock to advise him that things were moving slowly. Promptly at four-thirty, he grabbed his overcoat, hat, scarf and gloves and headed down the escalator and out the door. The day-long snow had accumulated significantly. Normally he would have been quite upset that he did not have his goulashes, but not on this day. No, he was finally about to become a father. On his way to the streetcar stop he whistled a medley of his favorite current hits from one of his favorite radio shows, *Your Hit Parade.*

When he got to the hospital, he took over for his sister-in-law on the right side of the bed to discover his wife had turned into a monster. "You did this to me," she screamed at him.

"Calm down," he urged.

"Don't tell me to calm down! I'm the one who's dying, not you."

Her mother patted her hand saying, "You're not dying sweetheart. It will be over soon and you'll have a beautiful little baby."

Finally, at a little before nine o'clock the doctor gave her a shot to help a bit with the pain. This allowed her to execute better. By ten o'clock they were telling her that the baby was about ready and wheeled her into the delivery room.

Harold was sent off to the Father's waiting room while everyone else was relegated to the hospital lobby to wait. Harold found a copy of the December 1st issue of *Look Magazine,* the cover displaying *Servicemen's Follies – "soldiers, sailors, marines at the Stage Door Canteen"*. Next to the *LOOK* banner it read: *"What I Learned About the Nazis from Stalin by Wendell Willkie".* He flipped through the pages of the magazine laughing at a cartoon by Carl Rose, reading a short poem by Ogden Nash, then on to a movie review of Road to Morocco with Bob Hope, Bing Crosby and Dorothy Lamour, which included several photos of the production. When he got to the back page showing a Chesterfield Cigarette ad with a colorful illustration of Santa delivering cigarettes, he gave up distractions and began to rehearse his speech about naming his little boy.

Unknown to him, I had finally decided to cooperate with my mother. At ten-twelve that night I took my first peek out of the secure cocoon that had been my only home. Once I took that first glance the rest happened quickly.

At ten thirty-five Doctor Gillespie still in his delivery outfit, mask hanging from his ears covering his chin, walked into the Father's Waiting Room with a smile running from ear strap to ear strap. He extended his hand and asked "Were you serious about that sawbuck?"

Harold thought for a second and then it clicked as he started to pump the doctor's hand. "Really?" he asked. "It's a boy?"

"That he is, and you owe me," Gillespie laughed. "He is eight pounds seven ounces and just under twenty-one inches. I wouldn't be surprised to see him playing quarterback at Kentucky in twenty years or so," he speculated.

"Would you like to see him?"

"Well, I'll be a son-of-a-buck, hell yes," Harold exclaimed.

After staring at me for several minutes through the window of the nursery, Harold was escorted to his wife's room.

"He's beautiful," she said. "But I wanted a girl so badly. And I don't think I can do this again. Well we can't call him Sandra and I don't want to call him Sandy. Maybe Randy? How about Randall? We could call him Randy. I like that don't you?"

Harold swallowed hard and said, "I was thinking maybe Lee would be a good name."

"No, I like Randall. We'll call him Randy," she insisted.

Harold looked into his wife's eyes seeing both her disappointment and that familiar determination.

"How about Randall Lee, then?" he asked. "I would like to name him for Robert E. Lee."

"I swear Harold, you and your Civil War heroes. Well, I guess I like that OK. So, that's it then. Our baby will be known as Randall Lee Stertmeyer. Yes, that sounds good to me."

"Randy," she murmured.

"Randy," he repeated bending over to kiss his wife's forehead.

"Well, get some rest," he said. "I'll go tell everybody about Randall Lee."

As it turned out everybody liked the selected name.

"When can we see him?" Lois asked.

"Not until we bring him home," Harold answered repeating what he had been told by Dr. Gillespie. "Only the father is allowed in the nursery. They will keep him and Paula here for four or five days."

Everyone was exhausted. All but the new father piled into the Packard. He had to wait twenty minutes for a streetcar to take him downtown. Yet he was oblivious to the cold and snow as December 10th turned into December 11th.

When he got off the streetcar at Government Square, he realized that the last bus across the river to Newport had long departed. Well, he thought, it won't be the first time I've walked the mile and a half across the Central Bridge to get home. As he headed south on Walnut Street the snow was blowing sideways from his right.

His chosen route took him right passes the Straus Tobacco Shop. He pressed his nose to the glass window looking at metal pop-up signs for Old Gold and Lucky Strike cigarettes alongside a dozen or more pipes and a handful of lighters.

As he stood there, he heard his wife's determined words, "You can just go ahead and get some of those *It's-a- Girl* cigars."

"I'll be back in the morning," he said to his image in the glass.

"And, I'll be needing a couple of boxes of the ones with the ***blue*** labels," he shouted in the air.

With that he began to whistle the University of Kentucky fight song and headed south toward where his day had started.

Lee, Grant & Sherman
by Alfred H. Burne

No Girl for Paula

1943

As days go by,
we're gonna fill our house with happiness.
The moon may cry,
we're gonna smother the blues with tenderness.
When days go by,
there's room for you,
room for me,
for gentle hearts an opportunity.
As days go by,
it's the bigger love of the family.

From As Days Go By (Theme from Family Matters)
By Jesse Frederick, Bennet Salvay and Scott Roeme

The Mishpucha

I first heard the word *Mishpucha* (meesh-puk-**khah**) from my new friend, Sandy Schwartz, a couple of months after we started junior high school at the new Woodward High School in the fall of 1954. I heard it again from my other friend Freddie Zigler not long after. And I learned from Freddie that this Yiddish word meant "family."

I loved the word immediately. Perhaps, I enjoyed saying *Mishpucha,* because you could not pronounce it correctly without spitting, like many Yiddish words. So, you always literally *spit it out.* And, therefore, I could not say it or hear it without a smile or a laugh. That's still true today.

So, as it were, I had a fairly large mischpucha scattered around Cincinnati and Northern Kentucky.

Not being a believer in divine intervention, I would submit that the time and place one is born is a matter of good or bad fortune. I would further suggest that the family environment into which fate deposits you is more important yet.

There is no such thing as the perfect family (with the possible exception of the 1950s television clan of Ozzie, Harriet, David and Ricky Nelson), but I was rewarded with a pretty damned good one. They checked many important boxes, like solid morals, hardworking, intelligent, complex, and yet, sufficiently imperfect.

It would be fair to say that I came from a predominately German heritage. Most, on my Mother's side, were also Jewish. The Germans would say *familie.* I liked the sound of *mischpucha* better. And without realizing it at the time, it was very likely that some of my *familie* in Germany were sending some of my *mischpucha* off to concentration camps.

With Hitler waging war all over the world when I was born, one might expect that the reaction in the United States toward German Americans would have been similar to that deployed against Japanese Americans.

And, to be sure, there was some push back toward citizens of German background. In places like Crystal City, Kenedy and Seagoville in Texas as well as Camp Blanding, Florida, Stringtown, Oklahoma, Fort Lincoln, North Dakota and Camp Forest, Tennessee, many German nationals were interned. But, with almost twenty percent of the US population being of German heritage, it wasn't likely that that number were headed to a containment camp.

So, while the internment of Japanese Americans during the war is considered historic, the small number of German citizens treated to a similar action is a mere footnote.

As stated, most of my relatives on my mother's side of the family were of the Jewish persuasion while my father's clan were Catholic and Lutheran. A recent DNA exploration indicates that there is a smattering of English and Scottish cousins scattered around somewhere. But who those may be, I could not say?

So, in keeping with the mores of the time in which I was born, let's go with the *ladies first* approach, starting with my mother's side of the family.

My mother, Paula Charlotta Theobald and her two sisters, Winifred Janet and Lois Joyce, were the children of Cosey Loewenstine Theobald and Louis Conrad Theobald. My mother was the oldest, born on October 24, 1907. My Aunt Win arrived sixteen months later on February 1, 1909. Aunt Lois, the baby of the sisters, who was what you might call a *whoops* addition, a little surprise package, was born on October 25, 1923, a day after my mother's sixteenth birthday. Thus, she was given the nickname "Babe."

Both Paula and Winifred were musical prodigies, the former on the piano and the latter on the violin. I suspect that my grandmother, Cosey, pushed them both a little too hard. Aunt Win put her violin in its leather case in her late teens and never drew a bow across the strings again.

My mother stuck with the piano longer, studying at the prestigious Cincinnati Conservatory of Music. She once played with the Cincinnati Symphony and became a piano teacher as a young adult. She was still giving lessons when I was a young boy, and there were some great parties in our living room where she would pull out sheet music of popular songs of the day from within the piano bench and lead great sing-a-longs around her Wurlitzer Baby Grand aided by a bathtub full of beer.

My mother too stopped cold turkey when I was around twelve years old, and the rich black mahogany veneer instrument became nothing more than an imposing piece of furniture, with the exception of the times I taught myself enough cords to bang out some simple little tunes. She tried twice to give me lessons when I was quite young. We both agreed that I was better served honing my skills with a ball and bat.

This decision paid her a small dividend during my last two years of college when I was awarded a modest grant-and-aid to play baseball for the Miami University Redskins in Oxford Ohio. Being both German and Jewish, my mother was a bit tight with the coins and most grateful for the financial help.

Of course, my mother's two sisters provided an important branch to my family tree. My Aunt Lois Joyce Theobald married West Virginia GI Joseph Anderson on Halloween night in 1942. That marriage begot my cousins Paul Merrick Anderson (October 19, 1948) and Richard (Rick) Louis Anderson (January 28, 1954). Paul and his wife Mary Lee begot Mike and Jon, while Rick and his wife Terry begot Michelle and Eric. And the begotting continued beyond that generation with six more cousins several times removed.

My Aunt Win married William "Bill" Sutton in 1933. Uncle Bill was both handsome and interesting. He played piano by ear with pieces of the fingers on his left hand missing, thanks to a mishap at Gilbert Avenue Pontiac where he worked as an auto mechanic. He was a man's man, which included chain smoking and some serious "chain" drinking as well.

As off-springs go, this union begot absolutely nothing. But it did provide enough misery that Aunt Win threw Wild Bill out for good on December

3, 1953, the day she moved from the old family home in Walnut Hills to a newer, more modern two-story house in Bond Hill. She turned over a couple of new leaves that day.

The gin, scotch and beer got the better of Uncle Bill's liver in 1957. To her credit, Aunt Win is now buried next to him at the Theobald and Loewenstine family plot at Rest Haven Cemetery.

I never got to consciously create any memories of my Grandmother Cosey as she succumbed to cancer when I was eleven months old, but I am told her greatest solace in her last months was rocking me in her wicker rocking chair. Her three girls viewed her as a saint.

Cosey was the second oldest child of Jacob and Jeanette "Jenny" Keyser Loewenstine. She was born on November 26, 1886 and passed away on November 3, 1943. She is also buried at Rest Haven Cemetery in Blue Ash Ohio.

Cosey's older brother Montgomery "Monte" Victor Loewenstine, was a highly decorated veteran of the First World War and was actually awarded a medal at the White House by President Herbert Hoover. A photo of that ceremony is part of our family archives in my possession. After the war, he had a long career with the Manischewitz Company, makers of world-famous Matzo products and really lousy wine. He spent the early part of his Matzo schlepping career in Cincinnati and later at their headquarters in Newark New Jersey. The four vacations to New York City that I took with my parents during my youth always included a visit to Jersey City to see Uncle Monte and his wife Aunt Carrie. The ferry ride from Manhattan across the Hudson River to Jersey City was a great highlight.

Uncle Monte and his wife, Aunt Carrie, had two sons, Rolland "Rollie" who was my mother's age, and Harry, who was Aunt Win's age. Rollie had a daughter Caroline who was three years ahead of me at Woodward High School. Sadly, I have lost track of her. Harry was a successful lawyer and lived in the upscale Village of Indian Hill.

Grandma Cosey also had three younger brothers, Clifford Jack, Hal Maurice and George Crawford. Cliff also worked for Manischewitz in Cincinnati. Hal worked as an insurance salesman while George ran the

Hamilton County License Bureau for many years.

Uncle Hal had a tragic event as a young married man when his wife shot their infant daughter and then shot herself. The baby died. His wife survived but was committed to Longview Mental Hospital. Divorce followed shortly after.

Uncle George also married a somewhat mentally lopsided lady named Marge. They had one daughter, Elaine, who was two years older than Aunt Lois. When that marriage dissolved, Elaine temporarily moved across the street on Spokane Avenue in the care of Grandma Cosey and Grandpa Lou.

Elaine married Jack Pittroff, a Clark Gable look-a-like, and had three children, my third cousins, Jay, Perry and Janet. I am still very close to Jay who was born on my mother's birthday a year before I debuted. We were great pals as youngsters and spent a good deal of time killing each other while playing cowboys and Indians or cops and robbers. Jay could really die, especially when taking an imaginary arrow to the chest. All of that glorious nonsense ended when his family moved from Dexter Avenue in Walnut Hills to a small farm in Milford in the early 1950s. Today Jay is retired and living in Columbus Ohio.

Uncle George, soon after his divorce, married a large and happy lady named Dorothy. They remained happily married until Uncle George passed away in 1984. Dorothy had a much younger sister named Shirley, a delightful and pretty thing that became an early role model for my cousin Jay Pittroff and me.

The first wedding I remember going to was in September of 1953, when Shirley married Marine Sargent Ken Eppert, resplendent in his dress blues, at the Walnut Hills Presbyterian Church, with Uncle George giving away the bride.

Ken and Shirley had two boys, Steve, or *Ske* as he was called (Steven Kenneth Eppert) and Douglas. Steve became a very successful businessman. Doug also had great success as a restaurant manager. He has always graciously provided me with a prime window table at the renowned Montgomery Inn Boathouse Restaurant over the past twenty or so years.

Sadly, Shirley passed away at a very young age from complications from childhood rheumatic fever. She would be very proud of the men her two boys became.

As is apparent, family trees are complicated. And the next generation on the Loewenstine side was loaded with kids. My great grandfather, Jacob Henry Loewenstine, who, among other things, was a Rough Rider and fought alongside Teddy Roosevelt in the Spanish American War, had ten siblings.

Jake was the third oldest, born on December 12, 1858. If you're keeping score, you can visit his grave site at the Judah Touro Cemetery in the Price Hill neighborhood of Cincinnati. Should you want to stop by to say hello, go to Section A, Lot 7, Grave 3. You will note that, for whatever reason, his headstone is facing in the wrong direction.

He became an Assistant Police Chief in Cincinnati. Coincidentally, he passed away on December 10, 1937, two days before his 79th birthday, and five years to the day before my birth.

The rest of that generation of Loewenstines were as follows:

Willard A (DOB unknown and passed in 1893)
Charles W (Born in 1856 and passed in 1933)
David C (Born in 1859 and passed in 1934)
Albert M (Born in 1861 and passed in 1939)
Maurice (Born in 1867 and passed in 1949) AKA Morris
Edward Charles (Born in 1870 and passed in 1940)
Blanche (Born in 1872 and passed in 1945)
George W (Born in 1874 and passed in 1897)
Sanford (Born in 1874 and passed in 1910)
Diane (Born in 1882 and passed in 1924) - Married name Fix

I would offer just a couple of notations on that bunch. First, it is clear that their mother, Theresa Loewenstine, was a busy lady over a twenty-five-year period. Second, my mother's Uncle George, born in 1900 was named for his Uncle George, who died at the young age of 23. This was in keeping with the Jewish tradition of naming children only for the deceased, never for the living.

As stated, my great great grandmother, Theresa Loewenstine, was a busy lady, but it served her well as she lived to be 75 years of age. Not bad for the Nineteenth Century. She was born in 1837 and passed in 1912.

The guy keeping Theresa so busy was my great great grandfather, Samuel Benjamin Loewenstine, who was born on March 3, 1831 and passed on April 4, 1909 (the same year my father and Aunt Win were born). Not having to go through the sheer terror and stress of delivering eleven babies, old Gramps Sammy lived to the riper age of 78.

Sam came from a fairly large family as well, being one of five children. His siblings with as much information as I can provide were as follows:

Jacob Henry (DOB unknown and passed in 1915)

Morris R (Born in 1834 and passed in 1880)

Jeannette Loewenstine Schwarzberg (Born in 1837 and passed in 1878)

David C. (Born in 1840 and passed in 1898)

Samuel's father was Moses Loewenstine. His date of birth is unknown, but he passed in 1890. Samuel's mother was Theresa Gross Loewenstine, who shared a first name with Samuel's wife. Again, I can't provide Moses date of birth, but I do know that he passed in 1874. There is no information for Theresa's date of birth either, but she passed away in 1878. They are both buried in the United Jewish Cemetery in the Walnut Hills suburb of Cincinnati at the corner of Montgomery Road and Huron Street. Our home on Spokane Avenue provided a clear view of that cemetery from our second-floor dining room window.

I can get back one more generation on Theresa Gross Loewenstine's side of the family. Her father was Jacob Gross, date of birth unknown. He was born in Kirchheimbolande, Germany. Her mother, Henrietta "Yetta" Gross, was also born in Germany, in Rhineland-Pfalz in 1814, and passed in 1881. I have been able to locate her grave marker in the same United

Jewish Cemetery in Walnut Hills.

My great grandfather Jake, may have been named for Jacob Gross. But this would have been a violation of Jewish law, as he was born before his namesake passed away.

One thing of which I am sure is that in a ceremony giving me a Jewish name right after I was born, I was assigned the moniker of *Ruben Jacob*, for my great grandfather Jake. I guess Rubin was as close to Randall as they could get in Judean parlance. As stated already, I was born on the fifth anniversary of his death.

That brings us to the Keyser side of my mother's family. The Keysers had settled originally in Elmira, New York.

My research has turned up considerably less on the Keysers than the Loewenstines, but this is what I do know.

My great grandmother, Jenny Keyser Loewenstine, was born in Elmira, New York on August 6, 1860. She didn't pass away until March 12, 1952. Thus, I was able to get to know her fairly well. She lived out the last years of her life under the care of her three granddaughters, my mother, and my Aunt Win and Aunt Lois. She resided in the front upstairs bedroom of the house in which the three girls were raised at 3315 Spokane Avenue in Walnut Hills. During the War, that modest two story, coal heated structure also housed Aunt Win and Uncle Bill, my grandparents Lou and Cosey Theobald (until my grandmother passed in 1943), my Aunt Lois and Uncle Joe (except when his army duty took him away) and my mother and me while my father was serving in the Merchant Marines, sailing the seven seas and dodging Nazi torpedoes. This was very typical of family life during World War II.

Great grandma Jenny rarely left her small bedroom situated at the top of the stairs directly over the living room. She spent most days swaying to and fro in her wicker rocking chair and reading popular fiction of the day with the help of a large round magnifying glass.

Every once in a while, with the aid of a cane she would slowly make her way to the small second floor kitchen that my grandfather had added over the main kitchen on the first floor. Armed with a soup bone, fresh vegetables and a bit of lard, she would fill the house with the irresistible aroma of her one of a kind soup.

She was a very sweet woman who became my surrogate grandmother after the death of Grandma Cosey in 1943. I would often visit her in her room where I would sit on the floor and listen to her incredible stories of days before cars, planes, radios, televisions, telephones and washing machines.

She even shared with me the tragedy of the assassination of Abraham Lincoln, which occurred a few months before her fifth birthday. She explained to me that word of the Lincoln murder came to her family in Elmira, New York via the local paper, the "Elmira Daily Advertiser."

She also spoke of houses draped in black and a spectacular memorial parade shortly after the assassination. For me, it was a connection to what seemed like real "ancient history."

I am grateful that I carry this vision of Jenny with me, as I have not uncovered much more about that piece of the Mishpucha. I can only go back to her parents, Joseph (DOB 1828 and passed in 1910) and Lena (DOB 1830 and passed in 1912).

I also know there is a close connection between the Keysers of Elmira and my mother's cousin Juanita Levy of New York City. Though she was my fifth cousin I had been instructed to refer to her as Aunt Juanita. On our trips to New York we would always visit her and her husband, attorney Lou Levy, in Manhattan where they lived in the opulent Broadmoor Hotel on the Upper West Side. Their apartment looked over Grant's Tomb and the Henry Hudson Parkway, with a view of the George Washington Bridge in the distance. It had a great Chinese Restaurant off the lobby that my father absolutely loved.

Aunt Juanita also had a very cool job. She was the executive secretary to the President of a toy company with an office across the street from Macy's Department Store. The company picked up the rights to distribute a new simple toy in 1958. It was called the Hula Hoop and was the invention of the Wham-O Toy Company. When my parents took my cousin Paul and me to New York in August of 1958, Aunt Juanita gleefully presented my ten-year-old cousin with a bright blue Hula Hoop. My father was unimpressed, calling it a piece of garden hose stapled end-to-end.

Ungratefully, my father reacted to this so-called gift by stating, "That's the dumbest thing I've ever seen. I'm supposed to haul that back to Cincinnati on the train?"

"You just wait and see," my smiling Aunt Juanita told my father, as my mother was giving him a good kick in the shin.

By Christmas of that year they were producing 50,000 of those little "garden hoses" per day. Touché!!

Let's move now to the Theobald side of my mother's family. This won't take nearly as long.

My grandfather, Louis Conrad Theobald, was born on July 8, 1886 and passed away on May 4, 1953. He died on a sunny Monday, a day I remember well. I was in the fifth grade at Hoffman School. My Uncle Bill met me at the end of the school day. This was quite unusual.

"Randy, I'm sorry to tell you that Grandpa passed away this morning," Uncle Bill said to me placing what was left of his left hand on my head.

I knew older people died. I had witnessed it with my great grandma, Jenny. She was there one day and gone the next, just the year before. But not Grandpa Theobald. He was my pal. The guy who read the funny pages to me. The guy whose lap I sat upon and listened to Waite Hoyte announce Cincinnati Reds games. The guy who let me help him shovel coal into the coal chute. The guy who could fix anything.

I felt a tear start to form in my eye as we drove back to Spokane Avenue in Uncle Bill's old black Packard.

"What happened?" I asked.

"He had a heart attack in his sleep. Aunt Win found him in bed this morning," Uncle Bill explained.

I knew that he had a heart attack twelve years earlier. And he walked a bit bent over with a slight limp. But he always seemed fine to me.

The day before, as always on Sundays at noon, he walked the two blocks up to where Hewitt Avenue dead-ended into Montgomery and Gilbert Roads. He boarded a trolley bus heading north on Montgomery Road through Evanston, Norwood and into Pleasant Ridge where he would exit at Losantiville and Montgomery Roads. From there he would walk the half block to the apartment of his uncle, Fred Hemple (more on him in a minute).

"He seemed fine when he got home last night," Uncle Bill stated. "He went peacefully, thank God."

I clearly remember that Monday. I was quickly taken a few doors up to the Goebbels', where my friend Chris lived. To distract me, Mrs. Goebbel took us the few blocks to Gluecksberg's Drug Store, where Chris and I enjoyed hot fudge sundaes.

My Aunt Lois had left less than a month earlier with my four-year-old cousin Paul, to join my Uncle Joe, who was serving in the Counter Intelligence Corp in Germany with the Army.

That night, we had dinner at Aunt Win's house. My mother sobbed through dinner while my more stoic aunt held things together. I found myself staring at the empty chair in which my grandfather had sat for the first ten and a half years of my life.

On Thursday, Gramps' funeral was held at Weil Funeral Home on Reading Road in North Avondale. I had a hard time keeping my eyes off of my Grandfather's body, lying in the polished oak casket, fully expecting him to wake back up and come home again.

The funeral home was packed, due mostly to the high rank Gramps had in the Masonic Lodge. He had been the President of the Board at the Masonic Orphanage, in Springfield Ohio. The service was short and very touching.

Around 11 AM, we jumped into two long black limousines and followed the Hearst on the trek to Rest Haven Cemetery. Behind us was a long caravan of cars requiring two motorcycle cops to manage the trip through a string of red lights and busy intersections.

With my father, Uncle Bill, Uncle George, Uncle Hal and two of his Masonic brothers acting as pallbearers, his coffin was carried to the site that we had gone to so often to visit the grave of Grandma Cosey.

There were more speeches, and he disappeared into a six-foot deep hole in the ground. With that, this wonderful gentle man left my life.

It is funny how memories string together. Because of my grandfather's passing on May 4, 1953, I am able to tell you that it was a thoroughbred named Dark Star that won the Kentucky Derby two days earlier that year.

Sadly, there isn't much known about Gramps' family due to a tragic accident in 1889. What is known is that his mother, Charlotta Hempel Theobald was killed in a streetcar accident in Covington, Kentucky, her date of death listed as April 30 of that year. I have heard that his father, Louis Conrad Theobald, also died that day, but there is no record of this that I have been able to find.

The marriage details of my great grandparent's union are as follows:

NAME: Charlotta Hempel (My GGM)
GENDER: Female
AGE: 22
BIRTH DATE: 1858
MARRIAGE DATE: 5 Feb 1880
MARRIAGE PLACE: Covington, Kenton, Kentucky, USA
SPOUSE: Louis Theobald
FILM NUMBER: 001943299
HOUSEHOLD MEMBERS:
Charlotta Hempel
Louis Theobald

Her death Certificate provides the following information:

NAME: Charlotte Theobald
BIRTH DATE: 1854 (Does not match the marriage certificate DOB above)
DEATH DATE: 30 Apr 1889
CEMETERY: Highland Cemetery
BURIAL OR CREMATION PLACE:
Fort Mitchell, Kenton County, Kentucky, United States of America

HAS BIO?: Y
SPOUSE: Louis Theobald

The only information I have found for my great grandfather is as follows:

Name: Louis Theobald
Gender: Male
Age: 26 (when he died)
Birth Date: About 1854
Marriage Date: 5 Feb 1880
Marriage Place: Covington, Kenton, Kentucky, USA
Spouse: Charlotta Hempel
Film Number: 001943299

Buried at Highland Cemetery

LOCATION:
2167 Dixie Highway
Fort Mitchell, Kenton County, Kentucky, 41017-2998 USA

As stated, Charlotta's date of birth is uncertain. I have discovered a birth date of 1854 for Charlotte Hempel and one of 1858 for Charlotta Hempel. What I can say with certainty is that my mother was given her middle name in honor of her grandmother. Charlotta and Louis Conrad were married on February 5, 1880 in Covington, Kentucky. The Marriage Certificate list Charlotta's age as 22 and Louis' as 26.

The only other piece of data available would indicate that they were both buried at Highland Cemetery at 2167 Dixie Highway in Fort Mitchell (Kenton County) Kentucky. But when I search the cemetery website, there are no results for either of them using any number of possible name combinations.

I do personally know just one more thing about Charlotta's family. There was a group of cousins who lived in Mattoon, Illinois. When I was very young my Grandfather Lou, my mother, father and I took a short trip to their farm in Mattoon, a full day's drive from Cincinnati on the country back roads of the day. They owned 80 acres upon which they grew corn, soybeans and hay. They sold the hay to a local broom factory that we visited.

It was also the first time I rode a horse and a tractor. While there, we took a drive down to Champagne, Illinois and visited the University of Illinois Football Stadium where I was summarily stung of the nose by a wasp. That day was a bitch. There are several photos in the family archives of that trip.

Unfortunately, I have very little data on the Mattoon crew. The photos from that trip note first names only including Bob, Elsie, Ralph and Stella. I also know that Elsie had three daughters. I do suspect that Charlotta was born in either that area of Illinois or in Covington, Kentucky.

There was also a small wing of the Hempel family in Cincinnati. Grandpa Lou had an Uncle Fred, mentioned earlier. Though he was an uncle, Fred was not much older than my grandfather. Fred's family took Lou Theobald in as a three-year-old, after the streetcar accident and raised him in Covington, Kentucky.

One more family fact of interest is that my grandfather's cousin was Cincinnati amateur golf phenomenon, Joan Hempel Comisar. Joan won several Cincinnati women's amateur golf championships in the 1950's and 1960's.

Joan was born in 1931. Her parents were Eugene D and Mildred E Hempel. I do know that Joan called Fred Hempel *Uncle Fred* and that she knew my grandfather very well.

She was married to Lee Comisar whose father, Nathan Comisar, was the founder of the renowned La Maisonette Restaurant in Downtown Cincinnati. Lee ran the restaurant for many years. No other restaurant received more Mobile Five-Star Awards in the history of that honor in the United States (41 straight years). They made the best Beef Wellington you could hope to find, with a side of impeccable service. The Maisonette was a very special place. Just as it was about to move from downtown out to the suburb of Kenwood, it closed suddenly on July 25, 2005.

With that, we now move on to the Stertmeyer clan. My father, like me, was an only child. But he had enough names to make up for that fact. Born on December 6, 1909, he was christened Harold Herbert Henry Joseph Stertmeyer.

Dad was a hell of an athlete, playing football, basketball and baseball at Newport High School, just across the Ohio River from Cincinnati. He had offers to play professional baseball, but his mother refused to sign the required papers, determining that their little family required him to get a real job instead. Thus, his athletic career at Newport High School concluded at the end of his junior year when he took a job as a runner at Fifth Third Union Trust, a small Cincinnati Bank.

As a runner he would "run" stocks and bonds and other bank papers from Fifth Third to other banks and brokerage houses. A popular slang word for money in those days was "scratch." And, early on, he was assigned the nickname of *Scratch* at the bank. He would spend a 47-year career at Fifth Third, the only place he ever worked except for his time in the Merchant Marines during World War II.

He met my mother at Fifth Third, where she worked as a teller, also leaving school after her junior year at Cincinnati Withrow High School. After a courtship of several years, they finally married on October 10, 1936. The announcement of their union as described in the Cincinnati papers read as follows:

Mr. and Mrs. Theobald of Spokane Avenue in East Walnut Hills, wish to announce the marriage their daughter Paula to Harold Stertmeyer, son of Mr. and Mrs. Henry Stertmeyer of Newport, KY, Saturday, October 10. As her only attendant, the bride had her sister, Mrs. William Sutton who wore a lovely wine-colored tunic style gown of crepe with a matching turban. Her corsage was of tea roses. Mr. William Sutton was best man.

The bride, who has lovely brown hair and fair complexion was a gracious figure in royal blue velvet, modeled along classic lines and falling in fold to the tip of her slippers. Completing this chic ensemble was a corsage of talisman roses. Following the ceremony, the bridal party motored to the home of the bride's parents for wedding supper and reception. After which the young couple were sped upon their wedding trip which will take them through Ohio. Upon their return they will reside in Newport, KY.

Among documents in the family archives remains a receipt from the Hotel Miami in Dayton, Ohio where they spent their wedding night. Dad was a big spender. Their receipt number A 47760 shows that the room cost $3.50 with an additional $0.25 for "Sundry." The grand total was $3.75. Dad knew how to treat a lady. The Miami Hotel was part of the Albert Pick Hotel chain as noted on the back of the folio.

My parents resided in Newport until my father went off to war in 1943. After the war, they purchased a two-family house at 3333 Spokane Avenue just seven doors up the street from my mother's family home on the beautiful cobblestone single block street lined with majestic pin oaks and maple trees. It was a great place to be back then.

My father was the product of the union between Henry Joseph Bernard "Henny" Stertmeyer and Emma Schneider. An interesting factoid about this *union* is that my grandparents were married on May 9, 1909 (Emma's birthday) in Aurora, Indiana. What makes this noteworthy is that their only child, my father, was born on December 6, 1909.

I only recently discovered the date of their marriage. Now the math is not too difficult here. It would appear that the trip to Indiana in May might well have been precipitated by the fact that Grandma Emma was a couple of months along with carrying dear old dad, so it is likely that the *union* preceded the marriage. Not that there is anything wrong with that.

As with my mother's side of the family, we will again go *ladies first* and explore my maternal grandmother's lineage.

My grandmother Emma Barbara Schneider was born on May 9, 1887. Her parents were Jacob and Elizabeth (Betty) Gantner Schneider. Her siblings were Wilhelm "William" Schneider, DOB June 13, 1885, Carl Jacob "John" Schneider, born on July 10, 1889, and Bertha Schneider DOB unknown. Bertha was married to Wilhelm "William" Fischer.

All I know of my great grandmother Betty was that she was the daughter of Johann and Emma Gantner. She lived for a while with Grandma Emma and Grandpa Henny on 8th Street in Newport when I was young. By the late forties she was pretty frail and then disappeared, although I don't recall her passing. And, I do remember a happy fellow who would show up every now and then named Buddy Gantner. He was older than my grandmother but much younger than Betty. I am fairly certain he had a given name other than Buddy. I am guessing he was Betty's younger brother and a solid role model for my father, who was quite fond of him.

Of my grandmother's siblings, I know the most about John. He had a daughter, Burnett, and two sons, Bob and Duke. Those three were all very close with my father.

My parents socialized regularly with Burnett and her husband Gilbert "Gilly" Rutz. In the fifties they owned and operated a delicatessen in Belleview, Kentucky and lived in a two-bedroom apartment behind the shop. I was fairly close to their son, Gilly, Jr., who was two years older than me. We often visited with them at the deli on Saturdays where they always served greasy but delicious hamburgers and some spectacular baked beans.

In the mid-fifties, they built a very modern ranch style house just outside Belleview where they lived with Gilly, Jr. and their baby daughter Janet.

Sadly in 1960, Burnett contracted cancer and passed away in late September of 1961 on the day the Cincinnati Reds clinched the National League Championship for the first time since 1940. At the time, Gilly, Jr. was studying to become a priest at a seminary in Newport and helped officiate at her funeral. He later eulogized my father at his funeral on September 6, 1984.

Burnett's two younger brothers, Bob and Duke, were an interesting pair. They both played football right after the war at Newport High School where, as the team's two halfbacks, they were known as *The Touchdown Twins*. Bob was a year older than Duke. Because we always visited my grandparents in Newport every Friday, we often attended the Friday night games to see *The Touchdown Twins* work their gridiron magic.

We missed a game in late 1949 when, sadly, their father John suffered a heart attack in the stands and died immediately. Bob was a senior and Duke a junior that year.

Bob and Duke were just over 5 feet six inches tall and not candidates for college football. After graduating high school, they both joined the Army and saw action in the Korean War. After the war, Duke took a job with Ford while Bob took a bad turn. He became a grunt for the Newport Mob where he ran "numbers." Thanks to my father, he quickly gave that up and went straight, also working for Ford as an assembly line worker in Cincinnati.

Through an exceptional consistence, I employed a great young kid named Doug Ruffner in 1975 when I was a VP and manager of the Cincinnati branch at Mooney and Moses of Ohio, a large insulation contractor. As it turned out, Doug's girlfriend and eventual wife was a tiny little lady named Terry Schneider. She was Bob's daughter.

Thus, I was reunited with Bob, who I quickly discovered was estranged from his brother Duke. At my father's funeral in 1984, Bob pulled Doug and me aside and told us a story that I had never heard.

As the tale went, when Bob was trying to screw up his life running numbers with the mob, my father had met him at a Newport bar one night. Dad had a very direct message for Bob. He told him, "Bobby boy, if you continue working with these thugs you are going to die. Either they will kill you or I will. So, here's what you're going to do. I've talked with your brother and he can get you on at Ford. On Monday you will show up at the factory, fill out an application and never again work for that big palooka, Frank "Screw" Andrews (real name Frank Andriolla and head of the Newport Mafia). Do we understand each other?"

A stunned Bob Schneider nodded his agreement after my father told him that he would make things right with Screw Andrews and that Bob would have no worries.

Bob told Doug and me that never once did he feel any heat from walking away from the numbers game and that he owed his life to my father. He wanted me to know that.

I'll never know how my father was able to pull that off with Screw Andrews and his Newport gangsters, but I do know that both he and my grandfather knew a lot of them over the years including Jimmy Brink, the owner of the original Lookout House Restaurant and Casino, Taylor Farley, Pete Schmidt, former Xavier University football star turned crook, Tito Carinci, a thug known as "Sleepout" Louis Levinson and the notorious Bridewell Brothers.

I suppose these relationships all started when my Grandfather Henny was the weekend night manager at one of Cincinnati bootleg boss, George Remus' speakeasies, on the edge of Newport during Prohibition. But I am also certain that my father never was directly involved with any of the nonsense that made Newport known as "Sin City" long before Las Vegas ever existed. Growing up in Newport, he got to know a lot of the local hoodlums but fortunately never became one.

Life didn't end well for Screw Andrews. In 1973, some mob goons showed up in Andrew's hospital room and instructed a nurse to take a break. Soon after Screw was tossed to his demise two floors below his room's window.

The only other relative I can speak about on my grandmother's side of the family is her cousin Stella Schneider. Though she was my distant cousin, I was instructed to refer to her as Aunt Stella, as my grandmother considered her to be like a sister.

Aunt Stella was born on January 26, 1885 to Johann and Katharina Mueller Schneider. She was married to a true gentleman, Ben Federle. Ben was an accomplished piano player who sang on the radio in the 1920s. They had no children and were extremely fond of my father.

During my younger years, they lived in a house in Ft. Thomas Kentucky that spoke well to their apparent affluence. I loved visiting them as their house was large, welcoming and just a short half block walk to an overlook with an expansive view of the Ohio River and Lunken Airport on the Cincinnati side of the river.

When Uncle Ben retired, they moved to Coral Gables Florida where we visited them in 1955. The highlight of that visit was swimming in the most interesting swimming pool I've ever seen, named The Venetian Pool, with caves and waterfalls. It still exists.

As to my paternal grandmother, I hope there will eventually be more to come. Some of the online research I have is as follows:

Schneider, Emma; (my grandmother): Daughter of Jacob & Elisabeth (Gantner) Schneider; born May 9, 1887 in Newport, Ky; Baptized -July 17, 1887 in Newport; Godparents -Johann Gantner & Emma Gantner

Elizabeth (Betty) Gantner (Dad's maternal grandmother): Daughter of Johann & Emma Gantner.

Schneider, Carl Jacob (My dad's Uncle); Son of Jacob & Elisabeth (Gantner) Schneider; born July 10, 1889 in Newport, Ky; Baptized - Sept. 15, 1889 in Newport; Godparents-Carl Siefers & Rosa Schneider.

Schneider, Wilhelm Jacob (Grandma's brother): Son of Jacob & Elisabeth (Gantner) Schneider; born-June 13, 1885 in Newport, Ky; Baptized-Aug. 9, 1885 in Newport, Ky; Godparents-Bertha Fischer & Wilhelm Fischer

Schneider, Stella (Grandma's cousin); Daughter of Johann & Katharina (Mueller) Schneider; born -Jan. 26, 1885 in Newport; Baptized - March 29, 1885 in Newport, KY; Godparents-Jacob & Rosa Schneider. Married to Ben Federle.

And now, finally, a brief exploration of the Surname of all this Mishpucha mess... the *Stertmeyer* clan.

From only two generations back, this part of the family is filled with confusion and a strange tale, yet I was able to trace the Stertmeyer name back over 250 years, the common thread being two small towns in Westfalen Prussia (later Germany).

We will start with Gramps, as I called him for the twenty-four years, we shared on the planet Earth. That would be Henry Joseph Bernard Stertmeyer, who was born on February 8, 1886 in good old Newport, Kentucky. His parents were Joseph Stertmeyer & Anna Kiewitt Stertmeyer.

Gramps had an older sister, Anna Maria Catharina Stertmeier, born on

June 3, 1883 and baptized the next day, June 4, 1883. And, gratefully, she had the same parents as my Gramps, Joseph Stertmeier & Anna Kiewitt. Her God parents are listed as, Bernard Stertmeier & Catharine Kiewitt. I should point out the different spelling of Gramps' sister and their parents' last names above, replacing the "Y" with and "I". This is how Anna's Birth Certificate is recorded at the Kenton County Library that contains the microfilm records in Covington, Kentucky. This disparity in the spelling of our last name appears from time to time in other records I have uncovered.

Aunt Anna Maria Catharina Stertmeier (or, probably Stertmeyer) was affectionately known as *Mamie,* a good move for someone with so much name with which to deal. These multiple names are something else that traditionally runs through my father's side of the family. After all, his full name was Harold, Herbert, Henry, Joseph Stertmeyer (with a "Y" not an "I" thank you).

Aunt Mamie married and moved to Racine, Wisconsin. The only time I ever met her was in 1950 when my mother, father and I vacationed in Chicago and took a short train ride up to Racine. I do remember she had a very nice home and a friendly husband named Heinz.

Gramps S had two other siblings, a sister Amelia, born on November 29, 1884and a younger brother, Edward, born on September 21, 1896 and passed in March 1985 at the ripe old age of 88. Uncle Ed never married. I met him several times, and he was always good for some pocket change when we hooked up. I never saw him without a suit and tie. Grandpa also had a cousin, John Henry Clement Stertmeyer, born on May 15, 1886. While I heard the name from time to time, I do not recall ever meeting him, nor do I have the date when he passed.

Sadly, I do not have much more detail about Grandpa Stertmeyer's immediate relatives, yet I have uncovered a litany of birth, marriage and baptismal records of the Stertmeyer kin. I will continue to research for more detail, but here is a brief list available from the International Genealogical Index in Germany to aid in that effort:

Anna Catharine Stertmeyer; Married on September 21, 1768 at Sankt

Callixtus Katholisch Church in Riesenbeck, Westfalen, Prussia.

Anna Margaret Stertmeyer; Married on June 18, 1771 at Sankt Callixtus Church in Riesenbeck, Westfalen, Prussia.

Anna Maria Stertmeyer; Christened on June 21, 1782 in Riesenbeck, Westfalen, Prussia.

Anna Cathar Stertmeyer; Christened on October 18, 1799 in Riesenbeck, Westfalen, Prussia.

Anna Catharina Stertmeyer; Married February 19, 1800 at Sankt Callixtus Katholisch Church in Riesenbeck, Westfalen, Prussia.

Anna Maria Theresa Stertmeyer; Christened on August 6, 1809 in Riesenbeck, Westfalen, Prussia.

Anna Maria Catharina Stertmeyer; Christened on September 27, 1812 in Riesenbeck, Westfalen, Prussia.

Anna Catherina Stertmeyer; Christened on September 30, 1816 in Ibbenbueren, Westfalen, Prussia.

Bernhard Hermann Stertmeyer; Married on April 23, 1844 in Ibbenbueren, Westfalen, Prussia.

Bernhard Heinrich Stertmeyer; Christened on September 2, 1845 in Ibbenbueren, Westfalen, Prussia.

Gerd Henrich Stertmeyer; Married on October 28 1767 in Sankt Callixtus Church in Riesenbeck, Westfalen, Prussia.

Hermann Stertmeyer; Married as a Catholic in July 1862 in Ibbenbueren, Westfalen, Prussia.

Johann Heinrich Stertmeyer; Married as a Catholic on July 21, 1813 in Riesenbeck, Westfalen, Prussia.

Josephus Henricus Stertmeyer; Christened on September 14, 1822 in Ibbenbueren, Westfalen, Prussia.

Joseph August Stertmeyer; Christened on October 30, 1849 in Ibbenbueren, Westfalen, Prussia.

Catharina Stertmeyer; Married on January 29, 1820 in Dreierwalde, Westfalen, Prussia.

Maria Anna Stertmeyer; Christened on August 10, 1810 in Ibbenbueren, Westfalen, Prussia.

Marrianne Stertmeyer; Born August 9, 1810 in Ibbenbueren, Westfalen, Prussia.

This provides an interesting, if somewhat incomplete list of Stertmeyers from a very specific area in the Westfalen region of Prussia (later Germany). All were Catholic. And many of the names connect the dots right up to my great grandfather, grandfather and father. The names Heinrich, Bernard, Joseph, Anna, Catharina and Maria bestow us with a clear thread from the late 18th Century and early 19th Century to my day, starting in the mid-Twentieth Century.

And what of the tiny towns of Riesenbeck and Ibbenbueren in Westfalen, or Westphalia, as it is known today?

The year 1146 is generally considered as the year that Ibbenbueren was founded as a small church village. Throughout much of the Middle Ages it was ruled by the Counts of Tecklenburg.

At the beginning of the 16th Century control fell to Charles V of the Habsburgs, who also controlled the Netherlands by his sister Mary. The Netherlands connection provides the thinnest of threads to the tale I will share in conclusion, as does Ibbenbueren's relationship to the House of Orange in Holland.

Ibbenbueren became part of the Westfalen district of Prussia until that union was dissolved and it became part of the German Republic. If you wish to know more about this, look up Bismarck and 1871.

Like Ibbenbueren, Riesenbeck sat on the southern slope of the Teutoburg Forest in Northwest Germany. And it was also controlled by the Counts of Tecklenburg.

In 1803, it became part of Prussia sharing a similar future fate with Ibbenbueren.

Today the two towns sit a short 15-minute drive apart, about 9 kilometers. The Saint Kalixtus Kirche (Calixtus Church) that appears as the place of marriages and christenings of so many Stertmeyers, still sits at the center of Riesenbeck today.

And now, in order to wrap up this discussion of my mysterious

Mishpucha, let me share one final rather bizarre and outlandish anecdote.

My father repeated this whopper frequently over the years, and I believed its validity until I became a critical thinker in my late teens.

You see, according to good old Dad, we were related to royalty. As detailed above, the Stertmeyer clan does seem to have some convoluted connection to the Netherlands and the once powerful House of Orange-Nassau. And if that connection exists, so could a further link to the American colony of New Amsterdam (the future New York City).

Without delving deep into the history, the basics of Dad's tale is that we were related to the 17th Century Royalty of the Netherlands and the House of Orange. What I am now certain is a fable, suggest that a fairly successful Stertmeyer (first name unknown) was a sea captain for the Dutch West Indies Trading Company often sailing the Atlantic to deliver goods to the Dutch colony of New Amsterdam.

Somehow, he connected with one of the princesses of the Netherlands, and with his great good looks and charm, rapidly impregnated her. What should have been a big problem for Captain Stert, and should have resulted with his head being separated from his body, was resolved by the Sovereign Prince Frederick Henry (yes "Henry"), the father of the new mother-to be, his eldest daughter, Princess Amalia (very close to "Amelia" I should point out).

To save Prince Frederick Henry and his wife Amalia van Solmes-Braunfels (perhaps the precursor to the wonderful little Texas town of New Braunfels) the embarrassment of a bastard grandchild, Freddie boy decided the solution lie in the New World. Thus, he gave the expectant couple a parcel of land in New Amsterdam and packed them on their way with instructions never to return to their beloved Holland.

I cannot provide the origins to this wild tale, but I do know that my father's Aunt Amelia in the 1920's hired a man to research this family legend. He promised detailed results. She gave him two-hundred dollars in cash and never laid eyes on him again.

We all have the capacity to believe what we want to believe, especially when it serves our ego. I think my dad truly deemed there was sufficient truth in the fairy tale to believe he had royal Dutch blood coursing through his German-American body.

All I can say is that there was a Frederik Hendrik who ruled the House of Orange, and he was married to Amalia van Solmes-Braunfels. History allows me to put a check next to that much, but the rest of this enchanting nonsense appears to be pure myth, a romantic fable, but fun.

Not to my cynical surprise, my extensive research has resulted in zilch, but I will say that reading about New Amsterdam was worth the time I gave to it.

The most gratifying aspect of my family is the fact that I have two wonderful children, Scott Christopher Stertmeyer and Allison Paige Stertmeyer Gunkel. Scott's wife Tami has given him a biological daughter, our sweet Ella, as well as two step-daughters, the spectacular Tori Tarvin and the fun-loving happy Tayler Tarvin. Tami, Ella, Tori and Tayler have filled our life with the greatest possible joy.

Allison is married to Sean Gunkel, who has done great work as a Reverend in the US, Argentina and Brazil. Their two daughters, Ashley and McKenzie, are bright, beautiful and full of life.

And my wife Peggy has also blessed our family with her two special sons, Lee and Gene.

So, the tree continues to grow.

I am sure there is so much more to be learned about the Loewenstine, Theobald, Schneider and Stertmeyer family units and the tree branches they feed. But for now, that is all from my Mishpucha.

Grandma Cosey Loewenstine Theobald
Wedding Day

My Uncle Mont Loewenstine (L)
Great Grandfather Jake Loewenstine (R)

Paula & Winifred
1912

Three Sisters.
Paula, Lois & Winifred Theobald
1926

Paula Theobald & Rollie Loewenstine
1918

Aunt Lois & Uncle Bill 1936
(Bill's newly missing fingers are bandaged on left hand)

Grandpa Lou Theobald
1936

Aunt Win – Wedding
February 6, 1933

Aunt Lois Wedding

Harold Stertmeyer.

Elizabeth Schneider

My Grandmother - Emma Stertmeyer

Emma, Henny, Paula & me - 1944

The Schneider Clan
From left: Al, Grandma Emma, Dad, Louise, Grandpa Henry S, Burnette, John, Stella and Ben Federle, Bertha Fisher, Elizabeth and William.
Circa Late 1930s

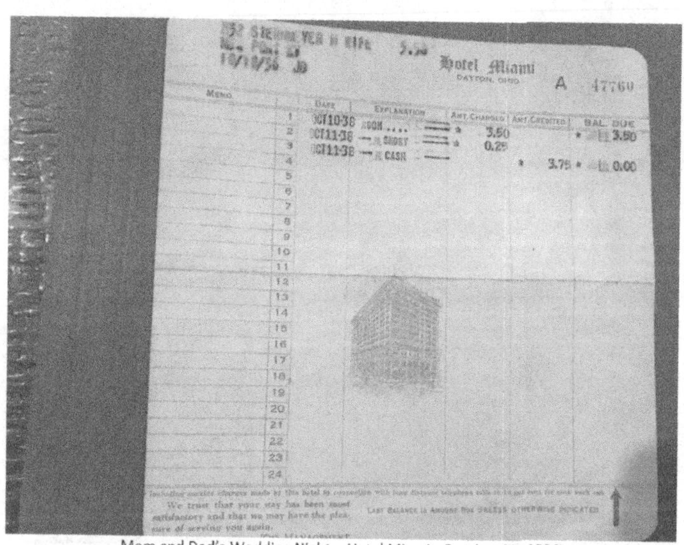

Mom and Dad's Wedding Night – Hotel Miami - October 10, 1936

Grave Site of Great Grandmother 5 times removed.
Henrietta "Yetta" Gross.
United Jewish Cemetery – Cincinnati

Paula, Randy & Harold Stertmeyer
Winter 1943
A New Generation from the Mishpucha

1946

Those magnificent men
in their flying machines,
They go up diddley up-up,
they go down diddley down-down!
They entrance all the ladies
and steal all the scenes,
With their up diddley up-up
and their down diddley down-down.
Up! down! Flying around!
Looping the loop
and defying the ground!
They're all frightfully keen.
Those Magnificent men
in their flying machines!

From *Those Magnificent Men in Their Flying Machines*
By Ron Goodwin

PIPER CUB

If being born a middle-class white boy in 1942 was like winning a lottery, then I almost lost it all in 1947. What were the odds of this close call? My life came within a black cat's whisker of being cut disastrously short in July of that year. It was during my first ever trip to the annual Fifth Third Bank Picnic. My father, less than a year back from the war, had not attended this yearly event since before I was born.

Now back in full swing in the Commercial Loans Department, and with an enthusiastically welcoming return as the Bank Soft Ball Team's first baseman, he was more than a little excited on this bright and sunny Saturday morning, as we prepared to depart for a day at the Martz Picnic Grounds in Ross Kentucky.

The Ross facility sat on the Kentucky side of the Ohio River, just upstream and across from Coney Island and River Downs Race Track. There were a series of stone buildings that ran up from the boat launch to a spectacular softball field that had a grass infield and an attractive outfield fence, resplendent with beer, soft drink and cigarette advertising posters. At age three and a half I was looking forward to spending the day with my two new little friends I had made through the bank softball team. Both of their dads had also just returned from the war and were now back to work at 5th 3rd and also regular members of the bank ball club that played every Friday night, under the lights, at Deer Creek Commons just north of downtown Cincinnati.

Little Pete Rose was almost two years older than me, yet an inch shorter. Joby Haines, though my exact age, towered a good 2 inches over me. Since the Bank League season had started in April, the three of us had become real tag-alongs, unofficial batboys and all-around mascots extraordinaire. Outfitted in our 5th 3rd ball caps, safety-pinned in the back to assure a tight fit, we were really something, or so we thought.

Unlike me, Pete and Joby were both named for their fathers. Pete's dad, Big Pete, was a great guy and a fantastic athlete. So good, in fact, that he was a running back for the old Cincinnati Bengals semi-pro football team, even though he was in his late thirties. Always upbeat and smiling, he took all three of us under his wing and taught us a lot of baseball. He had big expectations of Little Pete, who was a willing student.

Joe Haines was a quiet handsome man that, compared to my dad and Big Pete, seemed a bit aloof. He was clearly more interested in the ladies and whatever was on tap, than he was about the three little rascals.

So, since there was *Big Pete* and *Little Pete* and *Big Joe* and *Little Joe,* to the ballplayers on the bank softball team, my dad and I became *Big Stert* and *Little Stert.* And for a few of the old timers who had always called my father *Scratch* we were referred to as *Big Scratch* and *Small Scratch.*

That moniker had evolved from my father's first job at the bank. At the age of fifteen, he was hired as a runner; someone that ran documents and stock trades from Fifth Third Bank to other banks and brokerage houses. In another way of saying it, he was moving money or, in the jargon of the day, scratch, around downtown Cincinnati. Thus, in 1924 he was assigned the nickname of *Scratch.*

Still without a car of their own following the war, my parents borrowed my Uncle Bill's 1939 big Packard and off we went, departing our family home in Walnut Hills. The drive through Eden Park, then down winding Martin Drive past the Waterworks reservoir and finally across the L&N Bridge into Newport, Kentucky, was already familiar to me, as my father was from that little town on the banks of the Ohio River. But once in Newport we took a route brand new to me, which took us through the small towns of Fort Thomas and Southgate down to Route 8, which ran along the river.

As my father guided the big Packard east down the two-lane road, my mother pointed out the Coney Island Amusement Park with its two large roller coasters clearly visible across the mile-wide grey Ohio.

A minute or two later my father stuck his left arm out of the open window, signaling we were about to turn left. After a big truck blew by us with enough force to shake the Packard, we shot onto a long narrow dirt road, kicking up dust until we came to an unmarked railroad crossing. Dad navigated the tracks and we suddenly came upon Martz Picnic Grounds with a small pony track and a beautiful ball field to the right and a grass airstrip to the left. Just passed the runway where two small planes sat, we pulled into a large parking lot already quite full of cars.

Dad grabbed our baseball gear from the trunk and we headed for a large stone pavilion abuzz with bankers and their family members. The building was shaped like half of a hexagon with sizeable openings looking out on the ball field. On the opposite side of the huge room sat very large built-in concrete coolers, some filled with bottled beer, others with soft drinks, all on ice. About every six feet, attached to the front of the coolers were the required bottle cap openers with small cans beneath them to catch the discarded caps.

Our arrival was greeted enthusiastically by several of my parent's friends from Cincinnati's third largest bank. I found Little Pete standing by one of the large openings holding his ball glove and slugging back a Nehi Grape drink. I had my own Nehi in hand along with my black Ewell Blackwell model mitt that was too large for my little hand. Pete and I scrambled through the airy space leading to the ball field and started tossing a brand-new baseball I had brought for the occasion.

Shortly thereafter, Joby Haines joined us. We formed a little triangle along the first base line and started firing the ball to each other. I noticed a small crowd of my Dad's banker buddies gathered nearby, most enjoying the free beer, and commenting on how good the three of us handled the ball at such a young age.

We eventually worked up a thirst for another drink. Pete switched to coke while Joby and I stayed with the complimentary grape drinks. My mother caught me guzzling the Nehi and yelled, "You go easy on the drinks, you hear?"

Around noon we gave up on our second round of toss and headed back to the Pavilion for a charcoal grilled hamburger. Soon after a large group of men started a pickup game on the ball field. I had learned on Friday nights at Deer Creek Commons that both Big Pete and my dad could hit the snot out of a softball. And on this sunny Saturday they both put on a show in spite of the beer buzz they already had going.

Once they had finished my mother instructed dad to take me over to the pony ride. He threw me up on a brown and white creature and some teenager walked the pony and me around the rink.

After a couple of laps dad suggested we walk over to the nearby airstrip to watch the small planes take off and land. This attraction was providing all who wished a short flight back west up the river where they circled over downtown Cincinnati and then returned to land on the long grass runway. It was now four o'clock.

Just as we arrived there was a bit of commotion around a small yellow Piper Cub J-3 some twenty feet from where we stood. To start the plane, someone had to flip the prop. This process was called "hand propping." But they couldn't seem to get this one to turn over,

I watched as the pilot, a fellow named Chester Mason, got out of the plane. My father explained to me what was going on. Now the pilot reached up and gave the prop a twirl. Nothing. He tried again. Again nothing.

They say the third time is the charm. And sure enough, after and energetic effort by Mason, the prop began to spin.

We would learn later that what was to follow was a result of a young helper in the cockpit named Harold Ellison accidentally hitting the throttle on the plane. Before we could grasp what was happening the plane started to roll. Mason, reacting quickly, grabbed at a strut redirecting the little aircraft in our direction as he fell to the ground.

Suddenly the plane was headed right at me. My father's impulse was to try to push me out of the way. In so doing he probably saved my life. I started to fall raising my right arm to protect myself from the propeller, which looked ten times larger than it probably was. As I stumbled to the ground the prop nicked my right wrist and the plane rolled over both my father and me.

Then there was a terrifying grinding noise followed by a loud scream. With that Mason was able to get back in the aircraft and cut off the engine.

After a very short silence pandemonium broke out. People were running everywhere. All I can remember after that was my father rushing me back toward the pavilion holding my right arm, now totally covered in blood, high in the air. I felt no pain, but was clearly in shock as I realized I was sobbing uncontrollably.

We found my mother, who just about fainted when she saw my blood-soaked arm and shirt.

As it turned out, the grinding noise we had heard was the plane plowing directly into an eighteen-year-old boy who was on a bicycle. We would learn later that the impact had thrown both the boy and the bike several feet into the air. He had suffered a severe deep laceration of his upper leg and hip.

Unfortunately, little Ross Kentucky had only one ambulance. Clearly the other victim was seriously injured and needed the ambulance. So, my Father's good friend, the normally very funny Harold Girkin, or *Girk* as he was known, gathered my mother, my father and me and off we headed to Speers Hospital in his old Chevy coupe. There would be no joking from Girk now as we sped down the dirt road and zoomed west onto Route 8.

We reached the emergency room where I was rushed into a small room with two beds separated by a thick curtain. As a doctor rushed in with two nurses, the more seriously injured teenager was wheeled to the other bed in the room. As the doctor started to examine my right arm, we could hear a lot of commotion on the other side of the curtain.

My mother told my father to find a phone and call her sister my Aunt Win to tell her what was going on. The doctor was applying painful pressure to my wound trying to stop the bleeding. He told the nurse to attend to the top of my right ear and we learned for the first time the prop had also clipped it. The minute I heard that, I started to feel the pain there as well.

We heard someone say on the far side of the curtain that the other victim needed surgery immediately. He was wheeled back out of the room.

They finally got the bleeding to stop on my wrist.

The doctor said to me, "OK, little guy this is going to hurt," and he began to apply some auburn colored antiseptic first to my wrist and then my ear. He didn't lie. It hurt like hell. I tried to be brave, but could not hold back the tears.

The pain finally subsided and they stitched and bandaged my wound. He then explained to my mother that he wanted my arm in a sling until I could see Dr. Kendall, my pediatrician, who could take over the treatment on Monday. Before he dismissed us, he jostled my hair and said, "You're a very lucky young man."

Then to my mother, "He lost a lot of blood. He might be light headed for a while. I suggest you get him home and into bed."

Girk sat waiting for us in the in the lobby of the emergency room. Once he saw I was alive and breathing, the old Girk reappeared.

"Well squirt, I guess you're going to live. I assume you still have an arm under that thing," he joked with his familiar hoot, pointing at the sling.

I loved Girk. In my short life I had never met a happier, more upbeat guy. He was my dad's best friend on the ball team. He remained that way for the rest of his life, even keeping us in stitches years later at my father's funeral, with one tale after another of their hijinks at the bank.

My father reported that he had reached my Aunt Win. And a good thing that he had, as she had heard about the accident on the six o'clock news on WASI radio. They had even named both me and the other boy in their broadcast, erroneously reporting that we were both in critical condition.

Girk drove us back to the Martz Picnic Grounds. When we arrived, we were surrounded by a huge group of people. We learned that the boy on the bike was named Donald Osterkamp and that he was the nephew of the Branch Manager of the Peebles Corner Branch at Fifth Third.

We gathered our things and piled into Uncle Bill's Packard and headed for home.

My arm remained in the sling for ten days after which Dr. Kendall removed the stitches. All I have to show from this near-death experience is the memory of the trauma of the whole experience and a barely visible quarter inch scar on the inside of my right wrist.

We heard that Osterkamp had a very deep foot-long gash in his right hip that resulted in 53 stitches and several nights in the hospital. The report the next day in the Sunday *Enquirer* and then in the Monday *Post*, both reported that it was my left arm that had been injured. But I looked at the arm in the sling and it was clearly my right arm.

There would be many more picnics with my pals Joby Haynes and Pete Rose. They both became great athletes. Joby is in the Withrow High School Hall of Fame for his basketball prowess. And we all know a little something about Little Pete Rose

When I was about eleven or twelve, I found myself on the Ferris wheel at Martz with Pete. In those days, I was a bit of a goodie-two-shoes. Maybe to clean cut for my own good.

When the Ferris wheel stopped suddenly with us swinging near the top, I blurted out, "What the heck was that?"

Pete looked at me and said, "Jesus Christ Stert, don't you ever fuckin' cuss?"

I thought about that and realized that I didn't. Therein lied the difference between Pete Rose and me as kids.

I still see Pete from time to time, usually in Las Vegas. As a rule, the first thing Pete brings up is the fried chicken they served for dinner at the bank picnics. And he is right. It was damned good chicken.

Then Pete usually brings up our dads saying, "Those two son-of-a-bucks could sure play ball."

He is right about that too. And my son-of-a-buck dad would have loved hearing that from Charlie Hustle. As it were, dad probably saved my life on July 27, 1946. Thanks Scratch!

Piper Cub J-3.

Martz Field at Ross Kentucky

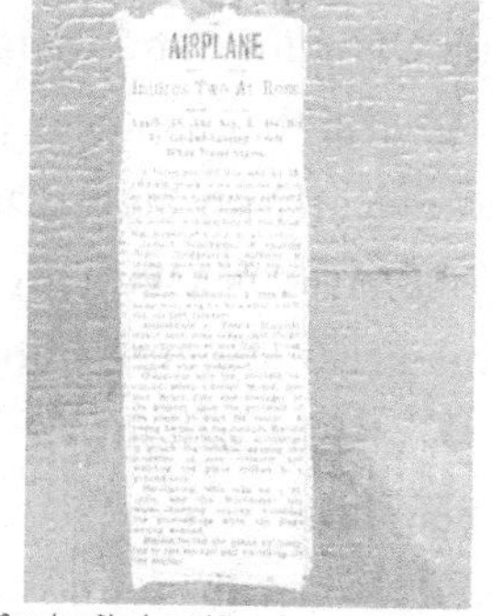

AIRPLANE

Injures Two At Ross

[illegible]

Sunday Cincinnati Enquirer - July 28, 1946

1947

They come from every point of the compass, from the 48 states — thousands of them—
of all colors and creeds, to man the ever-growing fleet of Liberty ships
that carry the goods to the men of the fighting fronts of this global war.
At the world's largest United States Maritime Service Training Station at Sheepshead Bay, Brooklyn, New York, more than 10,000 are studying the elements of seamanship,
are acquiring knowledge about lifeboats and life saving
that will protect them along the sea lanes menaced by Axis U-boats,
are learning to be clerks, pharmacist's mates, deck hands, engine room hands, ship's cooks...
Heave Ho! My Lads, Heave Ho!
It's a long, long way to go.
It's a long, long pull with our hatches full,
Braving the wind, braving the sea,
Fighting the treacherous foe;
Heave Ho! My lads, Heave Ho!
Let the sea roll high or low,
We can cross any ocean, sail any river.
Give us the goods and we'll deliver,
Damn the submarine!
We're the men of the Merchant Marine!

From, *Heave Ho! My Lads! Heave Ho!*

(Official song of The Merchant Marines)
By Lieut. (jg) Jack Lawrence, USMS, 1943

Pharmacist Mate

On November 17, 1945, my father departed La Harvre, France aboard the steamship Waterbury Victory. He was listed on the ship's manifest as Harold H. Stertmeyer, Lieutenant Junior Grade, Purser, Pharmacist Mate, and a 35-year-old American citizen who was able to read and was to be honorably discharged from the Merchant Marines upon his arrival at the Port of New York.

Named for the city of Waterbury, Connecticut, the Victory ship carrying my dad had been launched just four months earlier in Baltimore on July 26, 1945. The original plan for the vessel was to carry cargo needed for the war effort.

But by the time it was dispatched, the Waterbury Victory found itself hauling German POWs home and returning American GIs stateside.

Among my father's closer pals on board the Waterbury Victory were Master Mitch Decker, Chief Mate Don Gardner, Second Mate George Burke, Chief Radio Operator Herb Lecumberri and Fourth Mate Robert Erickson, who at 6' 3" tall, towered over the rest of the crew. Of the thirty crew members on board, only Deck Hand Karl Karlson and Chief Engineer Howard Tobias were older than my father.

On this final voyage home from the war were twenty-six US citizens, two Spaniards, one Irishman and Karlson who was listed as Scandinavian.

US participation in the war had been ongoing for more than a year when my father entered the Merchant Marines because none of the fighting services would accept him due to his age. He had tried more than once to enlist in the Navy. With no success, he finally settled on the Merchant

Marines rather than sitting out the war.

Thus, in 1943 he headed to Sheepshead Bay, a small body of water separating mainland Brooklyn from the eastern end of Coney Island. It was here and in Perth Amboy, New Jersey that he would receive his training before being thrust into the naval action of World War II.

My father would often talk about his last ocean crossing of his Merchant Marine career as being particularly rough due to late fall storms in the North Atlantic. But his main point was that the rough sea was a welcome change after three years of worrying about Nazi U-Boats.

The ship made port in New York just after noon on Tuesday, November 27th, having streamed past the welcoming form of the Statue of Liberty. After clearing customs, my father and a handful of non-essential officers were cleared to the Pay Master's office where they were handed an envelope with their final pay in US currency in a carefully sealed Merchant Marine envelope.

From there, he crossed the hall where he was handed his discharge papers and a second envelope of money to pay for two days-worth of food and a ticket for that evening's New York Central train back west to Cincinnati. He was advised that he was no longer to wear his uniform once he arrived home.

Just like that, the war that had officially ended three months earlier was now over for my father.

While my father was still streaming west in the Atlantic, America had celebrated Thanksgiving Day in a special way. President Harry Truman had declared November 22, 1945, as a day of national thanksgiving when he proclaimed, "Now, therefore, I, Harry S. Truman, President of the United States of America, in consonance with the joint resolution of Congress approved December 26, 1941, do hereby proclaim Thursday November 22, 1945, as a day of national thanksgiving. May we on that day, in our homes and in our places of worship, individually and as groups, express our humble thanks to Almighty God for the abundance of our blessings and may we on that occasion rededicate ourselves to those high principles of citizenship for which so many splendid Americans have recently given all."

For my father, the Nihilism that was Adolph Hitler and Nazi Germany, no longer posed a threat and was happily in his rearview mirror. Due to his rather late entry into the War, his had been a relatively short tour of duty, cram-packed with danger, threats, fear and the relief of survival. Yet to my father, that journey had been something of an epoch. In the jargon of the time, it was several *blue moons* or more than a *month of Sundays*.

Yes, it seemed *eons* since he first departed home. And he knew, as he settled into his seat on the Twentieth Century Limited in the bowels of Grand Central Station for the overnight trip home, he was returning a very different person.

Though he had been toughened and tempered and tarnished by the experience like most, he would usually share only the fun times, the comradery and even the hilarity of his years at war. Most of his stories in which he would take great pride and joy in telling to me during my youth, were filled with happiness and a kind of giddy glee that effectively masked the tragic toll caused by being a slowly moving target for German submarines and destroyers for over two years.

Most of his friends and family assumed that serving in the Merchant Marines was the safest place to be during the war. As it turned out, my father had signed up for what would prove statistically to be the deadliest assignment in the US war effort.

The US Merchant Marine suffered the highest rate of casualties of any service in World War II. Officially, a total of 1,554 merchant ships were sunk due to action in the war. Because the US government did not keep the kind of detailed records for the Merchant Marines as they did for the other branches of military service, an exact accounting of loss of life cannot be officially be stated. but what is known is that the comparative death toll of all of the U.S services for the war is as follows:

Merchant Marines 1 in 26

Marine Corp 1 in 34

Army 1 in 48 (This includes the Army Air Corp)

Navy 1 in 114
Coast Guard 1 in 421
Average 1 in 56

Yes, the supposed cushy service of the World War II Merchant Marine was more than twice as dangerous as the average of all who served.

Harold Herbert Henry Joseph Stertmeyer had dodged the proverbial bullet, or, more accurately, a passel of torpedoes. No one, including himself, could possibly grasp the emotional baggage attended with such an experience. Like so many others, he would deal with it for the rest of his life.

But, as the New York Central train rolled west through the November night, Harold's thoughts were of his wife, his young son, and how he might resume his life in Cincinnati. He spent the trip reading the latest editions of "Stars and Stripes", "Yank", "Life" and "Look" magazines, which he had stashed in his duffel bag. He especially liked the Bill Mauldin cartoons in "Stars and Stripes" and the "Sad Sack" comic strip, always to be found in "Yank" magazine. He was also able to squeezed in a couple of catnaps, plus a ham sandwich and a beer purchased from the porter, along the way.

The next morning, he arrived just after 8:30 into the still bustling Cincinnati Union Terminal. He threw the duffle bag over his shoulder and ascended the ramp up to the busy concourse to be met by my sobbing mother, with me firmly in hand. Behind us stood my Aunt Win and Uncle Bill. It was a greeting like so many that had been repeated time and again in the Art Deco colossus, which was one of America's last great train stations ever built.

Our little group worked our way from the concourse into the largest half-dome in the western hemisphere where above us were displayed the huge mosaics of Winold Reiss, detailing the history of Cincinnati labor in dramatic color and detail.

Of course, I did not understand the significance of my father's survival and return home. As he took me up into his arms, I had no way of knowing that this was ultimately an unusual display of affection, one which would prove to be uncharacteristic of my father's treatment of me in the future. I don't recall that moment very well as I was just short of my third birthday. But I also cannot recall any other such exhibition of affection from my father after that. Like so many of his depression and war-hardened generation, such warmth toward a son was just not typical. "Boys don't kiss boys," he would always say.

We worked our way through the busy station into the frigid November morning. We walked to the parking lot and piled into my Uncle Bill's long-nosed black 1937 Packard sedan with its striking chrome swan hood ornament and headed to the Spokane Avenue home in which my mother and her two sisters had been raised.

When we arrived, Aunt Win put some coffee on the stove and everyone settled around the green Bakelite table in the small kitchen of the two story house that was now home to my Aunt Win and Uncle Bill Sutton, my Aunt Lois and her husband Uncle Joe Anderson, as well as my grandfather Lou Theobald and my great grandmother, Jenny Loewenstine.

During the war, it had also been home to my mother and me. But now, she, my father and I would reside in an apartment in a two-family home on Monroe Street in Newport, Kentucky, my father's hometown, just across the Ohio River from downtown Cincinnati.

My Uncle Joe had just washed out of the US Army and had taken a job at the Cincinnati Stock Yard. Thus, for our family, the war had ended, seemingly with no harm done. My father and uncle had served and survived. Uncle Bill, due to his age, some bad knees and two missing fingers, had spent the war fixing cars at a local Pontiac dealer.

My father would often mutter to my mother or me in later years, "He was OK to work on Pontiacs, but he couldn't work on a jeep or a tank? Who's running this damned country anyway?"

At any rate, as the reunited family threw back some freshly brewed Maxwell House, the post war life of the Stertmeyers, Suttons, and Andersons was quietly launched in the humble confines of the 3315 Spokane Avenue kitchen.

I suppose that my father would have preferred to take the month of

December to decompress from the stress of his war service, but financial concerns demanded that he get back to Fifth Third Bank at Forth and Walnut Streets in downtown Cincinnati where, thankfully, his job in the Commercial Loans Departed awaited him. Thus, on Monday, December 3, three days before his thirty-sixth birthday and exactly one week before my third birthday, he put on one of his freshly dry-cleaned and pressed banker suits that had spent more than two years under the protection of mothballs and headed back to work.

Over the next half dozen years, a semblance of normal life would evolve for our extended family. Uncle Bill would continue his work at Gilbert Avenue Pontiac. Uncle Joe would quickly grow weary of his work at the stockyards and re-enlist in the Army Counter Intelligence Corp (CIC) soon to head off to Japan to help with the US efforts to rebuild the Japanese government into an American brand-like nation. My grandfather, Lou Theobald, now in his sixties, would continue to have trouble finding work. He did finally find a very cool gig at Shillito's Department Store playing Santa Claus during the Holidays from 1948 through 1951, a job that fitted him well and that he truly loved.

As to my father, he seemingly had no problem with his return to the banking life. But underneath the pschyo-surface, the scars of war remained and would pop up regularly. He often turned to the bottle as his medication of choice, using beer outwardly and whiskey secretly. Clearly, this approach was not what the doctor ordered, but it was a common cure used by many returning vets.

In early 1947, my parents bought a two-family house at 3333 Spokane Avenue, eight doors up from the family house at 3315. This fit the typical family profile of the time, wherein families found shelter in the same neighborhood. My mother's Uncle George Loewenstine and his second wife Dorothy, along with her younger sister Shirley, resided across the street from my Aunt Win and Uncle Bill. Uncle George's house was a large four-family with a bank of garages in the back, where Uncle Bill parked his Packard. George's older brother Cliff lived on Fairfield Avenue, one street to the west, with his wife Nell.

Being on Spokane Avenue in our three-story home built in 1897 was a great thing for me. Perhaps most significantly, I had three mothers. Aunt Win and Aunt Lois stepped up in my youthful development. All three sisters had a role. My mother was the worrying disciplinarian. Aunt Win was the nurturing teacher while Aunt Lois, being sixteen years younger than my mother and nineteen years older than me, was the fun-loving recreation director.

I also quickly made friends with our neighbors, Neil Van Outer and Chris Goebel, as well as my third cousin, Jay Pittroff, who lived a few blocks away. And with this move, the beginning of my father's story telling suddenly rained down on me.

Whether it be on a Newport bar stool, as he spoke with other vets over a Friday afternoon beer, or while tossing a baseball or football in our backyard on a Saturday afternoon, or in my little second story front bedroom in our new Spokane house, the "Legend of Harold," as told through his fascinating tales, became the glue that bound him to me.

Let's be clear, the vast majority of my father's tales were shared with me on Friday nights and Saturdays, while he was mildly, or even seriously, under the influence of pedestrian lager and/or cheap whiskey. Someone once said, "Whiskey is the drink which enables a man to magnify his joy, and his happiness."

That was often the case with post-war Harold. He would sit on the edge of my bed with a wide *gin grin* and spew forth his outlandishly funny and sometimes scary anecdotes, always accompanied with his distinctive high pitch giggle.

Yet there was the constant danger that a switch could flip in an instant, turning Dad from a most entertaining Dr. Jekyll to an angry, very frightening Mr. Hyde.

Most often that switch was my mother. Her certainty that she could control my father's drinking by simply confronting him was naively misinformed. She spent the next 14 years devoted to that singular approach. Only my more informed and firm intervention at the tender age of 17 would eventually solve the riddle of alcoholism and turn the direction of our little family in a new, improved direction. But that's another story.

Looking back on the years after the War, I am grateful for those Fridays and Saturdays. Alcohol or not, my father seemed like a prolific storyteller. But, in truth, he only had a handful or two of memorable yarns. And he would repeat them with such childlike glee and colorful detail that I never tired of hearing them.

My first clear memories of my father's early efforts at being a bard took place in my small front bedroom on the second floor of our new house.

A Friday tradition began soon after we had moved in, aided by the NBC radio program *Gillette Cavalcade of Sports*, which aired every Friday night at 9:30. Therein lay the first problem. At the age of five, this was way beyond the bedtime rules set by my mother. But bolstered by a couple of quarts of Hudepohl Beer (Cincinnati's finest according to Dad), he would go to battle over whether or not there was redeeming value in allowing me to stay up late and listen to prize fights and his stories.

Over a short period of time, my mother's position went from "absolutely not" to "OK, he can listen to the first round" to her falling asleep before the second round, making my father the ultimate victor.

When we first started tuning in, Bob Haymes, using the radio name Bob Stanton, was the commentator. He was the younger brother of the popular crooner, Dick Haymes, one of Aunt Lois' favorites.

Stanton had a high-pitch tenor voice perfect for calling a prizefight. My father loved Stanton, but not so much his singing brother. Every Friday night he would say to me, "Kiddo, you know Stanton's real name is Haymes and he is the brother of that sissy signer Dick Haymes? That son-of-a-buck is no Von Monroe, Bing Crosby or Frank Sinatra, I can tell ya. But, on the other hand, good old Bobby boy can sure call a fight. They must have different mothers."

On most Fridays by 9:30, I was pretty weary from a hard day of juvenile play. But the moment I heard the strains of the *Look Sharp/Be Sharp March,* an upbeat, bold tune that included the use of a prizefight bell, I became wide-awake, full of anticipation. The razor company jingle written by

Mahlon Merrick became an iconic piece of music that my friends and I still reminisce about to this day, along with its catch phrase "Look sharp, feel sharp, be sharp."

Many of the fights featured no-name boxers who my father referred to as chumps, stray dogs or worse. But every now and then, there would be great fighters on the bill including Willie Pep, Sugar Ray Robinson, Archie Moore, Jake LaMotta, Tony Zale and the two Rockys—Graziano and Marciano. On a very special evening, Heavy Weight Champ Joe Louis, and later, Cincinnati great Ezzard Charles, would strap on the gloves.

These were great nights, with my little radio next to my bed tuned to NBC, and me securely tucked between the sheets. My father was always perched on the edge of my bed calling our location the *cheap seats.* His only commentary during the call by Stanton would be an occasional *Uh, ah, son-of-a-buck* or his distinct giggle.

But between rounds, my father would throw himself into story telling mode. He could stop mid-sentence when the bell rang to start a new round, then pick his tale right back up at the exact point where he had stopped when the round ended. He would speak over the Gillette safety blade ads between rounds.

Early on, he did not speak of the war. Rather he would tell yarns of growing up in Newport Kentucky. For example, he loved to reminisce about playing basketball for Newport High School, explaining the only shot ever taken from the field was an underhand version of the two-handed set shot. The scores were always low. In his junior year, his last year in school (thanks to the depression and the need for him to find full time work), he played in a sectional final that ended with Newport losing by a score of 13-12, in overtime.

While providing a detailed description of the play by play of that game, he would throw his head back giving a big "hee, hee, hee, ha, oh, hee, hee, hee" giggle and say, "Son-of-a-buck, those were the days. We'd pass the ball a hundred times before we would shoot. If I shot too soon, I would find my young ass on the lumber. Old Coach McCabe didn't stand for any shit. Dammit to hell, we shoulda won that game."

He relished describing the tiny Newport High School gymnasium in which he perfected his underhand set shot, explaining how hard he practiced foul shots even though in his day fouls were rarely called. He played for Daniel McCabe, a real taskmaster, no non-sense coach, who also taught history. What really stuck with me was the affection with which he described his teammates, something that translated in my own playing days later.

In addition to going to school and playing football, basketball and baseball, starting at the age of nine, he worked as a pinsetter at the bowling alley on Monmouth Street, Newport's main drag. He explained the dangers of this kind of career. You had to be quick on your toes or you might lose a few toes. Everything *backstage,* as he called it, was manual. Automation of the bowling world was years off.

Here is also where he first started to drink. If he worked fast and hard, every now and then a happy bowler would send down a beer.

"You drank beer when you were nine?" I would exclaim in disbelief.

"Hell, yes, boy! That's how bowlers tipped you for hard work back then. Nothing goes better with a good cigarette than a cold beer!" he explained with a hardy giggle.

There were other stories about the dark side of Newport and the influence organized crime had over the town. When the Volstead Act was passed in 1919 establishing Prohibition, my father was nine years old. While he never mentioned the Volstead act in any of his stories, he did take great joy in talking about Prohibition and organized crime in Newport during his second decade of life.

Speakeasies, or *Tiger Blinds* as they were referred to in Newport, cropped up all over the little riverfront town. In fact, my grandfather, in order to supplement his meager income as a football shoe stitcher at the McGregor Goldsmith Company, managed a Tiger Blind on the outskirts of town on weekends. Dad would explain to me that while Gramps was technically breaking the law, it helped put food on the table. And Speakeasies were all over. The cops took bribes and turned their heads. That's just the way it was, he justified, making it sound like Henry Stertmeyer was doing a noble thing.

The name George Remus often came up in his Newport stories. Remus was the king of bootlegging in the Cincinnati area. Much of the subtleties regarding all of this were lost on me at my young age. But tales of Remus making Newport his center for producing illegal booze was clear. I suppose Remus stuck with me in particular because at that same time I was being exposed to jolly old Uncle Remus and *The Song of the South* in a record and book album about Briar Rabbit and his antagonists, Briar Bear and Briar Fox. So the name Remus struck a chord.

Sometimes Dad would scare the bejeebies out of me. For example, when he described how the crime bosses burned down Peter Schmidt's Beverly Hills Club for refusing to partner with them. My father thought this was funny while my reaction was fear, shock and anxiety. But there was something about my father's personality and demeanor that assured me he would protect me from evildoers, even mobsters.

In the category of lessons passed down is one of his tales from the baseball field that he told often and precisely. Dad was being wooed by the Pittsburgh Pirates at the young age of 15. To up his game, he hooked up with a semi-pro team in Cincinnati, where he was quickly welcomed by the more experienced and older ballplayers. Talent can trump experience.

But in this case, the experienced boys swept in with the mischief. A group of older players convinced Dad that to be a truly real ballplayer, one must chew tobacco.

So, at the start of their first game, the team's first baseman reached into his back pocket and produced a pouch of Red Man Chewing Tobacco and squeezed out a healthy pinch.

"Here, Stert, place this between your gums and your cheek," the teammate instructed. "Try not to swallow. Ya gotta learn to spit."

Obedient to a fault, my father slapped the chaw in place. As he explained, he spent the next 15 minutes doing a lot of spitting and not very much chewing. Finally, his turn at bat arrived. He rewarded his new team with a line drive down the right field line.

My father, now very animated, described the scene: "I was running like a scared rabbit, and I rounded first and headed to second. But their son-of-a-buck in right field was quick and had a hell of an arm. I could see it was going to be close, so I threw down my best hook-slide away from the ball and banged hard into their shortstop."

Now deep into his famous giggle, he said with great joy, "Well don't ya know I swallowed that Goddamned tobacco? Right down the hatch it went."

Very entertained with himself, he continued: "Well, shit fire if I didn't stand right up barf all over second base. That bag was covered in my lunch I can tell you. What I mess."

My giggle was now close to matching his when he told me, "Now you listen to me squirt. I never touched that crap again and if you are smart you won't ever go near Red Man, Oliver Twist, Mail Pouch or any other damned chewing tobacco. You just stick with that Double Bubble or Joe Palooka bubble gum, ya hear?"

Perhaps my favorite of his *growing up* stories was about the African American (sadly, not the terminology my father used at the time) Baptist Church that sat next to the railroad tracks on the west side of town. As a teenager, I surmised that this yarn was too outlandish to be true, but as a younger child it was a wondrous, happy account of mystical proportions.

As the narrative goes, on this particular Sunday, my father and a passel of his pals found themselves on a vacant dirt lot next to the church playing stickball. Given that it was a steamy hot summer day, the church windows were wide open, affording the group of young ballplayers easy access to the Reverend's loud and passionate sermon.

As my dad tells the story, the minister was praying that better times might be ahead for their little congregation. Certainly God would provide them with jobs and with more food and even enough coal to get the little church through the next winter.

Again, according to my father, the raconteur of this ridiculously irrational happening, no sooner had this last thought left the lips of the preacher man, when a coal train derailed, spilling three carloads of black gold at the door step of the church.

Wait it gets better. Everyone in the church rushed to the door to see what had caused the horrific crash outside. When the good pastor saw all of that coal, he screamed, "Praise Lord, thank God almighty. Our prayers have been answered."

I suppose any fable is born out of an element of truth. But that one was a doozy. The joy he derived out of telling this one was special. Years later I witnessed the delight my own young children got as he repeated this story to them. The merriment made whatever exaggeration there might have been worth it.

As to the war stories, they came to me in more circuitous fashion. He did not include these in his early Friday night bedside accounts. Rather, I first heard snippets of them as he sat on bar stools at Rudy's in Newport or the Bavarian Cafe in our Walnut Hills Neighborhood, with some of his cronies, having dismissed me to go suck down a Coke, or on the ball field before Fifth Third Friday night softball games, talking with other veterans who had returned to the bank from the war.

But as I pieced them together over time, I became curious and wanted to hear more. So I would ask naive questions like, "Dad, did you ever get seasick on those ships?"

"Hell, no, Kiddo. I got my sea legs fast. You had to," he would insist.

Eventually, this kind of banter broke the ice. Thus, I had opened the book cover on that *Encyclopedia of Harold Stertmeyer Goes to War.* Once opened, it was mostly the happy times that spewed forth. Even at a young age, I could see the conflict he had to confront as he spoke about his time at sea. Even as he told the funny tales, there were times when he would stop mid-sentence and glare into space, searching for something that I could not imagine. Then he would smile, shake it off and go on with the dialog.

For my father, the most difficult stories to tell, and for me to grasp, were accounts of the stress of German submarine attacks, as well as those related to his assignment as the Pharmacist Mate aboard any given ship he might be on.

Dad spent his time afloat between tankers and freighters. These two distinctively different types of ships were constant targets when at sea as they carried important fuel and other supplies for the American war effort. The tankers were distinctive when full, as you could barely see the middle of the ship weighed down by the oil it carried. But, as I was to learn, they could turn night into day if struck mid-ship by just a single torpedo.

Merchant mariners were on the front lines the moment their ships left US ports and were subject to attack by bombers, battleships, submarines, mines, and even land-based artillery in Africa and Europe. All World War II mariners received gunnery training from the US Maritime Service, including good old Dad.

Dad often told a frightening story of a 13-ship convoy he was on that sailed from Galveston, Texas bound for the Brooklyn Navy Yard. Of the original 13 vessels, only seven made it to New York. Of the six that didn't make it, three were sunk. The other three were badly damaged. He explained that the attacks were countered by US support from the air and by the use of depth charges, efforts that may have saved his life.

In truth, German submarines attacked fuel tankers and cargo ships with impunity and often within sight of shore. Fortunately, he survived that voyage, but as the Pharmacist Mate he had to treat several wounded mariners who had been plucked out of the ocean. The stress of this assignment, given his limited training, was obvious. Yet, he spoke of it all with a smile and a sense of accomplishment in helping to save several lives until they could get proper treatment. He knew, as did I, that he was very lucky he had lived to tell the tale.

Dad did have one funny account of standing on the bridge with his ship's captain at dusk one evening when they observed what they thought were two torpedoes headed straight at them. With his familiar giggle, he explained that just as the torpedoes were about to strike his ship, they realized that they were dolphins, not torpedoes. This was funny to hear, but maybe not so hilarious standing on the bridge at the time.

One aside of hearing of his war adventures was learning naval and sailing terms of the day. Things like, *Aye, Aye Sir, Port, Starboard, Carry On, Dog Watch (late watch on a ship... usually from 8-midnight), Bulwark,*

Bulkhead, Berth, Binnacle, Poop Deck, Quarter Deck, Gunwale, Bow, Stern, Hull, True Bearing, Able Seaman, Ahoy, All Hands on Deck, Buoy, Ashore, Battle Stations or General Quarters, Batten Down the Hatches, Galley, Below Deck, Brig, Capsize, Cargo Ship, Come About, Convoy, Crow's Nest, Jib, Destroyer, Carrier, Battleship, U-Boat, Fathom, Freighter, Gang Plank, Helmsman, Keel, Landlubber, Liberty (time off or furlough), Lookout, Mae West (Life Preserver), Mess, Minesweeper, The Old Man (the Captain), Skipper and Old Salt (an experienced mariner), Pilot Boat, Safe Harbor, Sea Legs, Sextant, Shanghaied, Shore Leave, Square Meal, Task Force, Tender, Waterline, Way-Lay, Weigh Anchor, and Wheelhouse, all became part of the lexicon of my Friday nights with Harold.

While my father and his mates would have been called *sailors* in the Navy, in the Merchant Marines they were referred to as *mariners.* And being a mariner ultimately took him around the world.

On the brighter side of his defense of the good old United States of America he was able to visit India, including Calcutta and the Taj Mahal, Australia including Sydney and Perth, North Africa, including Algeria and Morocco, and at the end of the war, Italy, France and England. He brought back some fascinating photos of Naples and Pompeii. He also sent home furniture and trinkets from his many ports of call, some of which I still own to this day. The one place he raved about most was Rio de Janeiro, calling it the most beautiful place he had ever seen.

During the war, Brazil was a loyal ally of the United States and sent its military to fight against Germany, even as German U-boats sank many Brazilian ships. The US provided $100 million in *Lend-Lease* money in return for use of airfields and ports to ferry troops and supplies across the Atlantic, including naval bases to help fight off U-boats. While Rio may have been beautiful, these were not the safest sailings my father took during the war.

With that said, the thing that he spoke of often with pure joy was his three crossings of the equator. His first and third sojourns over the earth's center line separating the Northern Hemisphere from the Southern Hemisphere were on journeys to Brazil. The other was on a sailing from Singapore to

Australia.

Perhaps he enjoyed describing these crossings and the requisite ceremony attached to the event more than any other recollection of the war. In rapid fashion, trying to get in as much information as possible between rounds of a fight, he would launch into a tirade, "So, they had this crossing ceremony, known as *The Order of Neptune*. It was a big tradition for sailors and mariners. Ya see, the point is to commemorate the first crossing of the Equator."

As he spoke, I gathered in my young mind that this tradition may have been sanctioned as a boost to morale, or perhaps was created as a test for seasoned sailors to ensure their new shipmates were capable of handling long rough times at sea. At least, that was how he spun it.

He would continue, "The guys who have already crossed the Equator are nicknamed *Shellbacks* or *Trusty Shellbacks* or *Honorable Shellbacks*, or *Sons of Neptune.* At any rate, those who have not crossed before are nicknamed *Pollywogs* or *Slimy Pollywogs.*" He would take a big breath then continue with great delight, "So, get this, the ceremony features King Neptune. There's this two-day event. It starts in the evening and then continues the entire next day, ya see?"

Another deep breath, trying to hurry to beat the bell signaling the start of the next round, "What ya need to understand, bub, this is a serious ritual where the old guys who were previously inducted crew members, the *Shellbacks* ya see, are organized into a *Court of Neptune*, in order to induct the *Pollywogs* into "the Mysteries of the Deep." By this time, I was more than a little confused. But each time he'd repeat the rant, it would come more clearly into focus, until I was laughing along with him at every turn, fully knowing what was coming next.

He explained that physical hardship, in keeping with the spirit of the initiation, was tolerated, and each *Pollywog* was expected to endure a standard initiation rite in order to become a *Shellback*. After another round of NBC boxing, he would pick up right where he had left off. " Listen close now because this is important. The night before the equatorial crossing was called *Wog Day* and, and the Pollywogs are allowed to capture and interrogate any Shellbacks they can find. But those son-of-a-bucks would hide." Another gasp of breath, and he would go on, "If they found one, they would tie the sucker up." A hardy laugh and then, "So then the Wogs would crack eggs or pour aftershave lotion on the heads of the captured Shellbacks, hee, hee, hee." "But," he would continue, with tears now running down his face from his own self-imposed hilarity, "the Pollywogs were made very aware that it could be much harder on them the next day if they were to do anything like this."

After one more round of boxing, both of us hoping for a knockout to eliminate further interruptions, he would pick things back up. "After crossing the Equator, Pollywogs received subpoenas to appear before *King Neptune and his Court,* usually including his first assistant *Davy Jones* and her *Highness Amphitrite* and often a bunch dignitaries, who are all represented by the highest-ranking seamen on board."

"What's a subpoena?" I would ask.

"Shit, squirt, don't you know nothing? A subpoena is a summons, a request, get it?"

After nodding that I got it, on he would go. "The seamen then officiate at the ceremony, which is preceded by a beauty contest of men dressing up as women. Each department of the ship is required to introduce one contestant in swimsuit drag. Afterwards, King Neptune might interrogate some of the guys."

"What is drag?" I might ask.

He would give me a frustrated look, think for a second and then advise me, "Well let's see squirt, what is drag? Well that's when men dress up like women, get it."

Actually, at first, I didn't get it. But he would forge ahead.

"Now listen to this this. They would use what they called *truth serum.* Ya wanna know what that was?" he'd ask.

Before I could answer, he would answer his own question, "The truth serum was hot sauce and after shave and whole uncooked eggs. And the Shellbacks would put that mess in the Pollywogs mouths, hee, hee, hee."

That part usually made me gag.

"But wait, there's more," he would say.

"During the ceremony, the Pollywogs had to undergo a number of increasingly embarrassing ordeals, like wearing their clothing inside out and backwards; crawling on hands and knees on coated decks so they would slide all over the place, hee, hee, hee."

At this point, he was lost in his tale of the Equator.

"There's more. The Pollywogs got locked up in wooden stocks. You know where the heads and hands stick out? Then they would get swatted with short lengths of fire hose and get pelted with mushy fruit. Then they would get locked in a water coffin of salt-water and bright green sea dye and forced to crawl through chutes or large tubs of rotting garbage and then kiss the Royal Baby's belly that was coated with axle grease."

I found all of this disgusting while Dad just screamed with laughter. I guess you had to be there. But to be there when he was playing dodgems with torpedoes and mortar shells? No thanks.

Once he had gathered his wits, Dad would finish the story with a final explanation.

"So, once the ceremony is complete, a Pollywog receives a certificate declaring his new status as a Shellback. I became a Shellback on April 17, 1944," he would proudly announce.

Fortunately, my father had several black and white photos of this ceremony he had brought back with him. Seeing him wearing a mop on his head, a grass skirt around his waist, a nicely crafted shell necklace and two coconut shells fashioned bra held together with thick cord, helped me to grasp both the term *drag* and the delight he took in having experienced this crazy ritual.

Who knew war could be so much fun?

This Friday night ritual continued right up until we moved from Spokane Avenue in Walnut Hills eight miles north to Grafton Avenue in Bond Hill (there are a lot of hills in Cincinnati). Thus, in August of 1953, our Friday night special came to an abrupt and unceremonial end. And with that, it seemed that my father's drinking grew worse as did our corresponding relationship.

Yet, over that seven-year period, my father's little story bank built into a multi-volume library, with weekly deposits being made from bar stools, bedside chats, backyard ball tosses and in 1953 at the smoky confines of the Evanston VFW.

The latter was kind of the icing on the cake and the final chapter. In the spring of that year, I tried out for and was selected to play for the touted Evanston VFW Class C knothole baseball team. When I was selected in March, my father became an assistant coach.

Thus, what followed was not only a very special year of baseball, but the complete opening up of my father's war archives. After every practice and home game, my dad would take me across the street to the VFW hall where he and the other coaches would aggressively throw back a passel of beer drawn from the taps behind the long shiny dark walnut bar.

And the stories would pour out as quickly as the beer from the tap. Now being the age of ten and being around thirty to forty WWII veterans two to three times a week filled in the color of the black and white picture of the war that my father had provided up to that point.

And like at no other time, being around all of his fellow veterans, helped to open Harold Stertmeyer's willingness to fill in some blanks. For the first time, I heard the actual blood and guts details about him having to treat half drowned, badly wounded seaman covered with in a mixture of crude oil and salty sea water, some with limbs missing. I learned of sailors and mariners dying in front of him as he tried to do what he could to stop their bleeding and sew them up with his limited first-aid training, too often to no avail.

And listening to the other vets tell their sad yet often funny accounts of the horrors of war, I realized two things. I discovered the importance of humor and booze as the universal antidotes to their emotional wounds that they had embedded in them after the war.

Then in August of 1953 we moved into our new home in the Cincinnati suburb of Bond Hill. That same month my baseball season gloriously came to an end when Evanston VFW went to the city knothole baseball finals. Both of these events occurred in the same week. After that, my father and

I never again set foot in the Evanston VFW Hall, nor did we ever again listen to a Friday night fight in my new bedroom. So, the stories, for me, had come to an end.

But my father's great stories endure, tucked away in a very special place in my memory bank. And I am grateful for the times he later spent telling these same stories to my cousins Paul and Rick Anderson on fishing trips and especially for the occasions with my own two children long after he had conquered the demons of drink.

I have never been able to look back on my times of hearing him tell his personal tales without thinking of his drinking. For me, they are forever attached. But, as he might have said at the time, "Don't make a federal case out of it."

And in an odd way, there was nothing in my relationship with him that brought us closer. But I still doubt the reality of that damned train dumping coal at the door of that Newport Baptist Church. Sorry, Dad.

Gi's aboard the Waterbury Victory

Cincinnati Union Terminal During WWII

"Yank Magazine"

Sad Sack WWII Comic Strip

Merchant Vessel Sinks off the U. S. East Coast

Comparison of Merchant Marine casualty rate to other services

Service	Number serving	War Dead	Percent	Ratio
Merchant Marine	**243,000***	**9,521****	**3.90%**	**1 in 26**
Marines	669,108	19,733	2.94%	1 in 34
Army	11,268,000	234,874	2.08%	1 in 48
Navy	4,183,466	36,958	0.88%	1 in 114
Coast Guard	242,093	574	0.24%	1 in 421
Total	16,576,667	295,790	1.78%	1 in 56

The King and the Order of Neptune

Tony Zale Vs. Rocky Graziano Friday, September 27, 1946

1948

I was thrilled to death
The day Babe Ruth signed my baseball...
I'll always remember that,
The greatest one of all...

From *A Man I Always Wanted to Meet*
By George Jones

THE BALL

Without any real appreciation for what I was experiencing, on May 8, 1948, I met a legend. Although to me he seemed huge, what little voice he had left was but a gravely whisper. "He's dying," my Uncle Joe explained.

Now, I was young, sure enough. But I was not so young that I didn't know that this was the great Babe Ruth who sat in front of me. The Great Bambino... the Sultan of Swat... the Colossus of Clout. This was the God of baseball. How could he be dying? As I stood next to him in the Cincinnati Reds' dugout, shaking his hand, I was sure he wasn't dying.

Letting go of my little hand, he signed a baseball using a very fancy fountain pen held in his big right hand and presented it to me. "There you are, little shaver," he murmured. He then tugged on the brim of my ball cap and tried to laugh, but all that he could muster was a smile and a cough.

It was purely the luck of the draw that had me in the third base dugout of Crosley Field, home of the Cincinnati Reds, on this warm sunny afternoon in early May.

When my Uncle Joe got out of the Army after World War II, he joined the American Legion and met a very special guy named Joe Hawk. This new friend of my uncle was the manager of the Bentley Post American Legion baseball team. In 1947, Uncle Joe, who had played one year of minor league baseball for the Williamson Red Birds in West Virginia with future Hall of Famer, Stan Musial, became an assistant coach for Hawk.

Hawk was already a legend in Cincinnati amateur baseball. His Bentley

Post team won the American Legion National Championship in 1947, my Uncle Joe's first year as an assistant coach, and no wonder. Their lineup included catcher Jack Gannon, hard hitting Hal Grote in left field, Stu Hein in center field, and a solid infield that included first baseman, Jim Frey, shortstop, Don Zimmer and his cousin Bill Zimmer at second base. Their ace on the mound was a lanky guy named Bill Crigler with Hein as a backup.

Also on the team was Glenn Sample who went on to become the Head Baseball Coach at the University of Cincinnati and the official scorer for the Reds for more than thirty years, including the Big Red Machine era. Hal Grot and Jim Frey both played in the minor leagues with Frey later managing two major league teams, the Kansas City Royals and the Chicago Cubs.

And, of course, there was the feisty little shortstop, Don Zimmer, who went on to have a half a century career in Major League Baseball as a player, coach and manager.

Zimmer is perhaps most famous as the recipient of a serious bean ball in 1953 when he was hit by a pitch causing him to lose consciousness. He suffered a brain injury that required surgery. He woke up two weeks later thinking that it was the day after the game. He spent the rest of his life with a steel plate in his head. This led to Major League Baseball adopting batting helmets as a safety measure to be used by players when at bat. New York Yankee shortstop, Phil Rizzuto, was the first player to use a batting helmet.

As for Joe Hawk, he went on to manage the Xavier University baseball team in the 1960s. I competed against his Musketeers while playing at Miami University from 1962-1964.

In 1948, it was my good fortune to become the bat boy for Hawk's ball club, thus fate brought me to Crosley Field on May 8 as Bentley Post played an afternoon exhibition game versus a Legion team from Cleveland before the Reds took on the Boston Braves.

Unbeknownst to any of us, the Reds had scheduled Babe Ruth to be there where he spent half of the exhibition game with the two competing teams.

It was after the game that each player, coach and I lined up to meet Ruth and receive an autographed ball.

That ball has had an interesting life.

In his infinite wisdom, my father, who was also in attendance that day, decided that the ball needed more autographs, so off we went before the Reds game with the Braves.

In 1948, the Red's Club House was a separate building sitting in the parking lot adjacent to the ballpark. The players would access the field through two tunnels. The first led from the Club House to the right field concession area under the stadium. This allowed fans to get a look at and request autographs before the players entered the second tunnel that lead onto the field.

It was to that concession area that dad and I went to seek more ink for my new prized baseball. Thanks to us so doing, the ball became one of a kind.

By the time the Reds started their batting practice the ball was signed with my father's Esterbrook fountain pen by some of the great unknowns in baseball annals. Along with the great Babe Ruth it now contained the signatures of Grady Hatton, Ray Mueller, Virgil Stallcup, Bobby Adams along with Reds stars Ted Kluszewski and Ewell Blackwell and many more.

We did not know it at the time, but this little exercise had greatly devalued the ball. Yet fate once again interceded. There was one large void on the ball on the exact opposite side from Ruth's familiar signature. In 1974, after Hank Aaron broke Ruth's record of 714 home runs, I ventured down to the new Riverfront Stadium in Cincinnati, ball in hand. It was three hours before the Reds took on the now Atlanta Braves. Of course, you couldn't get near Aaron.

But I was a clever young man. I took a little sojourn down the left field line to the area above the Braves bullpen. I shouted down to a player standing alone with his catcher's glove and a jaw full of tobacco.

I yelled down to him, "Hey there. I have this ball that is signed by Babe Ruth and would love to get Hank to sign it to."

"Let me see that," he replied.

Against my better judgment, I tossed the ball the five feet down to him.

He examined the ball for a rather long time and then asked, "Who the hell is Virgil Stalcup?"

"He was the Reds shortstop in 1948," I smiled back at him, thinking *who the hell are you?*

"Wait right there," he ordered, and headed toward the Braves dugout with my damned ball.

I sat there and waited and waited. Five minutes went by. Then ten minutes. I was really beginning to think I would never see that ball again, unsure of what to do next.

Then suddenly here he came, with old number 44 right behind him.

Aaron reached up offering me his hand, saying, "Hi, I'm Henry Aaron."

No shit, I thought. I reached down, shook his hand and introduced myself.

Suddenly I was surrounded with an army of kids anxious to get through me to touch baseball's hero of the year.

"How did you get this?" he asked.

With kids trying to climb over me, I gave him a very short version of my day on May 8, 1948.

"Do you have a pen?" Hank inquired.

I did. He took my ballpoint and scribbled his signature on the spot that seemed to have been destined for his autograph.

Then he handed it back and said, "Ewell Blackwell signed it. That guy had a wicked side arm delivery. I could never quite figure him out. They called him *The Whip*, you know?"

"Yea, he was great," I replied.

And Blackwell was great. On June 18, 1947, a year before the Babe signed my ball, Blackwell had pitched a 6–0 no-hitter against the Boston Braves. In his next start, on June 22, against the Brooklyn Dodgers, he took a no-hitter into the ninth inning, trying to tie the achievement of his veteran Reds teammate Johnny Vander Meer from nine years earlier, when Vander Meer tossed two consecutive no-hitters. Unfortunately, his no-hit attempt was ruined when Eddie Stankey got a base hit. The Reds won the game 4–0. Yes, Blackwell was special.

At that point, I looked like a fully poked piñata with kids pouring out of me.

"It's a real honor to sign that ball," Hank said with a genuine smile.

With that he turned away and jogged quickly back to the Brave's dugout, followed by a swarm of kids, leaving me standing alone with the unknown catcher who had been my autograph agent.

I thanked him and headed back to my seat in the sixth row opposite third base, the ball firmly in my grip. A few fans gathered around, curious how I had attracted Aaron to the Braves bullpen. I did a few show-and-tells and then settled in to watch the ball game.

Most of the twenty-six years between the Bambino and Hammerin' Hank events the ball stayed pretty much in hiding. Until I was in my teens, my parents supervised when and where it was allowed to appear. And we learned early that blue fountain pen ink would fade if left open to the elements. So that little sphere spent most of its time under lock and key in my father's roll top desk.

After Aaron signed it, I showed it off fairly regularly at cocktail parties, business meetings and holiday gatherings. It is hard to explain the subliminal pressure attended to caring for such a treasure.

I could go months without laying eyes on it or even thinking about it. Then the Yankees played the Atlanta Braves in the 1996 World Series. I had become the Senior Vice President of Sales and Marketing for Questech, Inc., in Vermont early that year. Our sales office was on the Upper East Side in Manhattan. Thus, I was in New York City often.

As it were, on October 26th, the day the Yankees won the Series, I was in the City. I had drinks with my old friend Fred Zigler that night at one of my favorite New York spots, Gallagher's Steak House on 52nd Street. Like me, Fred was in town on business. We watched the pregame at the bar.

When he had to depart for dinner, I walked nine blocks up to Mickey Mantle's Restaurant because symmetry and sentimentality are both part of who I am. Mantle had passed away the previous year, so watching the game at his watering hole just seemed right. There was a huge crowd of like-minded fans spilling out of Mantle's onto 59th Street.

Standing in the sidewalk section of the restaurant, I ordered a Bombay Martini (dirty) and watched the Yanks polish off the Braves. It was a great game six, with the Yanks scoring three runs early. The Braves staged a late comeback, scoring their second run in the top of the ninth. But John Wetteland held off the Braves, and the Bronx Bombers were once again the World Champs.

The next morning, I picked up a copy of the *New York Times* at the Warwick Hotel where I normally stayed. There were several stories about the previous night's game. The one that caught my eye was an interview with the Yankees *bench coach,* Don Zimmer. It began this way: "In the Yankee dugout, Joe Torre heard the voice of his bench coach, Don Zimmer. "Don't worry about it," Zimmer said. "This is the one for Frank. This is the last pitch.'"

Zimmer had been referring to Joe Torre's brother, Frank, who was critically ill at the time. And Don was right. On the next pitch. Mark Lemke lifted a pop-up down the third base line that Charlie Hayes easily caught for the final out of the series. I continued to read as Zimmer waxed sentimental about his years in baseball. And then, there it was. Zimmer talked about the day he met Babe Ruth at an American Legion game at Crosley Field in Cincinnati. He described Ruth's raspy voice followed by a description of Ruth signing balls for all of the participants. He joked that he and his cousin Bill Zimmer, not realizing the value of the gift, had both used their Ruth balls to toss around and had essentially ruined them. His old pal Jim Frey, on the other hand, had put his ball in a safe place and still had it. "Today that ball would probably be worth more than the Yankees are paying me," Zimmer joked. Reading Zimmer's comments about that special day in May almost fifty years earlier was a surreal moment. It just added to the mystique of owning such a treasure. By that time, I was keeping Ruth, Aaron, Kluszewski, Blackwell, Hatton, Stallcup et al tightly locked in a secure location back at my home in Cincinnati. When my son Scott turned forty in 2010, my wife Peggy and I took him and our daughter-in-law Tami out to dinner to celebrate. My gift to him was my baseball treasure from 1948. Now it's his problem.

The Babe's Autograph

1949

Oh, we're the men of Texaco
We work from Maine to Mexico
There's nothing like this Texaco of ours!
Our show is very powerful
We'll wow you with an hour full
Of howls from a shower full of stars.
We're the merry Texaco men
Tonight we may be showmen
Tomorrow we'll be servicing your cars!
We wipe your pipe
We pump your gas
We jack your back
We scrub your glass

So join the ranks of those who know
And fill your tanks with Texaco......And now, ladies and gentlemen... America's number one television star... MILTON BERLE!...

....The Milton Berle Theme song

THE BOX

It arrived in our home and into my life on the third Tuesday of October 1949. Along with it, came half of our Spokane Avenue neighbors. A large console radio had claimed center stage in our living room long ago. Not knowing what to do with this new contraption that my father had insisted we must have at all cost, my mother instructed the deliverymen to place it in a corner of our dining room. In so doing, she may have provided the original inspiration for something to be later known as the *TV Dinner*.

This new modern miracle was, of course, called a television set. Why it was called a *set*, I could not say, as there was only one television, unlike a *set* of golf clubs or a *set* of fine china or a new *set* of Goodyear tires. Ours was a Philco. It stood four feet high. Had it not been for the piece of gray glass situated in its top center, it might have been just another radio. This slightly bulbous glass was called a screen. It measured thirteen inches on the diagonal from one rounded corner to the other.

After the delivery men had uncrated this new marvel and situated it just so in the assigned corner, they plugged it in, and the taller of the two clicked the knob to the far left and waited. After fifteen seconds or so, something appeared on the screen that the smaller man referred to as *snow*. The neighbors now forming a large semi-circle around our dining room table gave out with a collective *ahhhh*.

Out of a separate box came a tenticaled monstrosity they called *rabbit-ears*, though it looked more like a basketball hoop with a praying mantis on top. It was the antenna. Without it, our only option was to watch *snow* to perpetuity.

The instant that the rabbit-ears were properly attached, a new kind of blur appeared. We were suddenly looking at a series of black, gray and white diagonal lines. The neighbors all looked at one another with questioning stares. One of the installers began to explain this diagonal phenomenon to my mother. But she had already been overwhelmed with snow. I was, therefore, instructed to listen and learn.

Over the next ten minutes, at the age of almost seven, I became the neighborhood expert on television. With that ten-minute lead, no adult relative would ever come close to understanding the technology of television as well as I.

It was explained to me that these lines on the screen could be eliminated by one of a series of small knobs situated just below the bottom of the screen. This particular knob was called the *vertical hold.* Sure enough, with some rather delicate tuning, the diagonal lines disappeared, replaced by a barely distinguishable vision of cowboys jumping up and down all over the screen to the point of distraction.

Not to worry. This dilemma was resolved by something called the *horizontal hold* knob. With a deft adjustment of this dial by the smaller installer, the very first clear image I was ever to see on television appeared. It was a cowboy racing down a hill on horseback in hot pursuit of a gang of villains, all with guns blazing. As two of the bad guys fell from their horses, our crowd of neighbors responded as if they were seeing a magic show. There were shouts of glee, smiles, and looks of wonderment as the protagonist continued to close in on the bad guys. I would soon learn that this hero dressed in white, astride a light-colored palomino, was Bob Steele, and the show was called *Six Gun Theater.*

As our neighbors continued to gawk in disbelief at the heroics of Bob Steele, I was guided to a spot where I could view the television from behind. I was advised of the danger of poking around inside the back of the set while it was plugged in. The view from the back revealed a dozen or so bulbous gizmos all lightly aglow. They ranged in size and shape. The man related that every so often these would burn out like a light bulb and would have to be replaced. He then pointed to the cylinder that was at the end of what he called the picture tube. It was the other side of this picture tube that, to no great surprise, provided the picture. This, and only this, I was told, carried a one-year warranty. For the first time, my mother understood something about the television that I did not. She was much more impressed with the warranty than with Bob Steele, who was now in a fistfight with four bad guys and winning easily.

The taller delivery guy turned back to me, ready to complete my training. He pointed to the largest dial on the front of the set that was surrounded by the numbers two through thirteen. This was the channel selector, or *dial*. A channel was the television version of what was referred to as a station on the radio. However, unlike the radio where there were several stations from which to choose, our television only offered three channels. The red mark on the channel changer was pointed at the number seven. The man explained that this was the CBS station, which stood for Columbia Broadcasting System. The other two options were channel 4, the NBC (National Broadcasting Company) channel and channel 11, the Dumont Network. I knew CBS and NBC from the radio.

The channel changer, I discovered, clicked as you turned it from one channel to the next, locking it into place for the given channel. However, it was surrounded by a dial that spun freely when turned. I asked the big guy what this was for. He explained that there were VHF stations like NBC and CBS and then there were also UHF stations. Unfortunately, Cincinnati had no UHF stations yet, so the big free-spinning dial was of no use. But the TV professor went on to explain that, if UHF were available, it would be accessed by putting the clicking dial on channel 13 and then fine tuning it to the UHF channel with the spinning dial.

I glanced at him with full understanding. I then looked to my mother whose eyes had rolled back into her spinning head. I was fairly certain that she would be tuning in to the *Shadow* later that evening – on the radio!

The short guy slid some paperwork under my mother's nose. She shook her head to clear away the shock, and semi-consciously signed the receipt. Mutt and Jeff thanked us all and headed for the stairs, the empty cartons in hand. Many of our accumulated neighbors exited behind them, several asking for an invitation to see more television soon.

Mrs. Van Outer from downstairs said to my mother, "Well, Paula, that thing is fascinating. But, if Dutch thinks he is getting one any time soon, he has another think coming." Dutch was Mae Van Outer's husband. They rented the downstairs apartment from my parents. Their son, Neil, was my best friend. He stood with his nose two feet from our new contraption.

This was a big event, and it required re-enforcements, I reasoned. So, I quickly asked my mother and Mrs. Van Outer if Neil could stay and watch whatever it was that we might see on our Philco television set. Neil looked at his mother with pleading eyes while I used the same strategy on my mother, who quickly nodded her consent. After a brief pause, Mrs. V agreed then stated sternly to Neil, "You get right down stairs for supper at 5:30 sharp, young man. Understood?"

Neil and I quickly scrambled to the two dining room chairs that afforded us the best view and turned our attention to the action on the screen. By this time, Bob Steele had successfully dispatched the six bad guys and was now planting a cowboy kiss on the gal he had just saved from harm's way.

What followed on that magical October Tuesday was beyond fascinating. After Steele's heroics on Six Gun Theater came a string of short shows, each incredible in their own way.

Six Gun Theater ended, and I decided I needed to test my tuning skills. I gave the channel changer a few clicks from channel 7 back down to channel four, the NBC station.

In so doing, Six Gun Theater was replaced by something called The Howdy Doody Show. This half hour extravaganza had a mix of real people and marionettes interacting as if they were all human. The theme was a combination of old frontier meets the circus.

Neil and I were quickly introduced to the host, Buffalo Bob Smith, dressed in pioneer garb, and the other three real humans, Chief Thunder Thud, Princess Sumer Fall Winter Spring (both woo-woo kind of Indians) and the very mischievous Clarabelle the Clown.

The rest of the cast all hung from the strings that controlled their motions. That portion of the cast consisted of a goofy and somewhat naive young boy named Dilly Dally, a wacky character known as Flub-a-Dub who seemed to be parts duck, dog, giraffe, seal and cat, a grumpy old Scottish-looking codger whose appropriate moniker was Mr. Bluster; and, of course, the hero of the whole party, the freckled faced redheaded "gee-wiz" character, Howdy Doody himself.

Howdy was adorned in baggy jeans tucked into cowboy boots, a plaid shirt and a big western-type scarf. His face was frozen into an inviting smile, and his wooden hair swooped low onto his forehead. I assumed his hair was red due the overstated freckles that covered his broad cheeks.

The show was performed in front of a live audience of laughing, screaming youngsters who sat in a small set of stands referred to as the Peanut Gallery. I had tuned to the new station just in time to hear Buffalo Bob exclaim, "Hey kids, what time is it?"

On cue, the Peanut Gallery responded as one, "It's Howdy Doody time!" They then broke into the show's theme song of the same name sung to the tune "Ta-ra-ra Boom-de-ay."

It's Howdy Doody Time.
It's Howdy Doody Time.
Bob Smith and Howdy too
Say Howdy Do to you.
Let's give a rousing cheer,
Cause Howdy Doody's here,
It's time to start the show,
So, kids let's go!

A big part of this first show that Neil and I watched that late October afternoon was based around Clarabelle confounding Buffalo Bob, Chief Thunder Thud and old Mr. Bluster in a way that kept all of the kids in the Peanut Gallery wailing with laughter, well aware of the clown's ploys. Thus, the kids continuously screamed their warnings to Clarabelle's victims... all to no avail.

The show concluded with Buffalo Bob scolding Clarabelle for all of his insensitive shenanigans followed by a short "life-lesson" speech by Howdy Doody, reminding the "kids" in the Peanut Gallery and out there in television land of the importance of respecting your fellow peanuts. Let's face it, I had already concluded that television was a powerful learning tool and I would no longer need to go to school. I must convince my mother of this obvious fact.

As Howdy dissolved from our little 13-inch screen, I heard my father bust through our front door a floor below and scream up the steps, "Did the television arrive?"

My mother responded with dismayed reservation, "Yes, Harold, your silly new gizmo is in the dining room."

"What the hell is it doing in the dining room?" he exclaimed.

Dumb question, I thought to myself. Everyone knew who was going to win that debate. My dad may have prevailed in his quest to buy a television, but it wasn't about to replace the grand console radio that sat next to my mother's baby grand piano in our living room.

My father hurried into the dining room; his face lit with the glee of a kid on Christmas morning.

"Hi boys," he cheered in our direction.

He immediately started attacking all of the dials, introducing himself to snow as well as horizontal and vertical television distractions.

"Son-of-a-buck," he whispered to himself as he looked to me for help.

So, the almost seven-year-old television professor (me) took over, explaining the art of TV tuning to my eager student (my father). He absorbed this new technology much better than my mother had. After a few *tell them, then show them, then have them do it,* lessons, the old man smiled with his newly gained mastering of the very complicated business of television. He was now in command.

After checking out the three program options, my father settled on something called "Paul Dixon's Music Shop" on channel 7. Dad explained to Neil and me that this was the same Paul Dixon that was a popular disc jockey on the radio. More magic... we now had a face that went with a familiar voice.

This show was built around current day musical hits that were played on a record player while Dixon and/or a gorgeous brunette named Dottie

Mack pantomimed the lyrics in front of some really corny settings. Twice during the half hour, another happy lady with very curly hair, who was introduced as Wanda Lewis, using what looked like a grease pencil, actually illustrated the premise of the song on a large piece of white paper hung from an easel. Her drawings were done right next to the goof ball (Dixon or Mack) who was pantomiming. It was all very peculiar, yet fascinating.

About ten minutes into Paul Dixon's Music Shop there was a rap on the back-hallway door that lead to a stairway which gave access up to the attic or down to the Van Outers' apartment. It was Mrs. V, who was very unhappy that she had to climb those old wooden stairs to collect Neil. She sternly reminded him of his earlier promise to be down for dinner promptly at 5:30. Neil was ten minutes late... not good.

My father and I allowed my mother to handle that nonsense. We were very busy watching television... your loss, Neil.

My dad did have the decency to yell in the direction of the hallway, "Hey, Mae, why don't you and Dutch bring Neil up at 8:00 to watch Milton Berle? He's supposed to have the best show on television."

Mrs. Van Outer replied, "We'll see. Neil has to be in bed at 9:00 on the dot. How long is the show?"

"An hour," my father came back. "C'mon Mae, this is television. It won't kill the little bugger to get ten minutes less sleep. Put him in his pajamas and you and Paula can listen to *The Shadow* on the radio in the living room. I hope you can come up. We'll keep the hall door open. Just let yourselves in."

I heard Mrs. V ask my mother if she was OK with that. My mother promised some potato chips and Seven-Up to Mrs. V, encouraging her to accept the invitation. Neil's mother loved Seven-Up, as did mine. With that, Neil started to lobby for Berle watching.

Finally, Mrs. Van Outer agreed with a quick, "Well, OK. That sounds like fun. We'll see you all at 8."

My father and I returned our attention to the Philco where Paul Dixon and Dottie Mack where pantomiming to the Johnny Mercer/Margaret Whiting version of "Baby It's Cold Outside," featuring a very fake fireplace.

We giggled through the rest of the show.

Just as my mother started to serve spaghetti and meatballs and my father was twirling the clicking channel changer, *The Camel News Caravan* with John Cameron Swasey was coming on the air. Swasey was a suave, well-tailored guy with a smooth baritone voice and a comforting smile.

My mother said, "OK, it's time to turn that thing off."

"Oh, for Crissakes, Paula, let us boys have a little fun with our new contraption, will ya," my father barked back. She either saw my eager joy or my father's determination or both. In any case, she capitulated.

So, through the spaghetti, we watched Swasey, the man who would later become more famous as the spokesperson for Timex Watches ("Takes a licking and keeps on ticking"), report the news and sell Camel Cigarettes. The big story that night was about China, and its leader, Mao Tse Tung, who had declared over the past weekend that China was a communist country and that the former leader Chang Kai-Shek had been dispatched to Taiwan.

What came after that was a cascade of memorable shows that live with me to this day.

First, on the Dumont network we found Captain Video and the Video Rangers. The show was set in the distant-future and followed the adventures of a group of fighters for *truth and justice*. Known as the Video Rangers, they were led by the incomparable Captain Video. The Rangers operated from a secret base on a mountain top. They wore uniforms that resembled what you might find in a US Army Surplus Store at the time. Their symbol was a prominent thunderbolt sewn on their shirt over their heart.

The show was pure science fiction. Captain Video received his orders from the Commissioner of Public Safety who was responsible for the entire solar system including human colonies on several planets and stars. One of the regular characters was a robot named *I Tobor*, or *Robot* spelled backwards. And, of course, there was the predictable antagonist, Dr. Pauli, an accomplished inventor and evil genius who wore gangster-style pinstripe suits and spoke with the snarl of many of the foreign villains to be found in the movies in the 40's. This show was as goofy and unsophisticated as was the *Paul Dixon Music Shop,* yet my father and I became completely immersed in this outer space odyssey. As we would soon learn, during commercial breaks Dumont aired special *Video Ranger* messages ranging from public service spots on morality and civics to advertisements for Video Ranger merchandise such as space helmets, secret code guns, flying saucer rings, decoder badges, photo-printing rings, and Viking rockets complete with launchers, all aimed at selling sponsor's products such as Powerhouse Candy Bars. This is how we spent 7:00 pm to 7:30 pm on this magical Tuesday. And then as the minute hand began to sweep north, I met some more new friends named Kukla, Fran and Ollie.

Long before something called the remote control was available, I was the remote control in our house. Eventually, on a typical evening, I would hear requests such as, "Randy would you put on channel 4? Honey would you mind switching over to channel 11? Ran, I hate this show, would you please put on something else?"

As it were, I cannot say what came onto the Dumont network at 7:30 that evening. But I can be sure that I was commanded to switch to NBC, where we discovered a big billed single-toothed dragon named Ollie, a round faced bald headed innocent boy called Kukla and calming blond, real human, mother figure who used her real name, Fran.

The show's creator was Chicago native Burr Tillstrom who acted as the out-of-site puppeteer. Fran Allison was a former radio comedienne and singer. Most nights she was the only human to appear on screen, filling the role of big sister and the sweet voice of reason as Kukla and Ollie engaged each other in hilarious conflict. On most nights Kukla would take on the role of leader of the troupe, while Ollie whose full name was Oliver J. Dragon, would constantly challenge his bald little friend. To show his endearing character, Ollie would slam his flat chin on the stage in frustration or roll on his back to enlist sympathy from the viewers.

Then there was an extended list of supporting characters such as Madame Ooglepuss, a retired opera diva; Beulah the Witch; mailman

Fletcher Rabbit; Colonel Crackie a Southern gentleman; and Dolores Dragon, Ollie's younger cousin.

This was the kind of show in which you became quickly invested. I loved it from the beginning. James Thurber once wrote that Burr Tillstrom was "helping to save the sanity of the nation and to improve, if not even to invent, the quality of television." Not bad for a bald kid, a middle-aged lady and a goofy one-toothed dragon. Just as the show's regular moral message was being played out at the end of the show, there was a soft knock on the hallway door. The Van Outers had arrived for Milton Berle viewing. Or, more accurately, Neil and his father Dutch Van Outer were there for Berle. Mae Van Outer and my mother headed straight to the living room placing themselves next to the radio and the upcoming addition of *The Shadow.*

In quick fashion drinks were served... Hudepohl beers for Dutch and dad, Seven-Up for the *Shadow* ladies and Orange Ade for Neil and me. Thanks to our round dining room table, the four television watchers sat in a neat little semi-circle that provided perfection for Berle watching. Good news for the dining room crowd. Texaco Star Theater starring Milton Berle was on NBC... no channel changing by the human remote (me) was required. First came the sound of a fire engine siren with the view of a curtain that said "Texaco Star Theater." The curtain opened to reveal four very happy Texaco Servicemen who broke into the show's theme song that included a riff of the melody from the song, "Put another nickel in the Nickelodeon."

Not only were we introduced to Berle on this 18th of October 1949, but the show also featured the comedy team of Dean Martin and Jerry Lewis. Martin was a singer and Lewis a comedian who had teamed up three years earlier, moving from night clubs to radio and then in 1949, to television. This show was one of their early appearances on this new medium.

Also, on the bill was Broadway performer Ethel Merman who displayed her bold, strong singing voice and her comedy chops as well.

The show was rapid-paced, slapstick infested and totally dominated by Berle who would soon become known as "Uncle Miltie" and later as "Mr. Television." As in Vaudeville, where Berle first gained notoriety, one guest act after the other took the stage including the Goetschis, a unicycle act; an adagio team called The Zoris; child performer Vera Raymond; Chuck Roe, who played the bass fiddle; champion trick roper, Junior Eskew; three singing - dancing kids known as the Madgid Triplets; and the beautiful Wally Wagner girls from Broadway.

The acts just came in waves, with commercials seamlessly weaved into the mix. Within the first ten minutes, Neil and I had moved to the floor within feet of the set. Thus, we were quickly admonished by my mother with a phrase I would hear thousands of times over the next few years, "You're sitting too close to that thing; you'll ruin your eyes."

Neil, Dutch Van Outer, my dad and I screamed with laughter for a solid hour. Jerry Lewis played off of straight man Dean Martin to perfection. Throughout the show, if Berle uttered the words "make up," a little guy would appear, yell "make-up," and smack Berle with a pillow-sized powder puff, giving off a huge powdery cloud. On this particular show Berle said to an angry Ethel Merman, "Ah, c'mon let's make up." Bam! Right in the chops, he took the powder puff.

Later in the show he said to Jerry Lewis, "Listen squirt, don't make up things about me." Sure enough, Berle was powdered again by the same little guy. Slap stick? Sure. Beyond hilarious? Yes.

The show ended with a big Western finale featuring Berle, Martin, Lewis, Merman, Raymond, the Magids, and performers from the World Championship Rodeo which was in progress at Madison Square Garden that week.

The merry men of Texaco reprised their gas station shenanigans to close the memorable evening. And with that, my mother and Mrs. Van Outer appeared from the living room. Bedtime had arrived. The Van Outers disappeared down the back hall, and I was steered to the bathroom where I quickly brushed my teeth and changed into my pajamas. My mother then guided me to my bedroom and supervised my nightly prayers. "Now I lay me down to sleep. I pray the Lord my soul to keep. If I should die before I wake (that part scared the hell out of me), I pray the Lord my soul to take. God bless Mom and Dad, God bless Aunt Win and Uncle Bill, God bless

Aunt Lois, Uncle Joe and Cousin Paul, God bless Grandma and Grandpa."

Then I felt this sudden compulsion to add, "God bless Howdy Doody, God bless Captain Video and all his Rangers, God bless Kukla Fran and Ollie, God bless Bob Steele, God bless Milton Berle and God bless Television." My mother indulged this slight diversion that night.

It was with a happy smile that I drifted off to dreamsville midway through my sleepy review of the day, tele-visions dancing in my head. Little did I know how my life and the world were about to be changed by *The Box*.

1949 Philco Television Set

Cowboy Hero Bob Steele

John Cameron Swazy

Kukla, Fran & Ollie.

Howdy Doody & Buffalo Bob.

Captain Video with a Ranger

The Merry Men of Texaco

Mr. Television - Uncle Miltie

1949

He's making a list,
Checking it twice,
Gonna find out who's naughty or nice,
Santa Claus is coming to town!

From *Santa Claus is Coming to Town*
By J. Fred Coots & Haven Gillespie

MY SCHWINN

I awoke earlier than normal on Christmas Eve 1949. Certain that I would find several feet of snow had fallen over-night, I rushed to the window of my bedroom, flung open the drapes to discover a still, moonlit, bone-dry Spokane Avenue for my view. It had not snowed since my birthday, two weeks earlier.

I reigned in my disappointment. Snow or no snow, it was Christmas Eve.

This special day and the magical day that would follow had taken on a singular and spectacular meaning to my seven-year-old-self. My belief in reindeer, chimneys, a fat-bearded-jolly grandfatherly character who liked cookies and milk, and finding all of my year-long wishes neatly wrapped beneath a beautifully decorated tree, had reached an apex on this particular Christmas. And, OK, there was just an iota of skepticism residing in the far reaches of my mind.

Without any urging from my mother, I hurriedly got dressed and wolfed down the French toast that awaited me in the kitchen, washed down with some delicious French Bauer brand orange aide (I hated milk and my mother had given up). As promised, my mother helped me on with my brown winter coat and dark tan woolen mittens with matching hat and walked me down the street to my Aunt Win's house, just seven doors away on Spokane Avenue. A deal had been struck that my mom and Aunt Win would take me to Shillito's Department Store for a Christmas Eve visit with Santa.

I rushed through the side door of the two-story house where my mother and two aunts had been raised. Aunt Win still lived there with her husband Bill Sutton as well as my grandfather, Lou Theobald, and my great grandmother, Jeanette "Jenny" Keyser Loewenstine. My grandmother, Cosey Theobald, Lou's wife and Jenny's daughter, had passed away at the age of 57, six years earlier.

Normally, my Aunt Lois and Uncle Joe Anderson and their baby, Paul, would have been living there as well, establishing four generations of our family under the same roof. However, on this Christmas, they were far away in Japan, where Uncle Joe was serving as a Master Sargent in the Counter Intelligence Corps of the US Army, spying and teaching young Japanese boys to play baseball.

My frail 88-year-old Grandma Loewenstine rarely came downstairs. Also, she was Jewish and did not want to have anything to do with this "Christmas non-sense" that her three granddaughters had brought into the home by marrying gentiles. I ran upstairs to give her the expected cheek-kiss. As always, she sat in her rocking chair next to her bed, book in hand, using the light of the front window to read. On this day, she was half way through the new novel, *Arabella* by Georgette Heyer. Ironically, the rocker in which she sat placed my great grandmother directly above the Christmas tree that was perched by the living room front window. While I had heard of Hanukkah, I had no idea what it was all about, and I was fully invested in Christmas.

"Hi, Grams," I said, looking into her sweet old brown eyes.

"Hello, my darling little boy," she slowly responded with her aged gravelly voice. "What kind of mischief are you up to today?"

"Mom and Aunt Win are taking me downtown to Shillito's to see Santa Claus," I explained.

"That's nice. You tell that old fraud I said hello. He'll understand," she assured me.

Having just turned seven, I did not yet know what a "fraud" was but Gram's tone let me know it wasn't good. How could this lovely old lady not like Santa? Oh well, anybody who would ride a sleigh through a dark cold winter's night and come down a chimney to deliver all of my Christmas wishes was OK in my book.

After receiving my regular pat on the head, I bid my great grandmother goodbye and took the steps two at a time back down stairs where I rushed to the kitchen to find Aunt Win opening a fresh can of Carnation cream with a well-worn red handled six-inch pick. Once she had poked two small holes in opposite sides of the top of the tin can, she put the fresh liquid into the icebox unused. She was a black coffee kind of gal. To my disappointment, she poured herself a cup of java, delaying our departure for my date with Santa. My mother was half way through a cup of tea.

Aunt Win motioned me to a chair between her and my mother and slid a Christmas card in front of me.

"This is from your little cousin Paul, all the way from Tokyo, Japan," she explained.

The card was unlike anything I had seen. It was a very delicately crafted watercolor vision of two unusual trees and a boat on a small body of water. It was bound with two colors of string. On the inside was some illegible scribble followed by the clearly hand-written message: "Ran, wishing you a very Merry Christmas form Japan… we miss you… Love, Aunt Lois, Uncle Joe and Paul."

My Aunt Win explained that the scribble was my 14-month-old cousin Paul's attempt to sign the card.

She continued to engage me in conversation, "So, Ran, what do you plan to ask Santa to bring you for Christmas tomorrow?"

I had a ready enthusiastic answer to that question. I looked at my mother for support and answered, "I am asking him for a brand-new Schwinn 26-inch American Flyer Bicycle!"

"Well, do you think Santa might consider you to be too young for a full-sized bike?" my aunt challenged.

"Heck no! Neil and I both want a big Schwinn. He wants a Black Phantom. That's a new model this year. I want an American Flyer. I just like it better than the Black Phantom. And it costs less too."

"But he doesn't believe in Santa," I explained. "So, I bet I'll get a bike and he won't." My downstairs neighbor and best friend, Neil Van

Outer, had been badgering me. Opening in 1832, Shillito's was the first department store in Cincinnati. In 1878, John Shillito built a magnificent new Department Store building at the corner of 7th and Race Streets that included massive display windows along the front facade. The Shillito's Department Store I walked into on Christmas Eve in 1949 was Cincinnati's version of Macy's in New York City. It was a grand sprawling department store with 9 stories counting the basement, where the bargains were sold (yes a "bargain basement"), and a balcony that housed the men's department, most of which overlooked the majestic and luxurious first floor that was devoted to women's wear, jewelry and a very nice sit-down Coffee Shop Restaurant. The massive front windows along Seventh Street were each decorated with wintry mechanical Christmas scenes like Santa's workshop and a Swiss ski village.

In the center of the first floor adjacent to ladies' shoes sat a bank of wide-door elevators with dials above each door in the shape of the top half of a clock. A sweeping minute hand arrow moved across floor numbers 1-7, plus a "B" for basement and an "M" for mezzanine, advising shoppers where each elevator was located and if it was headed toward or away from them.

When the elevator arrived, the beautifully engraved art-deco brass doors would part as shoppers poured out. There was a smartly dressed operator who would announce the floor and what specifically could be found awaiting the shoppers such as "first floor, women's wear, jewelry, candy, and Coffee Shop Restaurant. Going up."

I scrambled into the large elevator, tugging on my mother and aunt, anxious to get to the sixth floor as the operator repeated, "Going up."

With a slight movement of a lever, the door closed. The lady in charge then reached away from her small bench and pulled closed a second metal barrier and then moved another lever from left to right, and the car began to ascend. We quickly reached the mezzanine where the pretty lady in a maroon military-type uniform with a chest badge identifying her as Alice, deftly adjusted the car down then up and down again until she achieved perfect alignment between the elevator floor and the carpeted floor on the

Shillito's balcony. With that, she threw back the accordion metal interior door, then hit a lever that opened the exterior solid brass door.

"Mezzanine, men's wear, shoes, hats, boys clothing, shoe repair, employment office and toys," she announced. "Watch your step, please. Going up."

This process was repeated five more times until we finally reached the sixth floor. As the doors swept open, I heard Alice announce, "Sixth floor, dinnerware, cookware, appliances, lamps, sewing center, luggage, clocks, the Tea Room and Santa's Workshop. Watch your step please."

I patiently waited for some of the shoppers to clear the door, then I sprinted ahead looking back to see my smiling aunt and my concerned mother screaming for me to slow down. I knew where we were going... straight ahead through three rows of luggage, then past a row of lamps, then wall clocks and a dozen or so grandfather clocks, with a sharp right passed coffee makers and mixers. At that point, I came upon several decorated artificial Christmas trees, a fairly new innovation in 1949. Behind the trees stood a large curtain with a big sign that said *Welcome to Santa's Workshop*. A smaller sign informed me to *Enter Here*.

My mother and aunt caught up to me, and we entered into a maze of mechanical figures simulating what the real workshop surely must have looked like at the North Pole. It took almost ten minutes for us to work our way through the labyrinth before Santa appeared before us. He sat in a grand gold chair three steps above the path.

With Santa now in sight, I became nervous about the pending opportunity to make my case for my Schwinn eligibility. I had rehearsed my speech at least a hundred times. But now, all the words I had planned to speak had escaped my young mind.

There were five kids ahead of me, then four, then three, then two and finally one very little girl. She spoke clearly and happily to Santa then smiled while a very tall elf took her picture sitting on Santa's lap. She giggled and then climbed down from the great throne upon which the big jolly man in the red suit was perched.

My turn had come. *C'mon, Randy... don't blow this.*

I swallowed hard, took a big gulp of air and climbed the three steps. As this wonderful grandfatherly man bent down to help me upon his lap, Neil Van Outer's words came back to me. "There is no real Santa."

But my skepticism was temporarily erased when Santa, in a somewhat familiar voice, said to me, "Well, Randy, what would you like for Christmas?"

He knew my name! How could he possibly know my name? Neil was wrong. Surely this guy was the real Santa.

I blurted it out straight and clear, "I want a brand-new Schwinn 24 inch American Flyer bicycle," I proclaimed.

"Well," said Santa. "That's quite a tall order from such a young fella, isn't it? Tell me, have you been a good little boy?"

There was that question, just as Neil had warned me. "They just want you to behave."

A small dose of uncertainty attacked me again. So, I decided to test Santa.

I told him that I had been very good, which, in fact, I had. Then I asked him if it would snow for Christmas. With this question, he took great pause before assuring me that it most certainly would snow on Christmas Eve, for how else would he be able to softly land his sleigh on our roof. This made sense, although the past two Christmases had been bone-dry, yet not affecting the great assortment of gifts that Santa had left for me in 1947 and 1948… a minor detail when a Schwinn was on the line.

Then, as I was about to depart, he placed an old wrinkled hand on my shoulder and said something that left no doubt in my mind about his authenticity.

"Randy, you know your father works very hard at the bank, and though he can't be there for you as much as you might like, he still loves you very much. If you promise to remember that, then you will surely get what you want for Christmas."

Well, that was it. Did I have a flash for Neil Van Outer! Who else but the real Santa could possibly know that I sometimes doubted my father's love? I looked up into his warm, gentle face and promised to remember. With that, I leaped from his lap and ran to where my mother and aunt waited.

Completely forgotten now were the other questions Neil had planted in my young mind. Like, *how do reindeer fly?* Or, *there's another Santa around the corner at McAlpin's Department Store and another up the street at the Fair Store, and yet another ringing a bell outside on the corner of Fifth and Vine Streets. If there is one real Santa, then who are they?* No, these questions had evaporated, now unimportant. After all, I had just made the acquaintance of the real Santa Claus. There was no doubt.

One of the smaller elves came up to me and asked, "Why don't you climb back up on Santa's lap so we can take your picture with him?"

I subconsciously did as I was asked and shyly looked at the big elf with the camera. After two quick flashes, I was ushered back down as Santa patted me on the head and gave out with his best ho, ho, ho. I sprinted to my aunt and my mother with an unusual measure of glee. We exited Santa's Workshop to find ourselves at the entrance to the Tea Room.

I gushed to my mother and aunt that I now knew for a fact that this was the real Santa Claus. "He knew my name and he knew all about dad and he promised it would snow tonight," I explained.

They looked at each other with a knowing satisfaction. Aunt Win suggested we go to the Tea Room for lunch before doing a little last-minute shopping.

I didn't show much interest in the grilled cheese sandwich that they ordered for me, but finally wolfed it down when they promised me a scoop of pistachio ice cream as a reward. Throughout lunch, I fantasized about riding up and down Spokane Avenue on my new Schwinn.

Before heading home, my aunt made a few small purchases including some shoes that my mother liked but wouldn't buy for herself, as well as a lace handkerchief for Grandma Jenny.

We took the escalator down from the sixth floor traversing back and forth and stopping on the mezzanine where my mother asked if I would like to pick out a Christmas gift for my father. After great thought, I chose a silk maroon tie. They both agreed with my choice and my mother paid the clerk with a five-dollar bill, collecting two dollars and some change back with the tie in a fancy Shillito's gift box made for ties, then stored in a Shillito's holiday shopping bag regaled with some images of holly and a smiling rosy-cheeked Santa.

We exited the same door at Shillito's Alley through which we had entered. My aunt treated me to a soft pretzel. As I took the small bag from the vendor, I notice that it had begun to snow.

"I knew I should have had Randy wear his galoshes," my mother fretted. "We better get going. He just got those shoes for his birthday and I don't want him to ruin them.

So off we went back in the direction of Government Square. By the time we boarded the streetcar, the snow was coming down in heavy big white flakes, just as Santa had promised, and much to my mother's chagrin.

When we finally arrived at Aunt Win's house, there were a couple of inches of powdery snow on the ground creating the hush that comes with heavy snow. My mother hurriedly cleaned of my new shoes with a rag provide by my aunt.

As was the family tradition on Christmas Eve, dinner would be at my aunt's house. The rest of the afternoon I spent in the living room playing with my toy soldiers. At five o'clock, to top off what was shaping up as a perfect day, my aunt tuned the kitchen radio to WLW so we could listen to a fifteen-minute program where Santa read Christmas letters from Cincinnati's youth.

The Santa on the radio did not seem to have the same gentle and familiar voice I had heard at Shillito's. But I dismissed this without much thought. About two-thirds through the program I heard Santa say, "and here's a note from Walnut Hills from Randy and Paul. Paul is in Japan this Christmas and is asking for some toy soldiers like the ones his big cousin Randy has. And Randy is hoping for a new Schwinn Bicycle. They say here that they have been very good boys. Well, Paul and Randy, we will see what we can do. Ho, ho, ho and a Merry Christmas."

I couldn't believe my ears. Santa read our note on radio. Wow. This was unbelievable. My aunt was smiling from ear to ear.

My instinct was to run up the street and find my friend Scrooge Van

Outer and share some critical Santa information with him. I had all the marbles now, and he was going to have to concede. My mother put an immediate kibosh on that plan. So, illogically, I sat next to the Christmas tree by the front window just in case Neil might happen to walk by. The snow was coming down in buckets, and I saw Mr. Preston, who lived next door, busily shoveling the sidewalk in front of his house.

Then Uncle Bill pulled up in his big black Packard outfitted with chains around the tires to help the mammoth vehicle navigate through the snow. Before coming into the house, he started to match Mr. Preston's efforts to clear away the snow from the sidewalk with a large coal shovel that Aunt Win had set on the porch as a hint.

Just as Uncle Bill was putting the finishing touches on the walkway, my father appeared, bundled against the elements in his calf length black overcoat, collar up to ward off the snow, a matching black fedora with a silver-grey hatband and his ever-present grey gloves. Like me, he had left home in the morning without his "galoshes" that would otherwise be stretched over his cap-toe black Oxfords.

Per usual, my father and uncle entered the house through the side door, shaking off the snow in the small hall in front of the steps that led upstairs.

"I need a beer," Uncle Bill announced.

"Make that two," stated my father, offering to run to the icebox to retrieve a couple of Burgers.

My father was a Hudepohl Beer fan; with Bavarian brand a close second. On the other hand, uncle Bill preferred Burger, the exclusive sponsor of Cincinnati Reds Baseball. So, on this Christmas Eve, my father would be settling for Burger. As for me, I wanted to get on with dinner and try to get to sleep early in an effort to get to Christmas morning and a bike.

At 5:30, my grandfather appeared through the side door, brushing snow of his shoulders and his chocolate brown fedora. It was most unusual for Grandpa Lou to be away during the day. Yet for the past month or so he had been gone from morning until dinner Monday through Saturday. This particular evening, he carried with him a garment bag with a big Shillito's logo inscribed on it. He ran the bag up to his room. When he returned, we all sat down to dinner.

As always, Great Grandma Jenny took dinner in her room upstairs. My mother delivered a modest plate of food from the kitchen up to her as we were all gathering at the dining room table. I was just beginning to grasp the idea of traditions... and my family certainly had some.

Christmas Eve dinner was always pot roast with carrots, small red potatoes and green peas. Christmas Day dinner was a replication of our Thanksgiving dinner... roasted turkey, bread dressing, mashed potatoes, creamed corn and jelled cranberry sauce... a virtual carb-fest. The grease from the turkey was served in a gravy boat and mislabeled as gravy. In actuality, it was grease. But we all loved it lathered on top of our lumpy mashed potatoes, our otherwise dry bread dressing and the usual overcooked turkey. Yes, without the grease, Thanksgiving and Christmas dinners would have been a total bust.

Another part of the Christmas Eve tradition was that the adults opened their gifts after dinner, while the children (me), had to wait until Christmas morning to see what Santa had left beneath the tree.

The ritual continued after the adults had opened their gifts and all the ribbon and paper had been collected, when desert and coffee were served. Desert always consisted of my mother's rock-hard fruitcake and a large selection of Christmas cookies including my favorite, Lebkuchen, a traditional German Christmas treat that was a chewy gingerbread cookie made with molasses and full of warm spices and chopped walnuts. The white sugary glaze my mother crafted provided the perfect complement of a little sweet taste and just a hint of lemon. It was hard to believe that the same person could make that despicable fruitcake and those luscious Lebkuchens. Let's put it this way, whoever came up with the saying "nuttier than a fruitcake" must have had my mother's fruitcake. And, whoever first said "harder than a rock" must have had my mother's fruitcake. Hold the fruitcake... pass the Lebkuchens.

Half way through our 1949 Christmas Eve dinner, I was informed that I would be allowed the special treat of staying up later than normal and that the adults would open up their gifts at our house rather than at my aunt's home. This break with tradition did not excite me because, as I said, all I wanted to do was crawl between the sheets and quickly go to sleep in hopes of hastening Santa's chance to deliver my new Schwinn.

But, after the dishes were quickly washed and tucked away and a plate of cookies and a hot tea were delivered upstairs to Grandma Loewenstine, we all bundled up and headed up snow-covered Spokane Avenue to our house.

Once there, we all climbed the steps past the stained glass window to the left of the landing that artfully displayed a thin woman in a full-length Kelly green gown and a sleek reddish brown dog I had been told was something called an Irish Setter, and then up the three remaining steps to the center hall where our Christmas tree stood, bubble lights now aglow. I learned several years after my parents had sold this two-family house, that the buyer had ultimately sold the stained-glass window for about a fourth of what he paid for the house. This fact did not set well with my father.

Coffee was quickly brewed in the kitchen while my father filled his pipe and Uncle Bill lit a Camel cigarette with a kitchen match that he ignited with a flick of his thumbnail. His ability to do so always fascinated me.

Uncle Bill then sat down at my mother's baby grand and started to play *Jingle Bells*. This, too, mystified me, as he had lost the tips of his middle and ring fingers on his right hand to an accident while working on a car ten years earlier. Nonetheless, he played a flawless piano with a great flair. He invited me to sit down and play with him. He had taught me to play this simple tune with my right hand. I played the melody with my index finger while he played the bass notes with his left. He then took over again with renditions of *Silent Night* and *Santa Claus is Coming to Town*.

When the cups were filled and the granite-like fruitcake was distributed, I was assigned the chore of retrieving gifts for all but me to open. I recognized the box containing the tie I had chosen for my father and picked it first. Dad opened it with great excitement, and giggled his unique hee hee hee laugh, ripping off the tie he had been wearing and replacing it with the new maroon job from me. This pleased me to no end.

The next package I picked was for Grandpa, but I suddenly noticed he wasn't there.

I asked, "Where is Gramps?"

"He is going to the orphanage tonight," my Aunt Win explained.

"In this snow?" I exclaimed.

"Well, you know how devoted Grandpa is to the orphans," my mother said.

My grandfather was on the board of two orphanages. One was the Masonic Orphanage in Springfield Ohio, where he was President of their Board. The other was Saint Joseph's on Reading Road in Bond Hill. He was very devoted to the kids at both institutions.

It took more than 15 minutes for everyone to get through the wrapped packages beneath the tree. As everyone was finishing cake, cookies and coffee, our doorbell rang.

"Go see who that is," my mother instructed. My father escorted me down the stairs.

I opened the door and almost fell over. Standing before me was Santa Claus! In the same gentle voice, I had heard earlier in the day at Shillito's he said, "Well, hello, Randy. How are you on this fine snowy Christmas Eve?"

I thought I was going to pass out. Could a seven-year-old have a stroke?

He continued, "Don't you think that you and I should teach that Neil Van Outer a lesson about Santa Claus?"

Neil and his parents rented the downstairs flat of my parents' two-family house.

Santa reached out for my hand and pulled me onto the front porch. Sitting in front of the Van Outers' front door stood a Schwinn Black Phantom bicycle with a big red bow on the handlebars. I just stood there speechless.

Santa quickly rapped hard on the Van Outers' door. A few seconds later the door opened and Neil appeared with his parents right behind.

Santa gave out with a hearty, "Ho ho ho."

He then said, "Well, Neil, I hear you have been spreading the word around here that I'm not real. What do you have to say about that?"

Poor Neil stood there in total shock, trying to stammer out a response.

Santa continued, "Perhaps this will change your mind. I have a little something here for you."

With that Santa retrieved the black Schwinn Phantom and pushed it toward Neil saying, "Merry Christmas, my little friend."

At last, Neil found his tongue, running to the bike exclaiming, "Jeez, thanks Santa. Heck, I was only kidding. I knew you were real all along."

He beamed the biggest smile ever as he looked to me and then back to the bike.

"Well, go ahead climb aboard son," Santa said.

I stood there in total disbelief.

Santa said to Neil, "Now you listen to me. You have to let your dad teach you how to ride this thing and you have to learn all of the rules to ride it safely. OK?"

"Sure Santa. You bet I will," Neil promised.

I turned to see that my mother and aunt were standing behind me on the porch.

I stood there thinking, *What the heck... this kid didn't even believe in Santa ,and here he was getting my bike from the bearded guy.*

Mr. Van Outer finally weighed in saying, "Well, we better get your gift inside out of this snow."

"Good idea, agreed my father. "We need to get back upstairs."

Dad took my hand, guiding me to our door, and we followed my mother and aunt back up the stairs. I was happy for Neil, but more than a little disappointed.

My disenchantment came to a quick end when I reached the top of the stairs. Next to our Christmas tree sat a bright green Schwinn American Flyer, also regaled with a large red bow on the handlebars. I noted that training wheels were attached in the back.

I rushed to the bike with a mix of excitement and astonishment.

"Is this mine?" I asked.

"Indeed, it is," my mother assured me.

I tried to climb aboard, almost falling over, as the bike was big and a little unwieldy. I sat on the smooth leather seat, the training wheels helping me to maintain my balance.

All of the adults broke into joyful laughter as I continued to try to process the last ten minutes. Finally, I rushed to my bedroom window just in time to see Santa climb into Uncle Bill's Packard.

"Santa just got into Uncle Bill's car," I exclaimed.

Aunt Win then solved the entire riddle when she said, "They will be back soon. He has to take your grandfather to Saint Joe's."

I climbed into bed that night with my Schwinn American Flyer parked right next to me.

Well, Neil, I thought as I drifted off to sleep, *I guess for you and me, this Christmas debate was a draw.* From that day on, I knew who the real Santa was.

Shillito's Window Christmas 1949

1949 Green Schwinn American Flyer

My Favorite Santa and Me at Shillito's
Christmas Eve 1949

1949-1953

If you're blue and you don't know where to go to
Why don't you go where fashion sits
Puttin' on the Ritz

From Puttin' on the Ritz
By Irving Berlin

The Ritz

In the nineteen-forties and early fifties the two-block area where Woodburn Avenue sliced through the confluence of where Hewitt Avenue, Gilbert Avenue and Montgomery Road all met their end, was a vibrant commercial area abuzz with activity.

Scattered about on the east side of Woodburn, south of the intersection, sat Dow Drugs with its soda fountain and lunch area inside a large floor-to-ceiling window striking the pose of a Hopper painting. Next door was Cavenelli's fruit stand with rows of fruits and vegetables under a blue and orange canopy, then Franco's Barber shop with its spinning barber pole and Lasky's Bakery, a place that could fill your nostrils with aromas to be found nowhere else.

You would get off of a street car in front of Cavenelli's to find Buddy, the newsboy, crippled by what I would later learn was something called cerebral palsy. He commanded the corner screaming something such as, "Read all about it... read all about it... Frank Lausche elected Governor... read all about it."

Monday through Saturday, he limped in front of the corner newsstand waiving a copy of the *Cincinnati Post* in one hand and a thick copy of the *Cincinnati Time Star* in the other, ready to stick one under his arm in order to take a nickel in payment which he would quickly deposit in a change apron around his waist.

All of the street corner buzz was clearly visible from the soda fountain at Dow's Drugs through that large picture window. In the middle of the Twentieth Century, this was a neighborhood in its truest sense.

Across the street from Lasky's stood the Ritz Movie Theater. Without its small marquee and rounded ticket window it might have stood there unobtrusively enough between Walnut Hills Presbyterian Church and the long row of brick and glass store fronts. But this was no ordinary place.

To step inside the Ritz was to enter a land of fantasy, mystery, excitement and small doses of mischief. For me and my Walnut Hills pals, the Ritz was part amusement park, part candy store and part babysitter. On any given weekend afternoon, it offered a double-feature, a weekly news real, a cartoon and possibly the most important of all, the weekly serial episode.

It was the serials more than the movies that brought us back each weekend. Whether it was *Flash Gordon, Superman, Cody of the Pony Express, Brick Bradford* or *Son of Geronimo,* these little ten to fifteen-minute episodes were like a magnet that drew us to the Ritz on most Saturdays and some Sundays.

Most of these little gems were fifteen episodes or chapters. The genres included westerns, science fiction, cops and robbers or jungle stories. Many were derived from popular comic strips of the day, so *Flash Gordon* could keep you coming back all summer. At the end of each episode they would set the hook with something like this up on the screen: *Superman... The Mighty Man of Tomorrow Battles to Save the World from Destruction... One of the Great Serials of All Time...Don't Miss a Single Episode.*

When you entered the Ritz, a small concession counter stood to the left, with a second access inside the big doors through which you passed after giving your ticket to a uniformed usher so you could buy seconds between movies.

Once inside, the lady's room was again to the left followed by a narrow stairway that led up to the men's room and a closed door to the projection room. These were the days before air conditioning, so in the summer that door was often open providing a little cool air and a view of a very little old man who commanded the two large 35 millimeter projectors. It was the same guy from the first to the last time I came to this magical place. I hope they were paying him overtime.

After passing the stairs, you came to a warmly lit barrier behind which you could choose to go right or left to two aisles that led to the seats. I can't say why, but we always chose to go right. I had my favorite seat, ten aisles down. The seat I chose had a small aisle light on its side that stayed dimly illuminated during the movies. On the side walls were several multi-colored fixtures that brightened the seating area until the show began. Then they went dark.

I first entered the Ritz at the young age of three, too young to be allowed to climb the stairs to the men's room on my own. Thus, I was escorted to the ladies' room by either my mother or one of her two sisters, my Aunt Win or Aunt Lois. It was much larger and nicer than the men's room, with a large mirror with stools in front so the ladies could fix their hair or touch up their makeup and lipstick. The toilets had privacy doors, something not provided for the men… go figure.

Finally, at age five I was permitted to climb the stairs to answer nature's call. This was rare, as I usually was too transfixed on the small screen at the front of the theater to worry about nature.

The Ritz did not offer drinks, but for a nickel you could get a small box of popcorn or several candy options. My preference was usually Jujubes or Milk Duds plus a box of corn. This expense required that I carefully guard my ten-cents per week allowance, as I was given only a quarter for my day at the movies and admittance was a dime for children under the age of twelve.

If you were thirsty, your only option was a water fountain staged between the ladies' room and the stairs. It got a lot of use, particularly between the two featured movies where there might be several folks in line for a quick slurp or two.

On weekends, thanks in large part to the serials, the Ritz was packed with kids. When the lights went dim and the previews started, there was often a large cheer from the young demographic assembled. Youthful anticipation was something we all shared.

Each afternoon was filled with laughter, cheers and sometimes flying candy and popcorn aimed at a schoolmate seated nearby. A theater full of kids could keep even a young usher busy. Every now and then, an over-exuberant youth would be shown the exit, but that was rare.

The silver screen was full of heroes from cowboys like Roy Rodgers, Gene Autry, Gary Cooper and Randolph Scott, good guys like Jimmy Stewart, Cary Grant, Gregory Peck, Spencer Tracy, Clark Gable, Glenn Ford and Humphry Bogart, to great villains like James Cagney, Edward G. Robinson, Charles Bronson and Peter Lorre.

Then there were the youngsters such as James Dean, Mickey Rooney, Brandon DeWilde, the Bowery Boys, Shirley Temple, and Judy Garland. Some of my favorites were the song and dance stars like Gene Kelly, Frank Sinatra, Bing Crosby, Donald O'Conner, Debbie Reynold, Doris Day, Fred Astaire, Gordon MacRea, Jane Powell, and a swimming Esther Williams.

Not to be forgotten were the glamour girls—Jane Russell, Rita Hayworth, Betty Grable, Ava Gardner, Vivien Leigh, Loretta Young, and newcomers Elizabeth Taylor and Marilyn Monroe.

Perhaps the Ritz Theater favorites were the comedians—Bob Hope, Bud Abbott, Lou Costello, Lucille Ball, The Marx Brothers, Jack Bennie, Danny Kaye, Jimmie Durante and Ray Bolger.

And, finally the great character actors like Charles Colburn, Sidney Greenstreet, Andy Devine, Edward Everette Horton, Eddie "Rochester" Anderson, Eve Arden, Butterfly McQueen, Thelma Ritter, Hattie Mc Daniel and my all-time favorite, S. Z. Sakall, who was a dead ringer for my Grandfather Lou Theobald.

They all filled the Ritz Theatre screen in the late 1940s and early 1950s, providing, drama, laughs, excitement and great joy.

On any given Saturday, my cousin Jay Pittroff and I could be found with Jujubes stuck like glue to our teeth, affecting our laughs as Francis the Mule was guiding a confused Donald O'Connor through his latest predicament. Or I might find myself with my down-stairs neighbor Neil Van Outer tossing back popcorn while he cheered on the cowboys and I woo wooed it up for the Indians, just to piss him off.

We all loved the cartoons. I was especially fond of Tom and Jerry and Bugs Bunny (*That's all Folks!!*), with his nemesis, Elmer Fudd (*You cwazy wabbit*).

Many of my pals would head to the restroom or concession stand when the weekly newsreel came on. But I enjoyed the newsreels. I learned about Harry Truman and his battle with Korea, the Chinese and General Douglas MacArthur. I was informed of Dwight Eisenhower and his battle for the 1952 Republican Presidential nomination against *Mr. Republican,* Robert Taft of Ohio. Big news one weekend in 1951 was of an atom bomb test north of Las Vegas. These weekly news reports were usually entitled *The March of Time,* and were produced by Time, Inc., publishers of *Time* and *Life Magazines*. They were narrated by a silky-voiced Westbrook Van Voorhis. He had such command of the narration that no one dared doubt what he said.

If a cowboy movie or a gangster movie was on the bill, I was pretty much assured that my cousin Jay or my neighbor friend Neil would be there with me. On the other hand, if the marquee said *Doris Day, June Allison, Esther Williams* or the word *musical,* I was likely be there solo. I liked that stuff but the *girly junk* wasn't for Jay or Neil. I guess I wasn't as manly of a seven-year-old as were they.

One other thing was predictable. At some point over the afternoon in the dark, I was likely to get hit in the back of the head with a Jujube, a Milk Dud or, preferably a Dot, as they were softer.

There were a lot of cheers and boos each afternoon from the young crowd. And if something really bad happened on the screen, the ammunition would start popping off of the rigid silk panel of that period.

The naughtiest among us took joy in trying to make a saliva-coated Dot or Jujyfruit actually stick to the screen. This took a strong arm and a lot of spit.

This was the kind of behavior that could result in ejection, but there were a few pranksters who were more into mischief than movies.

One Saturday in 1951, my classmate Carl Riggs smuggled in a pea shooter along with a pocketful of small dried beans. Half way through the first feature, beans started banging off of the screen with enough force to actually move it in a wavy fashion. The usher had a hard time finding Carl. Eventually he started watching the crowd of kids who were laughing and pointing and, as we euphemistically said back then, it was *Drums Along the Mohawk* for Carl. His covered wagon was surrounded and he was off to the *Happy Hunting Grounds*.

Indeed, the Ritz was a happy place.

Yet, due to the times, and unbeknownst to me, these same movies were filled with racism and sexism. African Americans were relegated to stereotypical roles that reflected the deep prejudice of the day. Women were usually objectified, while Native Americans were always the bad guys in the many cowboy and Indian films. There is no doubt that many of the movies enjoyed at the Ritz embedded these widely accepted attitudes in the youth in attendance.

The work of Shakespeare has been called racist, sexist and anti-Semitic by many, yet it is still held in high regard. I guess context is an explanation if not an excuse. The conventional, and somewhat fair, justification is zeitgeist. There was just a cultural acceptance of such attitudes, and so it should be excused. Maybe so... But this observation about the films of the time must be noted.

I should also point out that, while African-American kids were not prohibited from the Ritz, I do not recall ever seeing any of my many black friends from Hoffman school in attendance. And that registered sufficiently at the time that I never discussed the movies I saw with my best black friend, Billy Tate, at school so as not to offend him.

From 1948 through 1953, the Ritz acted as the best possible babysitter, offering a safe venue for me and a respite for my parents.

When we moved north to the all-white neighborhood of Bond Hill in 1953, I bid adieu to the Ritz. The last movie I saw there was *Titanic*, starring Clifton Webb and Barbara Stanwyck. The Ritz was replaced by other great neighborhood movie houses like the Twentieth Century, The Ambassador, the Monte Vista, the Plaza, the Guild, and a new colossus in Roselawn called the Valley Theater. And there was no better place to watch a movie than the huge downtown theaters such as the Albee, the Palace, the Grand and the Keith. Each continued my fascination and joy of living vicariously through film. But there was, and always will be, just one Ritz.

1950

...I need this race!
Are you gonna push me, let me run and let me do?
I need it and I'm ready and I haven't got a clue
Any track is turning but the race is in my head
I'm attacking the illusion but the stopping drives me mad.

From *The Race*
By Yello

THE RACE

It is true. My father, Harold Herbert Henry Joseph Stertmeyer, had known to take a drink more than just now and then. And while I had seen many signs of his athletic prowess in the past, especially on the softball fields around the area, his drinking made him seem more and more vulnerable, and me less and less inferior.

On this given late spring Saturday afternoon, the day of the week he was most likely to be sporting his gin grin, he was in a happy-go-lucky mood. I, having hit two homers while playing a dazzling and faultless first base, was feeling a bit full of myself. Now, at age nine and one half, I was certain that I could take the old man in a short 50 or so yard sprint from my Aunt Win's house at 3315 Spokane Avenue up to our house at 3333 Spokane Avenue.

With great cockiness, I posed the challenge. "Dad, you know I'm the fastest kid in my class. I've been timed in the 50-yard dash at 7.1 seconds. I bet I could beat you in a race to our house."

He looked at me in a kind of way as if to say, *Did I just hear this runt say what I thought I heard him say?*

After digesting my challenge, his look of dismay turned to a huge smile. This made me even more certain of my impending success. For you see, my father on this particular Saturday, had no teeth. Gum decease had finally claimed his choppers. Each and every incisor, wisdom and eye tooth had been extracted two nights earlier by his friend and lodge brother, Doc Kushner. He would have to wait at least a week allowing his gums to shrink before he could be fitted for false teeth.

Though only forty-two years old, standing there smiling toothlessly back at me, he seemed ancient. No way could I lose to this semi-inebriated old man. As though he were reading my mind, he asked with perverted joy, "I suppose you want a head start?"

Feeling sorry for him, I responded, "No. Actually, I was going to give you five yards."

This seemed to sober him up considerably. The smile was gone.

I had insulted my own father. And now I was going to embarrass him in a foot race. I actually felt somewhat badly that I had started this whole thing.

Finally, he said, "Well, OK then, I'll take any break I can get. You know me. I hate to lose."

He laughed his silly giggle - that high-pitched *hee hee, ha ha, hee, hee, hee,* that I both loved and hated.

He pointed to a crack in the sidewalk in front of my Aunt Win's house and instructed me that this would serve as the starting line. He then pointed to three cracks back down the street indicating that was the handicap starting point that I had offered. I walked to the crack in front of the Prestons' house directly under a large freshly blooming pin oak tree.

There were no words from him now – only a frightening look of determination and that wicked, toothless grin. He stood with his hands on his hip, strangely poised, and indicated with a nod that he was ready. Reluctantly, I took my mark and offered to act as the starter. He nodded his agreement.

"All right then. On the count of three," I said.

His arrogance was starting to tick me off. I was determined to teach the old man a lesson. I would do more than beat him. I would humiliate him. With great confidence, I slowly counted, "One, two, three!"

I broke cleanly from my sprinter's stance, arms pumping, legs churning. My father did not move. I sprinted passed him, assuming that once I had won, he would offer some feeble excuse for not running the race.

There were nine houses from the starting line up to and including ours. As I sprinted passed the third house, a blur exploded by me on the right. I suddenly was looking at what surely must have been the fastest man alive. It was my drunken, toothless father. I expended every fiber of energy I could summon. He won by two house lengths.

When I finally reached our house, he awaited, not breathless as I expected, but as cool as you please, with a look of satisfaction I will never forget.

Then he did something that, in spite of all his foibles, would endear him and this day to me forever. He put his arm around my shoulder, gave out with his most genuine laugh, and said, "Someday, short stuff. Someday. But not today!"

1951

Life's a fastball, belt high,
Coming right down the middle.
Don't stand there and let it go by
Swing hard and aim for the stands!

From *The Baseball Song*
By Corey Smith

The Shot

Some would say that it's America's game
And, to many, it's brought unexpected fame

So, if ever you are looking for some baseball fun
Let me refer you to October third, nineteen-fifty-one

The event took place at the haloed Polo Grounds
And many have never forgotten the magical sound

The crack of a bat against the ball
Had become legend, of that early fifties fall

And millions around the country were able to see
The first game ever broadcast on national TV

To set the stage for this day, I should first report
The Giants had staged the most spectacular comeback of this sport

For they had won thirty-seven of their last forty-four
And by season's end, they had tied the score

It was a thirteen and a half game lead Brooklyn had thrown away
And the Giants had won the chance to continue to play

So, Brooklyn and New York faced a three-game set
Who might win now was anyone's bet?

The first game was played at Brooklyn's Ebbets Field
And the red-hot Giants refused to yield

But the Bums came back at the Polo Grounds in game two
A lopsided win, proving that they weren't through

The deciding game was played in an overcast chill
Would it be New York or Brooklyn with the ultimate thrill?

After seven innings the game was tied at one
And for all watching, the excitement had just begun

But the Dodgers had gone up by three at the end of eight
And for Giants fans, things did not look great

Dodgers starter Don Newcomb was pitching on only two day's rest
While pitching bravely, he was no longer at his best.

The Giants Alvin Dark scored a run on a Whitey Lockman double
Dodgers Manager Dressen decided continuing with Newcomb might lead to trouble

So, he went to the bullpen deciding to bring Ralph Branca in
Hoping the big right hander could preserve the win

But it was Bobby Thompson stepping in
Who homered off Branca for the game-one win

With first base open, Dressen should have called for a base on balls
But instead chose to pitch to Thompson, perhaps a very bad call

Branca's first pitch was a fast ball for a called strike
It was a pitch that Thompson just did not like

Branca came back with a fast ball high inside
You guessed it—Thompson gave that pitch a ride

The homer landed in the lower left field stands
Right in the middle of the hysterical Giants fans

Yes, it was to game-winning-homer-land that Thompson had sent it
As announcer Russ Hodges famously screamed, "THE GIANTS WIN THE PENNANT!"

Giants Manager Leo Durocher and coach Eddie Stanky both went crazy
While poor Ralph Branca stood on the mound, totally hazy.

"The Shot Heard 'Round the World" Thompson's homer was named
And you can still watch the replay today at Baseball's Hall of Fame.

Word on the street was that the Giants had cheated
Something that today is still repeated

Legend has it there was a signal steal, as you may recall,
But does it really matter? Thompson still had to hit the damn ball!

The Shot Heard 'Round the World

The Shot Heard 'Round the World
Polo Grounds October 3, 1951

1953

Here's where it all began
Here's where I heard that beat
In my simple humble neighborhood
On my simple humble street

From *My Simple Humble Neighborhood*
By Carole King

New Neighborhood

1953 started unobtrusively enough. But it would turn out to be one of those seminal years that, when looked back on later, was clearly life changing.

As to what was becoming a tradition with my father and me, the first day of the New Year was devoted to two things: eating turkey and listening to football on the radio. My mother and Aunt Win were in charge of cooking the turkey. Dad and I assumed responsibility for devouring the bird and the football. And, for the first time, most of the bowl games were on television in 1953.

New Year's Day saw Southern Cal unceremoniously dispatch Wisconsin in the Badgers' first Rose Bowl on a 22-yard touchdown pass from Rudy Bukick to Al Carmichael. Mel Allen, whose voice I knew from the Friday Night Fights on radio, announced the action. Although they lost, Wisconsin dominated the game, led by the rushing of fullback Alan "The Horse" Ameche, younger brother of actor Don Ameche.

That same day Georgia Tech trounced Mississippi 24-7 in the Sugar Bowl, Texas shut out Tennessee 16-0 in the Cotton Bowl while, in the Orange Bowl, Alabama demolished Syracuse 61-6 with Red Barber, the former Cincinnati Red's announcer, calling the game. Now that Babe Parelli and "Bear" Bryant had departed Kentucky, they were not playing in a Bowl, providing Dad with an excuse to get an early start on several quarts of Hudepohl fine lager.

After twenty years of Democratic Presidency (FDR and Truman), Dwight Eisenhower became the first Republican President since the start of the

Great Depression and the Second World War. Eisenhower had defeated Ohio Senator Robert Taft, known as "Mister Republican," in a close race for the Republican nomination in 1952. This was probably fortunate for the Republicans, as Taft died suddenly of a heart attack on the last day of July in 1953.

The Eisenhower campaign slogan the previous year had been, "I Like Ike," and it seemed most people did. He easily defeated Illinois Democrat Adlai Stevenson in the 1952 general election.

While Ike was busy trying to make peace in Korea by mid-year of '53, my state of Ohio was celebrating it's Sesquicentennial. The state sponsored a number of events to celebrate its first 150 years. For example, markers appeared across Ohio that described prominent people and events in the history of the state. The state government also issued a commemorative license plate, while the United States Postal Service issued a commemorative stamp.

On the humorous side, it was asserted that the United States Congress had never formally approved Ohio's admittance to the United States, and therefore Ohio was not a state. As it were, these stories were not true. But to set the record straight, President Eisenhower ended the debate by formally announcing Ohio's statehood as of March 1, 1803.

On a personal level, five things about 1953 stand out as major events in my young life. On April 10th Aunt Lois and my four-year old cousin, Paul, departed for Italy to join my Uncle Joe who was in Trieste defending the American way of life against the hated Commies. Less than a month later, my grandfather, Lou Theobald, died in his sleep in the early morning hours of Monday, May 4th.

As always, one thing leads to the next. Thus, thanks in no small part to my grandfather's passing, we moved from Walnut Hills to Bond Hill on August 5th. On August 8th, my Evanston VFW teammates and I played for the Cincinnati Knothole League Class C Championship. And, not without significance, on Labor Day my father switched from Gillette Blue Blade razors to Schick Injector Blade razors and from Lucky Strikes to Kools. Why these two things on this specific day? I could not say, but it was clearly a major event. Harold Henry Herbert Joseph had a way for making pronouncements about his life and committing to change on special days of the year… I guess so he could more easily remember these landmark decisions.

And, oh yes, make that six things. On Wednesday, August 5^{th,} I met Freddie Zigler. That morning, a moving van pulled up in front of the only home I had known in my 10 plus years of existence. I guess my parents felt the trauma of moving from Walnut Hills to the slightly more affluent neighborhood of Bond Hill might be too traumatic for me to witness first hand, so I was collected at 8:15 by my Aunt Win and whisked off to Woliver's Drug Store to help her at the pharmacy for a measly $.10 an hour. Wednesday was her short day. She illegally filled prescriptions for Mr. Woliver while I cleaned the store from top to bottom. At noon, with $.35 in my pocket, my aunt and I headed to the new neighborhood, stopping at Wherley's Tavern in Norwood to pick up some sandwiches. When we pulled up behind the moving van at 5426 Grafton Avenue, I sprinted from Aunt Win's black 1940 Chevrolet up the steps and into the front door of my new home. Sitting right in front of me as I entered was my mother's Baldwin baby grand piano. How the movers got the thing from the second floor of 3333 Spokane Avenue to the living room of Grafton Avenue was beyond my comprehension. But there it sat, totally unscathed. My mother and I were relieved.

The last few months had been a whirlwind. We had moved to Bond Hill for two simple reasons. As already stated, my saintly grandfather had died on May 4th. The resulting depression cast upon my mother and Aunt Win created the need to immediately vacate Walnut Hills, which had been their home for more 30 years.

The second, and more practical reason for my father and Uncle Bill, I am ashamed to admit, was that the first "Negro" family had recently moved across Woodburn Avenue, an invisible line of racial demarcation. Though I had been taught throughout my young life that racial prejudice was a distasteful, despicable thing, the fact was that, without admitting it out loud, my family decided to get the hell out of Walnut Hills before this slow invasion of colored people began to impact property values. It made little difference that the oldest child of the invading family was my classmate, teammate and very good friend, Billy Tate. This was an early lesson for me. The fact was that many people might disguise their prejudices, perhaps even from themselves, until the hidden bigotry is drawn out by an impact on their wallet.

They interred my Grandpa Theobald at Rest Haven Memorial cemetery on a gloomy, rainy Thursday, and two days later my parents were looking at houses in the modern Cincinnati suburbs of Mt. Washington and Bond Hill.

Thus, due to Gramps' demise and the unwelcome advance by the Tate family on our sacred Spokane Avenue, I suddenly found myself unhappily transplanted in the suburbs. If that wasn't bad enough, on this first afternoon in our new home, even before the movers had departed, I answered a loud knock on the front screen door and discovered myself face-to-face with a person whom, I would quickly learn, was my total opposite.

Freddie Zigler had thick curly black hair, brown eyes, distinctive Roman features and skin darker than Billy Tate's. I was a towhead with blue eyes, fair skin and, in my mind, a rather plain looking 10-year-old. Zigler seemed outgoing, almost arrogant, with a light frivolous attitude, and a high-pitched and all too frequent laugh. To him, everything seemed funny. I was shy, backward, soft-spoken, and too serious for my own good.

Staring back at me with a mile-wide grin, my new annoyance said, "Hi. I'm Fred Zigler. I live up the hill behind you on Laconia Drive. My mother insisted that I come down and introduce myself, although I really don't mind. You can never have enough guys for stickball. You do play stickball, don't you?"

Before I could slam the door in his face, my mother came up from behind and asked, "Why Randy, who's your new friend? Don't be so rude. Ask him in."

I didn't have to. He was through the door before I could get my hands out of my pockets. He left me standing at the door as he gave himself a tour of the house. Looking at his back as he walked into our kitchen, I felt certain that he would open our icebox and help himself to an apple. He did not.

After casing the kitchen for a moment or two, he blew by me without a word, but only a nod, suggesting I was to follow him. When he reached the hall off the dining room, he stopped to ask which bedroom was mine. Angry and dumbfounded, I pointed to the left.

He disappeared through the door and immediately yelped at his discovery of the vast collection of baseball cards I had spread out on the bed to reorganize.

"Get your hands off of those," I demanded. Nobody fooled around with my baseball cards; certainly not this halfwit.

He turned and smiled at me, not the least bit offended by my demand, yet offering not the slightest remorse for trespassing on such sacred property.

He finally said, "I know all about you. You're the kid who plays shortstop for Evanston VFW. We came to see you guys play Saint Mark's for the East Side Championship last week. You're playing Tony's Cafe for the City Class C championship on Saturday. No way you'll beat those guys."

He continued his perusal of my room. "Steve Goldman said you were moving into this house, but nobody really believed him."

I stared back at him, suddenly feeling a little superior due to his recognition of me. As I gathered up my baseball cards, carefully placing them back into an Ibold cigar box, I challenged his contention, "Whaddaya mean we won't beat Tony's Cafe?"

"Simple. They've got Eddie Brinkman, Jimmie Hargavy and Earl Stodtgruber. Nobody's gonna beat them. You guys got lucky against Saint Mark's. Forget it. Brinkman's pitched three no-hitters in a row. You might as well not even show up."

"Well, I've got news for you, eagle-nose, not only are we gonna beat them, we're gonna kill them."

I could see I had hurt his feelings with the remark about his nose, which is just exactly what I had intended. But I also felt bad that I had said such a thing. One thing I would soon learn about Freddie was that you could hurt him, but you couldn't break him. He was resilient. And he was used to abuse.

He attempted to make peace, "I guess it really wasn't luck against Saint Mark's. You hit the snot out of the ball on that Grand Slam in the 5th inning. And that Mauser kid throws bullets. You smashed that ball. But Mauser is no Brinkman. And anyway, who ever heard of Evanston VFW?"

"You were there?"

"Darn tootin' I was there. Our coach, Bip Bohl—he's Wally's dad—you'll meet Wally. Anyway, Bip took a bunch of us. Bip really thought you had a great, natural swing, and he ain't easy to impress. Just ask Wally."

Fred was good at making peace without giving up his stance. And, he had hit my weak spot—my ego. I decided to be conciliatory in my own backhanded way.

"We'll beat Tony's, OK. And Brinkman ain't gonna throw no no-hitter on Saturday. I promise you. If you want, you can come to the game with my mom and dad. My dad helps coach."

"You kidding? That's great. I'll root for you guys if you take me along. Jeezal Pete, this is keen. You really mean it?"

"Yea. Why not?"

Without realizing it, we had taken the first step to a life-long friendship. Freddie started to give me the rundown on the neighborhood.

"This is a fantastic place to live. I like it a lot better than Avondale where I used to live. Most of the kids around here are either Jewish or Catholic. I'm Jewish," he explained.

"What are you?" he asked.

This was the first conversation I had ever had with a peer about religion. I felt uneasy about having this discussion.

"Well, my mother is Jewish and my dad is... well I'm not sure what my dad is. But, he's not Jewish. We don't go to church."

"Your mom's Jewish? Well then that makes you Jewish. Don't ya know the rules?"

I didn't know there were any rules. "Whaddaya mean?" I asked.

"Simple. According to Jewish law, if your mother is Jewish, then you're

Jewish. So, that's neat, you're a Yid."

"A what?"

"A Yid. You know, like in Yiddish. That's another way of saying your Jewish."

This guy was really confusing me. I tried to change the subject.

"So, are there any other kids on this street?"

"Sure. The Gates live next door," he explained pointing out my bedroom window. "Janet is our age and Jack is a couple of years younger. And there is a little sister, but I don't know her name. They're Catholic, so they go to St. Agnes, not Bond Hill like you and me."

He continued, "Two doors down the other way are the Loewenstine's. There are four brothers. Leon is the oldest and he plays fullback for Purcell. They're Catholic too."

"I know about the Loewenstines," I said. Mr. Loewenstine is my mother's third cousin."

Freddie looked at me with a questioning stare. "How can he be related to your mother if he's Catholic?"

As if a magician had said alakazam, Freddie disappeared from my room. I heard him yell, "Hey, Mrs. Stuartmeyer," mispronouncing our name, "How can you be related to the Loewenstines if you're Jewish and they're Catholic?"

He had found my mother in the dining room unpacking boxes with my Aunt Win. My mother looked at Freddie with her typical patience while my Aunt threw off an obvious look of angst.

My mother explained, "Well, my cousin, Leon, married a Catholic girl and we heard that he converted to Catholicism. But none of us really know Leon very well."

Freddie responded as if he were on the debate team, "Mr. Loewenstine's name is Leon? Well then, he sure ain't Jewish. His oldest son is named Leon too. And Jews don't name their kids for the living—just for the dead!"

I had learned more about religion in the past ten minutes than I had in all of my sheltered ten years of life. My mother and aunt looked at each other as if to silently say, *Oh, boy, this kid is going to be a doozy.*

My aunt suggested that Fred might want to walk me around the neighborhood to show me the lay of the land and maybe find some other neighborhood kids to meet. Freddie thought this was a great idea, shoving me out the front screen door with the aluminum *W* on the center brace that stood for *Wagner*, the previous owners.

He led me two doors north, to the Loewenstines' buff brick two-story Cape Cod, where he rapped aggressively on their screen door with the appropriate *L* in the center brace. This initial-on-the-door thing was new to me. I assumed it represented a certain level of affluence that did not exist in Walnut Hills.

A very pretty lady, adorned in a yellow flower covered sundress and with a half-smoked cigarette hanging from her dark red painted lips, came to the door.

"Well, well, Freddie Zigler, what are you up to this afternoon?" she asked, giving me the once over. "And who is your little friend here?"

Fred responded loudly and enthusiastically, "Hi, Mrs. Loewenstine. This is your new neighbor, Randy Stuartmeyer (he was still mispronouncing my name), your new neighbor who just moved into the Wagner's house. His mom asked me to introduce him to the other neighbor kids."

"Well, hello there, Randy," she said. "I understand you are our long-lost cousin, right?"

"Yes Ma'am," I sheepishly replied, as she gave me the once over.

"Well, I'm sorry, but all four of my boys are at the swim club at Losantiville. I'll send Mike and Ron up to introduce themselves when they get home. Mike is about your age and Ron is a couple of years younger. Leon and Harold are already in high school at Purcell. Maybe you can come with us to one of their football games this fall."

"Yes Ma'am," I repeated, sounding like some creepy robot.

"Well, welcome to the neighborhood, Randy," she said, dismissing us with a smile while she and her cigarette disappeared back into the house.

As we skipped down the front steps of the Loewenstine house, Freddie said to me, "The Loewenstines belong to Losantiville Country Club. They're the richest family around here. My father says he's a shyster lawyer. Leon, Jr. plays fullback for Purcell and is a really good guy. But, the other three are assholes, if you ask me"

Not used to hearing kids my age use such language, I just processed this without a word.

He continued, "But there are some really neat kids in the neighborhood. My best friends are Wally Bohl and Carl Shiele. You will like both of them. They are really good athletes and Wally's dad, Bip, helps coach Loretta Foods. They're the best knothole team around here."

Over the next couple of hours, Freddie gave me the full tour of my new neighborhood. In 1953, I was pitifully introverted while Freddie Zigler did not seem to have an ounce of shyness in his body. He just forged ahead like a tour guide, taking me door to door like it was the most natural thing in the world.

First, we took a right to the last house on Grafton Avenue, where the houses met up with the three-story apartment buildings of a complex called Swifton Apartments.

Fred pointed to the right saying, "This is where the Fishmans live. Old man Fishman is a TV repairman. He has two daughters. Terry is three years older than us and uglier than sin, if you ask me. She's a redhead, and I hate redheads. But her sister Elaine, who is a year ahead of us, is really hot. Not as hot as the Wilkins twins up the street. But I wouldn't kick her out of bed for eating matzo."

"Why would you be in bed with her?" I asked.

He looked at me like I had two heads, then said, "Your kidding, right?"

My questioning stare indicated I was indeed not kidding.

"Man, I have a lot of work to do with you. I might only be 10, but I know what schtupping is," he stated with great insistence.

"What's schtupping?" I asked

"Fucking A, man!" he shouted at me. "Have you been living in Walnut Hills or on goddamned island?"

I fidgeted and just looked at him blankly.

We crossed the street where we stood in front of a house Fred identified as the home of Billy Hayes, a soon to be fifth grader at Bond Hill School.

"His uncle Frank is a great guy. Sometimes he gives me a ride to school if the weather's bad. But see that garden?" Fred asked, pointing at a blank lot next to the house filled with flowers and vegetables. "Billy's grandfather bought two lots and built his house on one and his cockamamie garden on the other one. If you want to die, try tiptoeing through the cabbage. Old man Griggs will kill you."

I made the quick assumption that old man Griggs was Billy's grandfather. I was already getting a bit overwhelmed with neighborhood data. But I decided that staying out of that garden was more important than learning what schtupping was… and why Fred would do that with Elaine Fishman even if she were eating matzo.

We continued up the other side of the street from my new house. Two little cape cods from the Griggs' garden, Freddie pointed at a white little house and said with great disdain, "That's where fat-assed Bertha Schwartz lives. See that little putting green she calls her lawn? Well, don't set foot on it unless you have earplugs. She'd kill you too, except she's so fat she'd never catch you. But she has a screech that would kill a cat."

It was beginning to sound like my new neighborhood was more of a minefield than a community. OK, I noted, no garden and no putting green lawn. The latter concerned me as it was across the street from my house where I had hoped to bounce tennis balls off of the front steps. Oh well, I'd risk the fat lady's screech.

As we headed on up Grafton Avenue, Fred gestured to the two-story house next to mine. "The Gates live there as I said earlier. Nobody is going to schtup Janet, with or without matzo. Not even with a bag over her pathetic head."

I had given up. Fred might as well have been describing the girls of Grafton in Greek. I just kept moving on up the street.

I learned that three more houses up on my side of the street lived the Listners. Richard Listner was our age and "way too fat for his own good," according to Fred.

His brother Don was already in high school at Walnut Hills because he was smarter than Richard. Their mother was divorced from their father and therefore had to work.

Then Fred pointed out the next house. "That's where Sy Berliner lives. He's loony tunes, if you know what I mean?"

"Crazy?" I asked.

"You can say that twice," Fred said with a hearty laugh. "Wally, Carl and I pull a lot of pranks on him. At first, I felt badly about it. But, he's not only nuts, he's also a mean prick. So, we mess with him now and then."

Get me back to Walnut Hills where the people are nice, I thought.

At the top of the slight hill where Grafton Avenue leveled off, we came upon two very pretty girls playing hopscotch on the sidewalk in front of their house.

The shorter one smiled and said, "Hi, Fred."

"Hi there, Diane," Fred responded. "Randy, this here are Diane and Donna, the Wilkins twins I told you about."

They didn't look like twins. The short one was pretty and athletic. The much taller one was equally attractive, but a bit gangly.

The short one pointed to her apparently shy sister and said, "This is Donna. You just moved in down the street, right?"

If Donna was shy, I was paralyzed. I just did not know how to act around girls. And if they were friendly, I was even more lost.

Fred covered for me. "Yep, Randy just moved in today. He plays shortstop for Evanston VFW, and he claims they are going to win the city championship on Saturday. I saw him hit one of the longest homeruns I've ever seen last Saturday when they beat St. Mark's."

Diane was impressed, while Donna seemed to care less.

"Well," Fred said, "I am going to take Randy up to meet Wally and Carl."

Diane flirted a very pleasant goodbye, while Donna yawned and went back to the hopscotch.

As we continued up the street, Fred pointed at the house across the street from the Wilkins and advised me that it was the home of Susan Hawthorne.

"I wouldn't kick her out..." he started, then stopped himself. "Never mind. We'll pick up on your sex education later."

After walking another block and a half, we came to the end of Grafton where it ran into Dale Road, a much busier street. Our jaunt continued east on Dale Road where we landed at a white and grey cape cod house with a porch similar to my new home. Fred forged ahead, advising me that Wally might be tinkering in the garage that stood at the end of an L-shaped alley. When we reached the back yard, we found two very athletic looking eleven year olds.

"Hey, cats," Fred said. "This is Randy Suartmeyer. Randy, this is Wally Bohl," pointing at the bigger of the two. "And, this is Carl Schiele," Fred advised, gesturing toward the much shorter one.

This guy just can't pronounce my last name, I thought. *If he knows so much about the schtupping thing, you would think he could get my name right.*

Fred continued, "You guys saw him play last Saturday when Bip took us to the semi-finals. Randy is the guy that hit that monster home run. Remember?" Then turning back to me, "Bip is Wally's dad. He helps coach Loretta's Food Shop, the best team around here."

Bip... not Mr. Bohl? I thought. *Oh, well. If they can call him Bip, it's OK with me.*

Carl stepped forward, extending his right hand. "Heck yea, I remember you. That was a heck of a game. But now you have to play Tony's Cafe. They're tough," he smiled.

Wally, clearly more reserved, but intently self-assured, walked up to me offering a handshake.

"How you doin'?" he grunted.

"Hello," I said to them both.

I already liked Carl. Wally, I wasn't so sure about yet.

But then he said, "let me grab a couple more gloves, and we'll have a toss. You can show us your stuff."

With that, he trotted to the back porch, returning with two right-handed fielder mitts.

"Freddie, you'll have to make do."

I looked inquisitively.

"I'm a southpaw," Fred advised. "But I can make this work."

Carl and Wally jogged to the other side of the back yard where Wally immediately threw a hard fastball to my right side. I backhanded it easily and tossed it softly to Carl. Wally tested me two more times, throwing the third one into the grass in front of me, which I scooped out of the dirt in a matter-of-fact manner.

From that point on, all went well. Wally let up on me, and we tossed the ball for almost a half an hour.

While we were enjoying it all, a maroon 1951 Chevy pulled into the driveway behind us. A pleasant-looking, crusty skinned man got out of the car.

"Hi, Dad," Wally shouted.

Carl, more respectfully said, "Hi, Mr. Bohl." Then pointing at me, stated, "This is Randy… I'm sorry, what's your last name?"

"Stuartmeyer!" Fred exclaimed.

"Hello, Mr. Bohl. I'm Randy Stertmeyer," I corrected.

Mr. Bohl smiled, offering me his hand and said, "Hello, son. I know who you are. We came to your game last Saturday. We could use a kid like you next year on Loretta Food's team. But you still have one more game to win this year, right?"

I was now starting to feel much better about my new neighborhood. I had found three new friends and a likable father figure.

Bip then broke up our game of toss when he said to Wally, "OK, little guy, time to clean up for dinner."

Then looking at me he said, "We'll be coming to your game Saturday. Maybe you can get another round-tripper."

Fred and I gave Wally the borrowed gloves and headed back to Dale Road with Carl, where we turned right, followed by a quick left onto Laconia Ave.

"This is the street that Carl and I live on," Fred advised.

Five houses down on the right we came to Carl's house, and he said, "Hey, let's all get together tomorrow down by Freddie's for a game of stick ball, OK?"

"Jeesal Pete, that's a great idea!" Fred chimed.

"OK. I think I can do that," I offered sheepishly.

Freddie and I continued on down Laconia almost to the dead end cul-du-sac where Fred lived. He pointed to his house and then said, "C'mon, I'll show you the short-cut to your house."

With that, we headed to the end of the street where he explained that the Graf family lived in a house situated right behind mine, a street over.

"Mr. Graf is a great guy and his daughter, Marsha, is a junior at the New Woodward where we will be going. And believe me, she's one of those matzo girls. But we'll get into that sex stuff some other time."

He then showed me how to take the Graf driveway to a clearing that led into my backyard.

"Neat, huh," he said pointing to the cut through.

"Are you sure he doesn't care?"

"Heck no, he's a cool old man. A real mensch. No sweat," Fred insisted.

What the heck is a mensch? I thought to myself.

"Well, I gotta get home. See ya tomorrow for stickball, OK?" Fred asked.

"Darn tootin'. It sounds like fun. Thanks for showing me around. I like Carl and Wally. Thanks again."

Fred pointed back at the Graf's house and said, "Good deal, pal. You bring the matzo and I'll explain what schtupping is."

With that, he gave out with that now familiar, if somewhat hideous, giggle and headed back up the driveway to Laconia Avenue.

When I walked in our back door and skipped up the four steps to the bright kitchen, my mother and aunt were waiting with a million questions. I told them about my tour with Fred, leaving out any reference to matzo. I could see the relief in my mother's eyes as she realized that my first day in Bond Hill had gone well.

My father broke through the front door a little after 5:30, anxious to see his new home with his old furniture. Dinner in the large dining room was a tuna casserole that my Aunt Win had brought with her.

The big after-dinner event was watching my father and Uncle Bill try to figure out the mechanical television antenna that was controlled by a box device attached to our TV. It rotated the antenna strapped to the chimney.

After figuring the thing out, my father advised everyone, "Well, this little son-of-a-buck beats the hell out of those damned rabbit ears."

And with that, my life in Walnut Hills... the only life I had known to that point, had been picked up and summarily moved north to Bond Hill.

That night, securely tucked between the sheets in my new bedroom, I fell off to sleep, much more optimistic about my new neighborhood than I had been when I woke up in my old neighborhood that morning. *This just might work out.*

And—to polish off this week in August—with Freddie, Wally, Carl, Bip, Mrs. Bohl, plus Jack Gates, Mike Loewenstine and my mother all in attendance at Owl's Nest Park, and with my father coaching first base—we beat Tony's Cafe 5-4 on a single by our pitcher Jerry Mauser in extra innings. I had three singles and a walk. I coasted home from third base on Jerry's single for the winning run. Evanston VFW was City Champions of Class C Knothole. Yes, it was a week to remember.

Ohio Sesquicentennial 3 Cent Stamp

1953

Let the cards fall
Let the cards fall where they may
All I can do, all I can say
Gotta move to trust my instincts...

From *Let the Cards Fall*
By 311

THE TRADE

Had the choice been mine, we would have moved to Mt. Washington rather than Bond Hill. This would have allowed me to reunite in the seventh grade at Withrow High School with all of my pals I had left behind at Hoffman School.

But, of course, the choice was not mine. And, I must admit, the anxiety of a new neighborhood and a new school was beginning to subside. I had made a few friends in the four weeks between moving to Bond Hill and the beginning of school.

When, on the second day of school, Mike Cohen, a cross-eyed rock-hard, fireplug of a guy, chose me first for the Cohen Cadets intramural football team, I became an instant celebrity at Bond Hill School. Mike had been picked at the end of the fifth-grade year in May 1953, as one of four captains for intramural sports. It took me a while to wade through all of this, because we had no such thing at Hoffman School. However, as I discovered, intramural sports were a big deal at Bond Hill. The sixth graders were kings of the hill. And the four guys chosen to be captains were each a king among kings.

As it turned out, Mike had heard of my endeavors in Knothole baseball with Evanston VFW from Freddie Zigler. Thus, he chose to single me out, take a risk if you will, in the hope that I was as good as Freddie had said. This simple act, by a person I didn't know, created an immediate buzz about me with almost every single sixth grader at Bond Hill.

But there were some exceptions. As we entered the second week of school, my prowess as a baseball player had failed to impress one small group. My new friend, A.J. Friedman referred to them as the Jewish Mafia. These four guys were not only some of the best athletes and brightest students in school, but more importantly, they came from four of the wealthiest families in Bond Hill. They all lived on the same exclusive street in the fashionable neighborhood of Paddock Hills. As a result, they were the rulers of the playground.

The largest, Louie Marcus, could not stay out of trouble. He was big and muscular. He was also nuts. He knew no fear. I had been advised by several of my new friends not to mess with Louie. When Louie was around, I tried my best to be invisible.

The other three of this elite group were all calmer and smarter than Louie. Alan Feinstien was the most studious. He loved and excelled at tennis, and had a compelling passion for all things scientific. Frankie Feldman was the most athletic of the bunch. He seemed to have a sensitive side, kinder and more open than the rest. I had heard he was studying guitar and was becoming an excellent musician.

The leader of the Jewish Mafia was Mickey Ross. Mickey was short and diminutive in stature. I would discover his size was deceiving. Mickey was one heck of an athlete—quick and tenacious. I also rapidly discovered one other, not so endearing, characteristic of his. He was never wrong. Unlike most, he could get away with thinking he was always right because he had Louie Marcus as his enforcer.

Like Mike Cohen, Mickey had been one of four team captains chosen for the year. It was predetermined that Alan, Louie and Frankie would be on Mickey's team. I soon learned that this group, who, taking a page from Notre Dame, called their team the Fighting Yiddish, was none to happy about Mike picking me first. They were even less pleased when our gym teacher, Mr. Landwehr, paired me with Frankie for our first running of the fifty-yard dash.

As he and I sprinted over the blacktop playground, I was greatly surprised at hearing the vast majority cheering me on. Frankie was fast, but I inched past him just before the finish line. Mr. Landwehr loudly reported the times.

"Feldman 6.8 seconds, Stertmeyer, 6.7 seconds." A huge cheer went up. I quickly learned from A.J. Friedman that we had both surpassed the old school record of 6.9 seconds. To his credit, Frankie smiled and shook my hand.

"I'll get you next time," he said with conviction.

His three compadres were not so happy. I realized I was making a name for myself at my new school while, perhaps, at the same time creating four formidable enemies. I became more certain of this when Louie Marcus bumped hard into me later in the day as I was carrying my lunch tray to join my new friends Freddie Zigler, Stuart Tobin and A.J. Freidman at a corner table in the second floor lunch room of Bond Hill School. The tray along with my chicken noodle soup, egg salad sandwich and bottle of government-subsidized milk went flying right into Freddie's lap.

I stood there gazing at Fred wearing my lunch, and then instinctively turned to see Louie Marcus wearing a wicked, evil-spirited grin. As A.J. and Stuart cowered on the far side of the table, Freddie jumped up and started a tirade aimed at Louie the bully. I was discovering how fearless my new friend Freddie was—and how lacking he was in good judgment as well.

Of course, this is just what Louie wanted. Fortunately, before Louie could get to Freddie, Mr. Landwher came up from behind and took Louie's right ear between his thumbnail and index finger, the immediate look of pain replacing the evil smile on Louie's face. At the same time, Landwher fixed his eyes on Freddie, pointing to a chair. Fred got the message and quickly wiped the egg salad from is shirt and sat back down.

The gym teacher said, "You just can't help yourself can you, Marcus?"

"Whaddaya mean?" Louie protested. Pointing at me he said, "This spaz wasn't watching where he was going and ran right into me. I didn't do anything. Then Zigler starts screaming at me like a numbskull. He's lucky I didn't rearrange his face."

Landwher pinching harder on Louie's ear said, "The only thing you're going to rearrange, young man, is your schedule. I saw the whole thing, and it's going to cost you a day's suspension." With that, he guided Marcus from the lunchroom in the direction of the principal's office.

As Landwehr and Marcus disappeared, A.J., with newfound courage said, "Hey, Fred, why don't you take off your shirt and let Randy eat what's left of his lunch?"

But Fred was paying no attention to A.J. He was looking across the lunchroom at Alan, Frankie and Mickey. Glaring back at Fred, Mickey smiled in a way that said *this isn't over.*

Well this is just great, I thought to myself. While there was a lot of talk around school for the rest of the day, about both the fifty-yard dash and the events in the lunchroom, nothing more came of it. At 3:30 the bell rang indicating that school was out for the day. I exited the side door with A.J. and Fred expecting to see the Jewish Mafia waiting for us. But there was no sign of any of them.

The three of us crossed over California Avenue, stepping into Brighthalle's Delicatessen where we each plopped down a penny in exchange for a piece of candy. Mr. Brighthalle had a wide array of one cent and two cents candies in long rows of trays displayed behind a slanted glass case just to the right of the entry door. At the door there was the requisite bell, hanging from the top, which announced anyone who entered the store. A.J. selected a grape sour-drop; Fred went with a chocolate kiss while I opted for a cherry hat. We then headed east past St. Agnes Church where my new Catholic neighbors went to school, savoring our respective treats. At Reading Road, A.J. headed south while Fred and I said good-bye and journeyed north.

When Freddie and I parted at the corner of Grafton and Portman Avenues, we agreed to bring some baseball cards to school the next day as card flipping was taking on new importance on the playground with the impending World Series between the Yankees and Dodgers less than a week off.

The next morning, a bright sunny Friday, held the promise of a great weekend just ahead. Freddie appeared at my front door at 7:30 sharp, and we were off. Freddie could talk of nothing but the Jewish Mafia, which was exactly what I was trying hard to forget. Thus, it was with great trepidation that we walked onto the Bond Hill School playground.

We approached a group standing near the hopscotch court. They were in a heated debate. As we neared them, I heard Spike Spiegel say to Carl Schiele, "What kind of name is Yogi Berra anyway?"

A.J. Freidman, towering a good six non-athletic inches over the rest of the group answered, "He's Indian. Not like woo-woo-woo Indian. Not like Tonto. I mean he's an *Indian*-Indian, like in the Taj Mahal. You know, sitting cross-legged in a diaper."

"You're nuts", Wally Bohl chimed in. "'Yogi' is Russian. It's short for something like 'Yogoslav Berralovski'. He's a Commie. My dad told me. He's a commie playing for the Yankees. How da ya like that?"

It was time for Freddie to join in the fray. "Geezooie, you guys don't know nothin'? He's Italian. His name is Lawrence Berra. Yogi is a nickname. He grew up in an Italian neighborhood in St. Louis. I read it in *The Sporting News*."

Spike Spiegel interrupted, "Freddie, when did you learn to read? And, anyway, if he's from St. Louis, how come he doesn't play for the Cards or the Browns? Did ya ever hear him talk? He's gotta be from the Bronx. He sounds just like my Uncle Moshe, and he's from the Bronx."

"I'll tell you one thing," A.J. said, breaking into Spike's tirade, "Mickey Mantle ain't from the Bronx. Have you heard him talk? He's gotta be from Mississippi or Arkansas or some place like that."

Carl Schiele, waving the Yogi Berra card that had caused the debate, said, "Well, wherever they're from, they've won four straight World Series, and I have a dime that says they'll make it five next week. They might talk funny, but they play for the Yanks. That's all that counts. Now do you want to trade this Yogi Berra for a Ted Kluszewski or not?"

Spiegel said, "Ain't no way I'm giving up a Big Klu for Yogi Berra. Forget it. But I'll take that dime bet on the Series. This is the Dodgers' year. Heck, DiMaggio is gone. And Mantel is good, but he's no DiMaggio. The Bums will kill 'em."

As I listened to the Dodgers vs. the Yankees debate escalate, I was thinking about the Berra for Kluszewski trade Carl Schiele was proposing to Spike Spiegel. Thanks to my Aunt Win and her job at Woliver's Pharmacy, I was getting more than my fair share of Topps Baseball Cards and the dusty stick of gum that came with every pack of six. She brought me some almost every time I saw her. I knew I had six Ted Kluszewskis sitting in my Ibold cigar box at home and one more in my back pocket.

On the other hand, I needed two more Yankees to have at least one card of their entire starting lineup. I was only missing first baseman Joe Collins and, of course, catcher Yogi Berra. I saw my opening and sheepishly entered the negotiations.

I said to Carl, "You know, Carl, I might be willing to give up a Kluszewski for a Berra, but only if I can get a Joe Collins with it."

That quieted the crowd. Just as Carl was about to respond, I noticed him looking over my shoulder with some obvious concern. I turned to see Mickey Ross approaching the circle. Alan Feinstine, Frankie Feldman and Louie Marcus were right behind him. I was surprised to see Louie who had been given a one-day vacation the previous day my Mr. Landwehr. It was obvious that Mickey was more interested in Fred than he was in me.

"What are you guys doing hanging out with that big mouth Zigler?" he asked.

"Eat me, Ross." Fred replied. "And what are you doing here Marcus? I thought they suspended you."

Marcus proudly stated, "I took three swats instead so I could be here today to kick your ugly tuchus, ya schmuck."

Ignoring Louie, Mike Cohen, who was less afraid of Mickey Ross and his merry band than even Freddie, interceded, "Hey Mickey, don't be such a Putz. We have some serious card-trading going on here. You like to trade cards. Why don't you join in?"

Ross took the bait, "Yea? What's up?"

Mike filled in Mickey who looked at me and said, "So, you're trying to cheat Schile out of a Joe Collins?"

Swallowing hard, feeling my pulse quicken, I said with as much confidence as I could muster, "No. I just think a Kluszewski is worth more than just a Berra. That's all."

Carl said, "Hey, don't worry about it, Ross, I don't have a Collins anyway."

Ignoring Carl, Mickey said, "Why don't you and Carl just flip for it. You flip your Kluszewski for his Berra."

Carl quickly said, "OK, that's keen. Whaddaya say, Stuartmoor?" he asked, badly mispronouncing my name.

Knowing that I was loaded with Kluszewskis, my instincts told me I had more to gain than to lose from this proposal.

"Sure. Why not?"

The group moved into a large circle now with Carl and me at its center. I liked what I had seen of Carl so far, other than he insisted on calling everybody by their last names and the fact he found mine impossible to pronounce. We exchanged friendly smiles.

An impatient Mickey Ross said, "OK. Stertmeyer proposed the trade so he flips first."

Stating what everybody in the circle already knew, he continued, "Heads beats tales. Two heads or two tales, you flip again until someone wins. The photo side is heads. The statistics side is tales. Go ahead, sissy-pants, flip your Kluszewski."

Knowing that I was *sissy-pants,* I took my Big Klu card between thumb and fingers and let it fly. The card tumbled end over end toward the blacktop. When it landed, a muscular Ted Kluszewski with his rippling muscles showing under his cut-off uniform sleeves was staring up at me. Heads!!

Carl took a quick look around the circle and launched his Berra. Heads!!

Carl and I smiled at each other and then bent over to retrieve our cards. According to the law of the playground, Carl would now go first. Of course, Mr. Big Shot, Mickey Ross, had to step to the center of the circle to proclaim this fact.

Carl gave Berra another spin. Tails!

Wanting this over, I spun Kluszewski toward the ground quickly. Tails!

For those gathered, this was now becoming serious fun. It seemed the crowd was balanced as to for whom they were pulling. It was obvious I had Freddie, A.J. Friedman, Stuart Tobin, Mike Cohen and a couple of others in my corner. It was equally clear that those anxious to see Carl walk off with the win included Mickey Ross, Louie Marcus, Alan Feinstine and Wally Bohl, a good friend of Carl's. But interestingly, Franky Feldman seemed to remain quietly uncommitted. Was this just my imagination, I wondered?

Before Mickey could state the obvious yet once again, I picked up my card and let her go all in a single motion. Heads!!

Just as Carl was about to let his card go, the school bell rang loudly, announcing it was time to line up by classroom groups at the entrance assigned to our given class.

Ross stepped in and said, "Nobody move! Go ahead, Schiele, flip your doggone card."

Carl launched Yogi Berra. Tails! A significant cheer followed. I noted just the slightest smile at the corners of Franky Feldman's mouth. As I bent over to claim my Yogi Berra, Mickey's foot came down on it.

He looked at me angrily and said, "We'll continue this after lunch. I'm going to take both of those cards from you, so be ready."

He spun away from the circle, and we all made a beeline for our assigned groups. I stood in line wondering what he had meant by, "I'm going to take both of those cards from you, so be ready." Did he want to fight me for them? Did he think I would just hand them over? Was he serious when he called me *sissy-pants?*

I had never had a schoolyard fight in my life, but I knew that I could not let Mickey bully me. If I did, I would be in for a miserable future at my new school. A bloody nose was better than not standing up to him.

I thought of advice I had always gotten from my Aunt Win—*You don't have to fight. You're bright enough to outthink people. Use reason and calm with bullies.* That sage counsel had served me well in the past.

Then there was dad's approach—*Don't ever take any crap from knuckleheads who think they can push you around. You just have to push back harder.* This had worked with Roy Mitchell a couple of years before when reason had failed. Well, at least I had on a black shirt. It wouldn't show the blood should it come to that.

As we marched single file up the stairs and down the hall to room 208, I continued to ponder my conundrum. We all took our seats, and Miss Cooper took the roll in alphabetical order finishing with Stertmeyer, Tobin and Zigler. After confirming we had a Friday full house, she launched into an hour of square roots. Normally I devoured math, but on this day my mind was on Kluszewski, Berra and Ross rather than that crazy little square root thing that some of my classmates still confused with the division sign. I stayed lost in my thoughts, gazing out of the half-opened window, at the passing traffic on California Avenue. Somehow, I made it to lunch without being called upon in either math or science. While I was sweating out my after-lunch date with Mickey Ross, Freddie and A.J. Friedman were focused on lunch.

"I don't get it," Freddie complained. "All of the Catholics are across the street at St. Agnes, and yet every Friday they insist on serving us either fish or egg salad."

"Yea, and always this doggone tomato soup," A.J. Friedman added.

Freddie continued, "Send this dreck across the street and get me a hunk of meat, will ya?"

"Hey, Zigler, I'm Catholic," shouted Tommy O'Brian from the next table over.

"Eat me, O'Brian," Freddie snapped back.

Then, "Oh, wait. That's right. You can't eat me. It's Friday and you can only eat this crap," Freddie said, pointing at his lunch tray.

While Freddie continued his banter with O'Brian, I pulled out the pack of cards from my pants pocket, neatly held together by two of my dad's thick bank rubber bands. I removed the Kluszewski card from the top of the pack. First, I studied his likeness on the front with his famous rippling biceps bulging from the cut-off sleeves of his Jersey.

I then flipped the card over. It was a Topps card, rather than the old Bowman cards that I had first collected.

"THEODORE BERNARD KLUSZEWSKI" it said at the top next to the baseball with the number 29 at its center, meaning this card was number 29 in the set. In smaller white print over a red background, I read:

First Base: Cincinnati Reds Home: Cincinnati
Born: September 10, 1924, Argo, Ill. Eyes: Grey Hair: Brown
Ht: 6'2" Wt: 225 Bats: Left Throws: Left

Then next to a big red star it said: *The Reds spotted Ted in 1945 when they were training at the University of Indiana. Not only was he a star baseball player, but also an All-American end on the football team. After leading two minor leagues in batting with .352 in 1946 and .377 in 1947, Ted became the Reds first baseman in 1948.*

It then listed his statistics for both the 1952 season and for his career. At the bottom was printed:

TCG TOPPS BASEBALL PRDT. IN U.S.A.

I twirled the card between my fingers, wishing I was 6'2" and 225 pounds. That would fix any and all of the Jewish Mafia. Micky Ross wouldn't mess with Big Klu. But I wasn't Big Klu, and my date with Ross was rapidly approaching.

As I continued to flip the card over and over in my right hand, an epiphany jumped from Big Klu's big biceps on the card right into my 11-year-old brain.

There was the answer right in my hand. I had to "become" Kluszewski. I had to remain soft-spoken, yet intimidating. Somehow, I had to convey to Mickey Ross that I was not to be messed with. Rather, I was someone to fear. As my dad had told me so often, "Don't ever go looking for a fight. But, more importantly, don't ever run from one."

Maybe I couldn't bulk up my muscles, but I sure could bulk up my attitude.

I turned to Fred and said, "Hey, Freddie, come with me. We need to find Ross and take care of this 'Big Shot' baloney of his."

First Freddie looked at me dumbfounded and then a wry grin crept onto his Roman face. He jumped up, ready for action.

I then heard A.J. Friedman asked no one in particular, "Is he nuts?"

He then answered his own question, "Stertmeyer is out of his mind. The

Mafia is going to cream him." Then to Stuart Tobin he said, "C'mon, Stuey, we don't want to miss this."

From that point on, I was too focused to hear much of the collateral clatter, but I would learn that just about every fifth and sixth grade boy formed a small parade and followed Freddie and me out onto the school playground. There was no sign of the enemy army.

We all knew that the Jewish Mafia never had lunch in the lunch room on Fridays for the same reason about which Freddie had been engaged with O'Brian. Instead of settling for egg salad or fish sticks, they rode their bikes the six blocks down Reading Road to Frisch's for a Big Boy and an order of fries. Their lunch cost $.60, ours $.12; the poor and humble vs. the rich and spoiled, if you will.

Like an impatient batter waiting for the pay-off pitch from a pitcher who is taking too long to make his next delivery, I surveyed the field of play. I had to somehow become Big Klu. I felt intimidating. I was ready.

Suddenly, there was abuzz from the large group that had gathered on the playground. And there they were, the Jewish Mafia; Allan, Frankie, the reinstated Louie and, of course, my nemesis, Mickey Ross.

They locked their expensive 3-speed bikes to the bike rack and began to move in our direction.

I tapped into my Kluszewski persona and quickly took a bead directly toward Mickey. The group of 5th and 6th graders on the playground parted like the Red Sea as if I was Moses. I heard someone over my right shoulder shout, "This is keen. Who are you pulling for?"

Somebody else said something about the potential for me to end the day with fewer teeth than I had when the day started.

As I approached Mickey, his bodyguard Louie Marcus stepped in front of me.

I quickly said quietly but firmly, "Get out of my way, Marcus. This isn't about you. This is between me and your little sister there," pointing at Mickey. This brought a smattering of laughter from those with the courage to laugh at Mickey Ross.

I walked around Marcus and stood toe-to-toe with Mickey. I realized

I was looking down at him. I almost called him a runt but then thought better of it. One insult was probably enough. Instead, I challenged him with, "So, Mickey, this is between you and me, right? You don't need help from Marcus to handle a sissy-pants like me. Right?"

I sensed that I had gained an advantage. Mickey had never expected me to take him on. Now it was time to be smart as well as tough.

"Mickey, here's a couple of things for you to think about," I said to Ross looking him straight in the eye. "First, I may be the new kid at Bond Hill, but I am not going to let you, or anyone else, push me around. It's important you understand that."

He didn't move or say a word. I could tell he was trying to digest my words and my posture. Louie Marcus grabbed me from behind, twirled me around with his superior strength and said, "This is a lot of BS. I'm going to knock your block off, you punk."

I threw his hand off of me and turned back to face Mickey and summoned the most courageous and confident smile I could.

"Mickey, are you going to embarrass yourself by letting this Neanderthal turn this into a fight?"

"What did you call me?" Louie asked.

From behind me I heard Frankie Feldman shout, "Shut up, Louie. Stertmeyer is right. This is between him and Mickey."

Then I saw it in Mickey's eyes. He didn't want to fight. He wanted a way out.

I continued, "As I said, there are *two* things you need to understand. The second thing is that you and I are both smart enough to not settle this with blood. Why ruin two perfectly good shirts and get thrown out of school?"

Mickey smiled and finally broke his silence. "I'm listening."

This was going better than I had expected. Mickey had opened the door, and now I had to walk through it. With my ability to continue to get way more than my share of the Topps six card nickel wax packs of baseball cards from my aunt, this was not really about the trade for me. It was more about acceptance, saving face.

"Alright, Mickey, here's the trade I propose. I'll give a Kluszewski to not only you, but also Frankie, Allan and your goon, Marcus. In addition, I will give Schile any other Red I have doubles of in my collection as extra for the Berra I won from him."

"What's in this for you?" Mickey asked.

"In return, you quit picking on everybody around here. And your team agrees to play Mike Cohen's team next Friday after lunch, three innings of softball. If we win, you all four give me back my Kluszewskis. If you win, you keep them, and we are all friends."

Before Mickey could reply, Frankie Feldman ran up to me, stuck out his hand and said, "That's fair. Cohen's Cadets vs. the Fighting Yiddish. You got a deal, Stertmeyer."

We shook hands.

Then he turned to Ross and said, "Right, Mickey?"

Mickey looked around at the circle of kids on the playground, then at Frankie and finally, at me. "OK. Deal," he said offering his hand.

I took it, and we smiled at each other.

As if it were scripted, the bell rang, summoning us all back to class. As we headed to get in line, I found myself next to Frankie Feldman. He put his hand on my shoulder and said, "I know why you get along so well with Zigler. You both have guts. Now, where's my Kluszewski?"

I had made a new friend.

The following Friday, the Fighting Yiddish beat Cohen's Cadets by a score of 8-7 with Louie Marcus driving in Frankie Feldman for the winning run. So, it had cost me four Big Klu's in return for my acceptance at my new school, not a bad trade.

Twelve days later, on Wednesday, October 6th, Frankie Feldman invited Freddie, Mike Cohen and me to join the Mafia at his house to watch the Yankees finish off the Dodgers, Billy Martin providing the winning hit in the bottom of the ninth inning.

That evening, my Aunt Win stopped by for dinner. After we ate, she handed me another 6-Pack of Topps cards. I ripped off the wrapper and discovered under the dusty piece of bubble gum the face of Joe Collins, the first baseman of the World Champion Yankees, looking back at me. A good trade? Indeed!!!

1953 Topps Baseball Cards

Ted "Big Klu" Kluszewski

Yogi Berra

Joe Collins

1954

Most any afternoon at five,
We'll be glad we're both alive,
Then maybe fortune will complete her plan,
That all began with cocktails for two...

From *Cocktails for Two*
By Sam Coslow & Arthur Johnson

SOPHISTICATION TRAINING

You usually do not comprehend at the time when a single day comes around and has a profound and lasting effect on the rest of your life. I had such a day in the summer of 1957 that involved a special lady, a big red brick downtown building and a bare room with only hardwood flooring and a full wall mirror.

My connection to the red brick skyscraper that helped to define the 1950's Cincinnati distinct skyline had started a decade earlier.

Shortly after my father returned home from the war, my parents began the weekly tradition of visiting my Grandma and Grandpa Stertmeyers' home in Newport, Kentucky every Friday for dinner. This weekly sojourn would eventually connect me to this modern building that I watched grow out of the ground each week.

In the summer of 1946, a rhythmic routine was quickly established. At around 4:00 PM every Friday afternoon, my mother and I would catch the number 7 streetcar at the corner of Woodburn and Hewitt Avenues and head for downtown. We would exit the streetcar under a maze of wires at Government Square and walk the short block to the Fifth Third Bank Building where we would enter through the large polished brass revolving door on Walnut Street.

My mother, with my little hand in hers, would guide me up the escalator which deposited us in the center of the second floor of the bright, polished three-story high bank lobby. We would then walk off to the right, her high heels clicking loudly with every step on the hard, shiny travertine marble floor.

Always my father would magically appear, and always with hat in hand. After my father wished a half dozen or so banker-people a good weekend, the three of us would take the down escalator, exit through the same revolving door, turn right and cross over 4th Street where we would enter the Dixie Terminal Building. One more down escalator would drop us at the Green Line bus terminal. Here we would jump on the *Newport* bus and depart through a hole in the south façade of the building. After the short ride across the Central Bridge spanning the mighty Ohio River, the bus would drop us at Eighth and Washington Streets directly in front of my father's favorite watering hole, Tony's Tavern.

Even at age four and five, I loved the next portion of the Friday adventure. My mother, after dictating to my father he was to have no more than one beer, would continue the block and a half west on 8th Street to my grandparents' second floor apartment. But dad and I would enter Tony's diagonal door into the smoky wonder of a *real man's world.* The high dark-stained oak bar stretched far enough to allow for 15 bar stools. To accommodate the tobacco chewers, and there were many, on the floor between every other stool sat a polished brass spittoon that matched the brass footrest bolted to the bottom of the bar (spit to the left, spit to the right, stand up, sit down, fight, fight, fight!). Near the center of the bar top was a large, clear glass vessel filled with hard boiled eggs. Behind the bar were rows and rows of bottles containing what my father called *hard liquor* and another big jar full of raw eggs for those who actually wanted an egg in their beer. This, too, was not uncommon at the time.

During the fall, my father, unbeknownst to my mother, would play a "fin," as he called it, on the weekly college football pool. This was at a time when five bucks was a chunk of change. My mother would have had a stroke had she known. He would sometimes also play the numbers, by dropping a couple of dimes on the bar for the chance to punch out a pimple-sized piece of paper from a "punch board." If his number happened to match any of several numbers listed on a framed list perched on the bar, my father would win some "serious scratch."

This never happened.

Tony's had a back room with tables and a separate entrance from Eighth Street clearly marked with a sign over the door as the "Ladies Entrance." In 1948, women were still not welcome in the bar at Tony's. In the back room stood a 12-foot treasure called a shuffleboard table, a very popular divergence for both the drunk and the sober at Tony's.

After his 15-20-minute hangout at Tony's, we would head the block and a half to Grandma and Grandpa's second story apartment on Eighth Street, just two doors away from the house in which my father was born. After a quick dinner that always included fish for my Catholic grandfather and meat of some fashion for the rest of us, we would wrap up our visit and head back across the Ohio River to what my Aunt Win called "Civilization" and the rest of us called Cincinnati.

It was on these Friday night drives north across the L & N Bridge that I started my connection with the Terrance Plaza Hotel. I had watched it grow out of the ground like a well-fed plant. Each subsequent Friday I saw it bloom from a small steel structure into a red brick mini-sky-scrapper that would help to define the Cincinnati skyline in 1950. Dad said it would put the Sinton, the Gibson and the Cincinnatian hotels to shame.

In a way, he was right. It was a special place indeed. This magnificent creation designed by the prestigious architectural firm Skidmore Owings & Merrill had its grand opening on July 19, 1948, and drew a crowd eager to see what the hubbub was about. Featured in an issue of *Harper's Magazine*, it was said of the Terrace Plaza, "If you want to discover what your grandchildren will think of as elegance of this postwar era, you will have to go to Cincinnati." At first glance, the building looked like a stack of boxes, but it was one of the first hotels in the mid-century representing a new modern style. The straight utilitarian design may have seemed shocking to some at the time, but it was a harbinger of modernism. Every room had air-conditioning. Beds slid out of the wall at the push of a button. The first seven floors were retail space for Bonds and J.C. Penney department stores. From the second floor to the seventh floor, there were no windows but only a red brick façade. The highly touted Gourmet Room sat atop the hotel, 20 floors from street level like a jeweled crown on a very plain looking queen. The circular restaurant, almost entirely exposed by windows, had a spectacular view of the city that truly set it apart. The hotel also included true modern art throughout, which included a stunning abstract mural by Joan Miró, an expansive mural of Cincinnati landmarks by cartoonist Saul Steinberg, and an Alexander Calder mobile. If that doesn't impress you, you'd better look up those three guys.

To enter the lobby, you had to take an elevator ride to the eighth floor. The fancy brass elevator doors opened to a bright sweeping panorama of huge floor-to-ceiling windows lighting up the registration desk and an abundant sitting area with modern sofas, chairs and small cocktail tables. The eighth floor also included two restaurants, an outdoor garden, and an outdoor ice rink. Just off the garden and rink sat the Terrace Garden Restaurant that had the feel of outdoor dining. It was open for breakfast and lunch.

Tucked on the opposite end of the lobby, behind the registration desk, sat the Skyline Room with a three-level terraced dining room consisting mostly of open booths facing the large windows that looked out at the Cincinnatian Hotel and the Cincinnati Enquirer Building located at Sixth and Vine Streets.

In its early days, I had toured the lobby with my mother and two aunts and loved every inch of it, as well as the ice rink and the peek-a-boo looks I got into the two eighth floor restaurants. We sometimes went to the basement Plaza Cafeteria for breakfast on shopping days in downtown. This was a switch up to our customary practice of grabbing breakfast at Mills Cafeteria, on Fourth Street. Twice-a-month shopping trips had been a part of the family routine since before I could walk. It included my mother and her sisters, Aunt Win and Aunt Lois. By the early 1950s, Aunt Win was working at Heinke's Pharmacy so these little *shopping trips* were always on Wednesdays... her day off. It was as if I had three mothers, each with a separate role. Paula, my real mother, was *The Enforcer*, Aunt Win *The Teacher* and Aunt Lois *The Recreation Director*. All three embraced these roles and excelled at their perceived assignments. Truth be told, there was way more mothering going on than any one young man needed. But, that's definitely another story. It was my Aunt Winifred who was on the mission to teach me some powerful lessons, a few beyond her pay grade, in the summer of 1954. It was her determined mission that brought us to the Terrace Plaza Hotel on a sunny, but muggy Wednesday, in mid-July. Her objective was to continue my education on how to be a gentleman as represented by your average sophisticated businessman. She had deemed that there was no better place to start than center stage at the Skyline Room, just off the lobby at the Terrace Plaza. She had made a reservation, insisting on, and getting, a window-facing table in the center of the room, assuring that there would be something to learn in every direction. It was clear on the streetcar ride into town from our neighborhood of Bond Hill that she was determined to turn me into a Bon Vivant… a Homme du Monde, in a single afternoon. Well, good luck with that, old girl.

The plan called for lunch at the Skyline Room followed by dance lessons at the Arthur Murray Studio on Fifth Street and concluding with cocktails (Coke for me) at the Gibson Girl Lounge at the Gibson Hotel. This was costing her an arm and a leg, she pointed out, so I had better watch, listen and learn!!

At the Terrace Plaza, she marched off of the elevator into the hotel lobby with me in tow. With clear determination, she guided me up to the Skyline Room Maître d', and confidently announced, "Twelve-Thirty reservation for two… Name Sutton… middle booth center of the room." Aunt Win was dressed nicely and had me in a tight-fitting charcoal grey suit. I was growing faster than my parents' finances could possibly keep me in clothes that fit. As good as we may have thought we looked, it was clear to me that the Maitra d' was of the opinion that we belonged in the hotel basement taking lunch at the Plaza Café, not in the luxurious confines of the Skyline Room with its fine linen table cloths and napkins, not to mention more fine logo embossed china and silverware than I had ever seen set before a single person.

Yep, we were frauds, and Pierre von Terrace knew it. He was not pleased having any proletariat littering, or loitering in, his fine eatery. Aunt Win seemed totally impervious to his chill. After many seconds of hesitation,

Pierre motioned to one of his captains who responded immediately. Von Terrace circled a table on his schematic, gave the captain two menus and nodded toward the center of the dining room. It looked like Don Quixote (Aunt Win) and Sancho Panza (me) were granted entry to the kingdom, no matter how unworthy we might be.

The captain was far less crusty than the Maître d', helping Aunt Win into our bench seat booth by gently spinning the table allowing her access to easily slide behind the table in a very lady-like manner. Then came my turn, on the opposite side, where I summarily banged my right knee hard against the table, while successfully fighting the urge to scream bloody murder. After asking Aunt Win if she would be requiring an ashtray, he disappeared, only to quickly return with an etched glass receptacle with the Skyline Room logo engraved in the center along with a black book of matches with the very same logo embossed in cherry red.

Aunt Win immediate dug deep in her pocketbook retrieving a red pack of Pall Malls from a faux leather canary yellow cigarette case, doing her best impression of Marlene Dietrich or Rita Hayworth preparing to light one up. Before she could even reach for the matches, the captain reappeared and deftly held out an elegant Skyline match to the pedestrian Pall Mall. Aunt Win, playing her role perfectly, leaned into the flame and took a long draw, blowing smoke in the air in a manner fit for the silver screen as well as the Skyline Room.

And with that, the real lesson began. Aunt Win scanned the table, took a deep breath, and forged ahead in an attempt to explain everything that sat before me. There was a small plate which sat upon a larger plate. Immediately to the left was a large fork with a smaller fork to its outside. To the right of the plates from left to right sat a knife, then a small spoon, then a large spoon. Aunt Win was able to explain all of this to me. She also defined the water glass, white wine glass and red wine glass that all hovered above the knife and two of spoons. I recognized the coffee cup and saucer directly to the right, and the butter dish with its companion small knife was easy for Aunt Win. Where she finally balked was with the fork and spoon that sat above the plates. I could see that she was stumped.

Never one to fake things, she smiled at me and said, "Well, that's why we are here. We will watch all of these refined people go about their lunches. Eventually someone will put that small fork and spoon to use. Then we will know."

Most important, she explained, was that I watch how the well-dressed businessmen conducted themselves. How they drank their Martini or Manhattan, how they sipped their wine, how they held their wine glass, how they cut their meat, where they placed their silverware when not in use, how they used their napkin, how they added cream or sugar to their coffee, how they stirred it, how they ate their soup (that required the big spoon to the outside, I discovered), how they spoke with their waiter, how they asked for the bill, how they paid the bill (this was a time when cash was still king), and if they were with a lady, how they treated her.

Every so often we would notice someone upon arriving or leaving slip some paper money to the Captain. At first unsure, Aunt Win finally concluded, "Ah ha, I get it. They are tipping the Captain for good service or maybe for sneaking them in without a reservation." Then there was some special table side service that Aunt Win seemed to understand. The first big production we saw was the captain come to a table with a trolley full of stuff including a big bowl. The process included chopping, spinning, the breaking of an egg, sprinkling grated cheese and adding some really tiny dried fish that Aunt Win called anchovies. The result of this big production was something Aunt Win identified as a Caesar Salad, which, according to the menu would add $3.50 to your bill. That was an insane amount of money in 1954, worthy of a hardy laugh. Who spends $3,50 on a salad? The 70-cent dish of olives listed on the menu also cracked us up. As we continued our lesson our waiter arrived, very smartly dressed in a short jacket with three inch cuffs and large lapels, a narrow black bow tie, dark black trousers with a black silk stripe on the outside seam, patent leather shoes and a clean white towel neatly laid over his left arm and a bright Gene Kelly smile. He looked pretty much like a happy penguin. He politely asked if we would like a cocktail. Aunt Win, fully prepared, ordered something called a Whiskey Sour and then ordered me a Shirley

Temple. I didn't like the sounds of that Temple thing, but she explained it would arrive in a Martini glass with a cherry. So, I would be able simulate drinking a real mixed drink. Our waiter smiled and went off to fetch the *cocktails*.

Before he returned, Aunt Win opened her menu as if it were a prayer book and ask me to follow along. We were both to have the chopped steak, the only main course on the menu available for less than a dollar. It cost a nickel more than a plate of olives and came with an order of mashed potatoes and beef gravy. We were there to learn, not to feast. A hamburger without a bun worked for me. Our penguinesque waiter returned with Aunt Win's orangey-peachy-colored cocktail and my sissy-pink fake martini. Aunt Win proposed a toast, something that was usually done when drinks arrived, she explained. We raised our glasses to me learning the foxtrot later that day. That seemed to match up pretty well with the Shirley Temple. We had to take our time with our drinks, she told me. No need to rush into ordering lunch. It just wasn't done. Sophisticates took their time, she insisted. Well, that settled it for me. If I was anything, I was a sophisticate-in-training who at the moment felt more like one of the Bowery Boys... *Sach Jones* to be specific. But I must admit, the environment was both intimidating and interesting. And I was certainly learning. After an appropriate amount of drink nursing, we finally ordered our rich man's hamburgers listed on the menu as "Savory Chopped Beefsteak served with Creamy Idaho Mashed Potatoes and our Classic Smooth and Succulent Beef Gravy."

When lunch arrived, the *Savory Chopped Beefsteak* proved to be pretty much a hamburger. But the potatoes and gravy were the smoothest, tastiest I had ever eaten...and, yes, that doggone gravy was succulent, just as advertised.

We made our way through our modest lunch, quickly learning what that the extra fork and spoon above our plates were for dessert. We watched as several diners around us engaged the spoons for ice cream and something listed on the menu as chocolate mousse, while the small fork was for navigating cakes and pies. Aunt Win wanted this to be a special lunch, one that would be remembered for the cuisine and the lessons, so she ordered us dessert… Chocolate Mousse for her and the *Seasonal Georgia Peach Pie* with the Skyline Room's own *Sweet Butter Crust* for me. By the time we wrapped up the first period class for that day, *Sophistication Training 101 (Eating out like a pro)*, we had managed to use everything on the table excepting the wine glasses. Not bad for a couple of amateurs.

I was assigned the task of requesting and paying the bill, something the man must do. This would now be a piece of cake after watching all the *expense account* business guys go through the process. I raised my hand to get the attention of our penguin, who attentively rushed right over, placing the check next to my right hand as if I might have been the CEO of Proctor and Gamble. "How much?" Aunt Win asked, knowing full well she had added every penny in her head. I answered any way, advising that we were $6.85 into this well-fed lesson of mine. "OK, then. We must leave a ten percent tip. So, here is $7.50 which is plenty close enough. Just put it on that tray and thank anybody in a uniform on your way out. Next stop is Arthur Murray's dance studio. We have to hurry. We're due there in ten minutes."

With that my *Fine Dining Class* was dismissed. We were off to dance class… Yikes!! Down the elevator we went, exiting the hotel on Sixth Street, where we took a right walking past the entry to Bond's where Aunt Win's husband, Bill Sutton, often shopped for clothes. I was excited when Bond's showed up as one of the two national chain stores at the Terrace Plaza as I knew it well from my three trips to New York with my parents. I had hoped there would also be a Camel's Cigarette smoke-ring-blowing sign like the one on Broadway near the Bond's Clothing Store. No such luck. This was still Cincinnati.

After working our way a block south on Vine Street, we came to the Carew Tower where we headed east on Fifth Street past Wiggins Restaurant and the Albee Theater, finally coming to the Traction Company Building at the southeast corner of Fifth and Walnut Streets.

An unimpressive elevator lifted us to the third floor where we exited before a sign announcing that we had found the Arthur Murray Dance

Studio. I knew about Arthur Murray long before Aunt Win and I walked through the door. He and his wife Kathryn had a very popular TV show, The Arthur Murray Party. Arthur would smile and dance while Kathryn provided the chatter and personality while dancing even better. They had parlayed their little dance brand into several hundred dance studios around the world.

We entered the Cincinnati version to be greeted by a very pleasant and attractive receptionist who sat behind a sign that said, *"If you can walk, we can teach you how to dance."* That was encouraging... I had met the rather meager standard—I could walk.

We took a seat as instructed. Within thirty seconds, an even more beautiful young lady popped through a door to our right. She had short, dark brown hair, soft and small features with blue eyes that reeled you in like a dead fish. She was petite, yet generously endowed, if you will, and was dressed in a tight jersey-type shirt, pleated skirt that came to just above her perfect knees, dark hose and black high-heeled shoes that fluted at the bottom of their three-inch heels. Or, I could have just said she was breath-taking.

"Hi there, I'm Kathy," she announced exposing her perfect teeth. "Are you ready to have some fun? I'm going to teach you the basics of the foxtrot, the waltz and the jitter-bug this afternoon. Wadaya think?"

I was too captivated to think. And by captivated, I meant intimidated. I had already forgotten her name. But Aunt Win came to the rescue.

"Kathy, dear, this is the introductory special, right? Three dance steps in one hour for ten dollars, correct?"

Kathy... that's right... her name is Kathy.

My little instructor confirmed Aunt Win's questions. "Well, that is exactly right, ma'am. With Mr. Murray's system, we can accomplish a great deal in the first hour. Are you his mother?" "No, I'm his aunt. But I'm paying for this and sure hope we get our money's worth," Aunt Win forcefully responded.

"Well then, let's get started," Kathy suggested. "Our room is right this way. By the way, darling, what's your name?" she asked looking me straight in the eyes.

I had no name as both my brain and tongue were numb.

Aunt Win to the rescue again. "His name is Randy." Kathy reached her right hand out to me and said, "Well, hi there, Randy. It is so nice to meet you. An hour from now you will love to dance. I promise."

At that point, we followed her through the door from which she had come, stepping into a room approximately twenty-five feet square, with flooring like a bowling alley and one wall that was fully covered by a mirror.

Kathy walked over to a record player sitting on a small table, while advising Aunt Win to have a seat in one of two chairs by the door.

"OK, we are going to start with the Foxtrot. Come over here by the mirror, and I will show you the basic step before we try to do it to music," she advised.

Like an obedient lapdog, I scurried over to her where she took my left hand her right hand and had us face the mirror in the middle of the room, saying, "Please hold my hand and do as I say. I will do your steps and you just do exactly the same. OK?"

She continued, "So, with the foxtrot you will start with your left foot and take two slow steps forward and then a quick single step to your left and close. Got it?"

No. I didn't have it. Holding her hand, I couldn't remember which was my left foot or what was forward, backward or sideways.

Sensing my confusion, she said, "Why don't I do it a couple of times first and you just watch?" Well, she was easy to watch. I liked that idea and nervously nodded my agreement.

She went right to it, describing her moves, "Start with the left foot, and forward slow, and the right foot forward slow, then quickly take the left foot to the side and closed. And again, forward slow, bend a little at the knee, and forward slow and to the left quick and close quick. See?" It may have seemed easy to her, but it seemed more like calculus to me.

I must say her patience was incredible. She took my hand with us both facing the mirror. Before you could say Fred Astaire, I was going forward slow, forward slow and sideways quick and closing.

But then it went sideways again. It was now time for me to *take her in my arms*, she advised. This was a problem on a couple of levels. First, other than sixth grade folk dancing in gym class, I had never held a girl in my arms. And I can tell you, a twelve-year-old Stephanie Shuman was a whole lot different than holding Grace Kelly. And Kathy was really aggressive with how to hold her, moving my right hand to the small of her back and pulling me close enough to her that I knew without question she was a woman.

Yet again, she worked though it all, and the next thing you know she had put *Walking my Baby Back Home*, by Nat King Cole on the record player. Within the allotted time I was foxtrotting my ass off with a fox named Kathy.

We quickly moved on the waltz. This one was a bit easier. We did something that Kathy called the box step. Add a little knee flex and a little *hipsy*-doodle, and the waltz was under control. It wasn't quite as much fun as Kathy wasn't pressed quite as closely as she had been with the *trot*.

Now down to our last twenty minutes, it was time to take on the jitter-bug. Kathy picked the Andrew Sisters Boogie-Woogie-Bugle-Boy which proved to be a little fast for my amateur talents. But she pressed ahead with great encouragement as I stepped all over her delicate little feet.

By the time the clock announced the end of our ten-dollar adventure, Aunt Win was sporting a big grin, Kathy was giving me a big hug, and I was contemplating if it was too soon to propose marriage.

The smile on Aunt Win disappeared when Kathy went into her pitch about the tango, the Cha-Cha and the Rumba. Aunt Win had invested the last penny she had intended to throw at my dancing talents. Plus, it had hit me half way through the jitter-bug that Kathy was supporting a sizable diamond on her left ring finger. Marrying two guys was against the law in Ohio.

Aunt Win politely turned down the tango deal, and we took our leave of the Arthur Murray Studio, never to lay eyes on Kathy again.

Aunt Win explained as we exited onto Walnut Street that it was too early for cocktail hour lessons. Her solution was a quick jog through Rollman's Department store at the other end of Cincinnati's Fountain Square, the centerpiece of downtown. The Tyler Davidson Fountain had stood in the center of a pedestrian island on Fifth Street since 1871, a gift to the city from business magnate, Henry Probasco as a memorial to his late brother-in-law.

As the two of us walked through the first two floors of the old store, my aunt reviewed every single lesson of the day, including the nuances of the foxtrot and waltz as she had perceived them from her perch at the dance studio along with the new news that there was a special place for your desert fork and spoon on a properly set table.

At 4:45, she deemed it time to stroll to the other end of Fountain Square to the Gibson Hotel. As we entered the hotel lobby, just two doors to the north of Fifth Third Bank where my father worked on Walnut Street, we took a sharp left to find ourselves gazing into the Gibson Girl Lounge.

The fact that I was a minor prohibited me from sitting at the bar (though that had never been a problem at the bars where my father hung out). Aunt Win strategically selected a table that would afford us the opportunity to see how the same businessmen from the Skyline Room lunch proceeded to get drunk after work.

The one thing my professorial aunt had not anticipated was the after-work flirting factor. There were a lot of dark grey suits hitting on some very attractive secretaries, shop clerks and bored housewives who had just finished a day of shopping at Shillito's, McAlpins, Giddings-Jenny to name a few.

Aunt Win had this little finale pretty well planned. When an attractive waitress known as (you guessed it) a Gibson Girl, arrived to take our order, the old girl was ready.

"OK dear, here is what we need for you to do. We will each have a ginger ale. But you will be serving them in champagne flutes, follow?"

No, she didn't follow. This poor, beautiful sweet young woman was probably working for a quarter an hour, plus tips. So, the tip was the goal.

Now, you need to understand that the Gibson Girl was the invention of late nineteenth century artist, Charles Dana Gibson. His illustrations usually included a corseted waistline and a piled-upon pompadour hair style with a waterfall of curls to frame a pale face with very red full lips and finely designed eyes. And, oh yes, rather full-busted, without being vulgar.

Kathy would have made a wonderful Gibson Girl had she not determined she would rather be Ginger Rodgers.

Aunt Win noticed the blank stare and tried again, "Darling, now pay attention. This is quite simple. You go over there to the bar and asked that nice man in the black shirt and the red vest to get down two champagne flutes. Are you with me so far? Then you request very nicely that instead of pouring champagne into them, he fills them up with some nice and bubbly ginger ale. That should be simple enough, don't you think?" This time she grasped it, smiling and politely responding with a rather sophisticated, "Yes, Ma'am."

If nothing else, Gibson Girls must be refined and polite.

When our ginger cocktails arrived, Aunt Win pulled out a Pall Mall. Having to light it herself at this establishment, she flicked the gold lighter that my parents had gifted to her the previous Christmas, placing the flame to the cigarette, taking a long smooth draw, and confidently blowing a long stream of smoke into the air.

While my forty-five-year-old aunt may not have been Gibson Girl material, she sure knew how to smoke a Pall Mall.

We nursed our ginger ales for almost forty-five minutes when my aunt gave me the signal that I was to signal for the check. Little Miss Gibson scurried in a hurry to our table. For less than a buck I had enjoyed my first real cocktail hour. I would never refer to my father's after work beers with the boys as *cocktail hour*.

As she had done at lunch, she slid some dough to me, and it was time to head back to the secure and less sophisticated confines of our homes in Bond Hill. We walked the half block up to Government Square and boarded the number 37 bus, marked with a header that said *Bond Hill – Roselawn*. Less than a half an hour later, we arrived at our stop at Lawn

Avenue and Reading Road, our adventure complete.

I could tell my aunt was quite pleased with the day. We rounded it off with dinner at my house on Grafton Avenue. My mother had made her less than famous meatloaf, not a great choice after the chopped steak at the Skyline Room.

I still remember looking across the table that night at my aunt. This was the same person who had taught me to tie my shoes, to read a clock, how to count to one hundred, how to color within the lines, how to swing a hammer, how to light a match, how to shoot a marble, and so much more. She usurped a good bit of mothering from my mother and had done it so well.

On this particular summer day, she had managed to smooth off some of my rough edges. It had been quite an adventure. But she still had a lot of work left to do.

The Terrace Plaza Hotel

Kathryn & Arthur Murray

The Skyline Room
Saul Steinberg Mural on Right

The Gourmet Room
Miro Mural on Left

1955

Moon over Miami
Shine on as we begin
A dream or two that may come true
As the tide comes in
Hark to the song of the smiling troubadours
Hark to the throbbing guitars
Hear how the waves offer thunderous applause
After each song to the stars

From *"Moon Over Miami"*
By Edgar Leslie / Joseph A. Burke

Beach Lessons

This story is about a new wonderland to which I came with high expectations. Many of those expectations were met, or even exceeded. But this little sunny paradise also provided some unexpected lessons about America in the mid-twentieth century.

Thus, it is also, in no small part, a story about Cleveland… not the city, but rather, the janitor at the Penguin Hotel in Miami Beach in 1955 and 1956.

This poor "Negro" from Cleveland, Ohio (with no last name… "Just call me Cleveland") and a smile that stretched the width of the hotel lobby, was a wonderful, unexpected discovery on my very first trip to Miami Beach Florida.

The Miami Beach I came to with my parents in 1955 was full of happiness, sunshine, sand castles and breaking waves, but also one that chased my new Uncle Remus-like friend off the Beach and back to the Miami-mainland by 6:00 each evening. Yes, African-Americans were not allowed on the resort island of Miami Beach after the sun set on the Bay. Moon over Miami had a different meaning for them. The beach and the surf were for "white folks only" once the sun set.

As for the "Negroes", as they were properly referred to at the time, they could come over every morning to clean the hotel bathrooms, change the bed sheets, and mop the terrazzo and marble floors. But they were not welcome to walk into a restaurant for dinner or play a trumpet or sing from their deep soul in the many nightclubs that came to life each night in several of the spectacular hotels along Ocean Drive and Collins Avenue.

They were considered, at best, second class citizens, relegated to the back of the bus for their ride out of the resort that they had spit-shined for the rich and middle- class tourists to enjoy each night.

For, you see, Miami Beach was one of several American cities that had "Sundown Laws" or "Twilight Laws" as they were known. These laws prohibited "Negroes" from being within the city limits after sundown.

In the earliest days of Miami Beach, the only blacks allowed there were those employed as hotel workers or servants for wealthy whites. It wasn't long before the city codified that rule into law.

In 1936, Miami Beach passed a new ordinance that required more than 5,000 seasonal workers at hotels, restaurants, and nightclubs, as well as domestic servants, to register with police and to be photographed and fingerprinted. Once registered, those workers, most of whom were black, were required to carry ID cards at all times in the city, and they were required to be out of Dade County, including Miami Beach, by sundown. Jews were also restricted from staying at many Miami Beach hotels until 1947 when a law was passed eliminating such restrictions. Prior to that, it was not unusual to see advertisements that stated, "Always a view, never a Jew," or signs displayed at hotels that said "restricted" or "gentiles only."

This level of prejudice in action was a new thing for me. Not that my city of Cincinnati was without its own disgraceful racism. The swimming pool at Hoffman school, where I attended grade school until 1953 and waded into its shallow water in the summers, restricted access to African Americans to Tuesdays and Thursdays only. And our great Coney Island Amusement Park did not allow African-Americans into the park well into the late 1950s. And even then, they were restricted from entering Sunlight Pool, the largest recirculating pool in America at the time.

I arrived in Miami on an early June Sunday morning in 1955 via the services of a Delta Airlines DC-6 that had departed Cincinnati at 11:00 PM the previous night. After short stops in Atlanta and Jacksonville, I exited the plane with my mother and father at the Miami airport at 4:30 in the morning, greeted by a warm and balmy breeze unlike anything I knew in Ohio.

Our little Delta sojourn south was both exciting and frightening for me, starting with the initial sprint down the runway at Indy 500 speed, which had me thinking that the ghost of Bill Vukovich was at the controls. This was not a comforting thought, as Vukovich, known as the Fresno Flash, and the winner of the race in 1953 and 1954, had been killed in a fiery crash a month earlier at the Indianapolis oval.

It only got worse once we were airborne. I was comfortably seated by a window, next to my mother, just behind the right wing. In the dark night skies, I saw flames blasting from the engine strapped to the wing. I was sure the plane was on fire. But a very nice, smartly dressed, stewardess assured me that this was normal and I was just looking at the exhaust from the propeller. She further calmed me with a dry turkey sandwich and a Coke. But I still wasn't so sure. It looked to me like the damned plane was on fire.

Ultimately, we survived with stops in Atlanta and Jacksonville. When we stepped off the plane in Miami, I was struck by the balmy breeze and the fresh smell of the tropic air. We shared a hotel shuttle across Biscayne Bay into Miami Beach with several other airline bargain hunters. After a few stops, including one at Miami Beach's new colossus, the Fontainebleau Hotel, we were finally dropped at our hotel, the Penguin, on Ocean Drive in the Art Deco area of the beach-side city. It was now 6:30 in the morning. The sun was just beginning to rise on the horizon as we heard the breaking waves of the Atlantic, just across from the hotel. Soon, we were in room 301 and fast asleep, Mom and Dad in a double bed, and me in a roll-away cot.

Later that morning, after sleeping a mere three hours, I sprinted down to the lobby to find a very pleasant looking African-American chap cleaning the terrazzo floors. At the front desk stood an attractive girl about my age. I quickly learned that this beauty was the daughter of a Jewish couple, George and Rose Rone, who owned the Penguin Hotel as well as The Betsy Ross Hotel, a few doors north. Her name was Patricia as displayed on her copper name tag attached to a flowery, loose-fitting blouse.

"Hi, I'm Patty Rone," she happily announced. "And that there, is

Cleveland," she stated pointing at the janitor.

"Well, hello there, youngster," Cleveland said with a happy smile and a hearty laugh, extending his meaty right hand.

I nervously introduced myself to them both, shaking Cleveland's catcher's mitt sized paw.

Cleveland, holding on to my hand said, "I understands youse be quite a ball player. Mr. Losenstine, told me all about you," he said.

After processing that, I realized that he meant my Uncle George Loewenstine, who had been coming with his wife, Aunt Dorothy, to the Penguin for three weeks every June since 1946. Actually, they were my mother's aunt and uncle. George was the youngest brother of my late grandmother, Cozy Loewenstine Theobald. He worked as the head of the Hamilton County License Bureau back in Cincinnati.

"Well, Mister Randy, wees gonna have to go out back in da alley and toss some ball during my break, ya hear?" Cleveland stated.

"Sure. That would be great," I answered.

While I continued my chat with the janitor, I found myself constantly glancing back at Patty. Damn, she's good looking, I thought to myself. She returned my silly peeks with a shy but constant smile.

At that point the elevator door opened and my mother, father, Aunt Dorothy and Uncle George walked out.

"Common, Ran. We're headed to Hoffman's for breakfast," Uncle George announced.

With that we walked from the lobby down the long first floor hallway that exited into a narrow alleyway behind the hotel. After walking a half block north in the alley and then a half block west we came to the entrance of Hoffman's Cafeteria.

Hoffman's was a very cool rather large bight art deco cafeteria on Collins Avenue, Miami Beach's main thoroughfare. I learned that breakfast at Hoffman's was a daily routine for Uncle George and Aunt Dorothy.

When we got there, we ran into Mr. and Mrs. Freeman, the parents of Marty Freeman, a Masonic Lodge brother of my dad and Uncle George. They were also the grandparents of my secret love, Margie Freeman, who was a year behind me at Woodward High School. If Penguin Patty was pretty, my little Margie was gorgeous, and thoughts of Margie quickly put Penguin Patty out of my mind… no contest.

This was the Freemans' first trip to Miami Beach. They were there at the urging of Uncle George and their son Marty. As I said, I currently had a serious crush on their granddaughter, Margie Freeman,

Mr. Freeman was digging into a small bowl of prunes, and raving about them. Who the hell loves prunes? I was not yet aware of the woes of old age.

We went through the line where I ordered pancakes. They were big, fluffy and so good, they became my go-to breakfast for the next two weeks. While two eggs and toast cost fifteen cents, my mother allowed me the extravagance of the two-bits pancakes with Vermont maple syrup.

After Mr. Freeman cleaned up his prunes and I polished off my pancakes our little three-generation army headed back to the Penguin, where I rushed up to our third-floor corner room that looked out at the Atlantic, to quickly change into my navy-blue bathing suit.

I ran down the stairs to wait for my parents where I found Cleveland cleaning ashtrays and talking to a young boy about my age. Cleveland introduced him as Master Allen Rone, Patricia's brother. He was an engaging, talkative and animated chap to put it mildly. Cleveland put down a blue Penguin logo ashtray and the three of us started talking baseball. Cleveland and Allen were big Brooklyn Dodger fans while I was, of course, a Cincinnati Reds fanatic. They had much more to brag about than did.

Just as Cleveland returned to ashtray polishing, the elevator opened and out stepped my mother and father along with Aunt Dorothy and Uncle George, all with beach towels in tow.

As we headed out the lobby door of the Penguin, Allen introduced himself to my parents and promised to be over to the beach later, inviting me to walk with him down the beach to Pier 1.

We crossed over the two-lane Ocean Drive into a fifty-foot grassy area loaded with palm trees with one or two spotlights attached to each. There was a paved walkway that separated the grass from a hip-high stone wall. Uncle George led us just south to an opening in the wall that gave us access to the sugar-like long white beach. Uncle George was on a mission to get to "his spot" on the sand where he spread his beach towel, as did Aunt Dorothy.

My dad threw down his towel on the hot sand and said to me, "Common' Bub, the last one in the Atlantic is a good-for-nothing," and started sprinting toward the breaking waves.

I had only been in the Atlantic one other time when we went to Coney Island in New York. The ocean looked quite different in Miami Beach. It had multiple colors of blue and green unlike anything I had seen.

I sprinted behind my father, doing as he did—diving head-first into a breaking wave, stirring up sand and drinking in salt. The briny taste of the ocean was both nasty and exhilarating.

After splashing around in the waves for a short time, I headed back to where my family had fortified our little piece of Miami Beach across Ocean Drive from the Penguin, to find Uncle George and Aunt Dorothy slathering on some raspberry red liquid as my mother stared on in horror.

As it turned out, this was their home-made suntan lotion—a simple mix of olive oil and iodine. They brought a couple of gallons with them from Cincinnati. Once covered head to toe, they glistened like a brand new, burnt orange Corvette (the Corvette was only three years into its long history in 1955).

"This is the best tanning formula you'll ever find. We get so dark after a couple of weeks, we can't get into half of the hotels on the beach," Aunt Dorothy tastelessly joked.

Uncle George, determined to outdo her said, "I don't go back to Cincinnati until I'm darker than Cleveland." (I knew he meant the janitor, not the city).

My mother smiled while my father responded with one of his patented "hee, hee, hees."

At age twelve and a half, I was already becoming the only liberal in the family. So, instead of laughing, I wondered why, if their ambition was to become Negroes, had they been so anxious to sell their homes in Walnut Hills before some Black family moved onto our street. But I kept it to myself.

My mother and I, being both fair of skin, had developed a new, much redder hue by noon.

Aunt Dorothy suggested we walk up the beach about one hundred yards to the White House Hotel, where the public beach ended. The hotel which, to no surprise, looked like the White House in Washington, had a basement coffee shop that was entered right from the beach.

My mother and I tried the potato soup, which like the pancakes at Hoffman's, became my go-to lunch for the next two weeks. For twenty-five cents I got a big bowl of luscious thick soup and a Coke.

After lunch, we retraced our steps back to where Uncle George, Aunt Dorothy and my dad sat cooking away in the hot Florida sun. Sitting with them was Allen Rone. As stated earlier, he was an outgoing, very animated kid, a year younger than I was, who would eventually do his best to get me into trouble.

After my mother insisted that I put on a light blue tee shirt to protect my pink skin from cooking further, Allen and I went to the edge of the water and tossed a pink rubber ball he had. In the next ten minutes I learned more about him and his family than I wanted to know. He advised me that his sister was quite enamored with me. My typical response to this news was silent embarrassment.

He insisted that we walk south the 15 blocks to Pier 1. By the time we returned, I had heard the entire Rone family history, including something very significant about Allen's father, and Uncle George's friend, George Rone.

As mentioned earlier, George Rone owned both the Penguin and the Betsy Ross Hotels, just a few doors apart on Ocean Drive.

As it turns out in May 1953, more than 150 black church pastors and their wives had booked rooms at the Betsy Ross Hotel. But this wouldn't be allowed in the Miami Beach of 1953. They quickly canceled their reservations after Rone had received a rash of telephoned threats to "blow up the place." In town for a convention, the pastors and their wives were forced to find other accommodations at predominately black hotels across the Bay in Miami. Even if they stayed, they would have been in violation of the sundown laws, but Rone had been willing to fight that.

According to a report in the popular African-American *Jet Magazine*, Betsy Ross owner George Rone told the delegates that if any of them were unable to find rooms in Miami, "the hotel will still be opened to them. I don't care what threats are made — I'll abide by my agreement."

Allen rightfully told the story with great pride. I was impressed, feeling that perhaps Cleveland was very fortunate to be working for the Rones at the Penguin rather than at one of the multitudes of other Miami Beach Hotels

When Allen and I got back to our section of the beach between 14th and 15th Streets, my mother summoned me back to the family enclave where I was advised that she, my father and I had already had too much sun and it was time to seek shelter before we turned into human ash.

We bid George and Dorothy farewell. As always, Mom referred to Uncle George as *Porge*, as in the ole nursery rhyme, *Georgie Porgie, pudding and pie, kissed the girls and made them cry. When the boys came out to play, Georgie Porgie ran away*. To my mother, these two Loewenstines were "Porge" and "Dor," no disrespect intended.

So, off we went, with Allen Rone trailing right behind us.

We found my new friend Cleveland mopping the porch of the Penguin (or *Veranda* as the hotel described it in its brochure). He greeted us all with a broad smile and advised me not to let Allen get me involved in his mischief. It was beginning to sound like Allen Rone had a long rap sheet.

Then he said to me, "go gets your ball glove son. Ise be taking my break in ten minutes, and we can go out back in da alley and toss a few if yas like. You can joins us if yas like, Allen, if yas promise to plays nice."

Ten minutes later the three of us were in the alley behind the Penguin tossing an old hardball that Cleveland brought with him. Two things became immediately apparent. Old Cleveland was quite a ballplayer and Allen was woefully lacking in baseball talent. But my new *Negro* friend was extremely patient with Allen and very complimentary of me.

At 5:30 sharp that afternoon, Mom, Dad, Uncle George, Aunt Dorothy and I gathered in the terrazzo lobby of the Penguin. Dinner would be at a place called Wolfie's, three blocks away at the corner of Collins Avenue and Lincoln Road.

We entered the revolving door at Wolfie's to discover a huge rectangular counter surrounded by several booths and tables. After being seated at a big booth, we were each handed a large menu with a smiling wolf in a tuxedo and waving a black cane on the cover. After opening it, I quickly learned that the specialty of the house was a thick corned beef sandwich on Jewish rye bread. Guess what we all had?

The sandwich looked just like the photo in the menu, about two inches thick, and almost impossible to bite into. It was served with a nice side of delicious coleslaw and a greasy potato pancake. More grease equaled more flavor, Uncle George explained. No one seemed to disagree, as all five of those slippery little buggers completely disappeared quickly.

The real surprise was the restaurant's version of my favorite dessert, banana cream pie. Wolfie's version had a cake crust and a thick banana-loaded custard topped with rich swirling whipped cream. I liked Wolfie's.

I realized on the walk back to the Penguin that I was going on less than three hours sleep, exchanging yawns with my parents.

But Uncle George insisted we sit on the Penguin veranda while he smoked a big Roi Tan cigar. Apparently, watching the "South Beach" busy sidewalk featuring tourist and the Ocean Drive traffic that included an inordinate number of fancy sport cars and an abundance of big-finned Cadillacs, until his corona was smoked to a nub, proved to be yet another Miami Beach Loewenstine tradition.

Across the street, the lights on the tall palms lit up the grassy park and its stone wall like Cincinnati Fountain Square at Christmas. And, of course, there was the constant, soft hypnotic crashing of waves, muffled by the steady stream of people and cars.

In 1955, the color combination of the year was unmistakably pink and charcoal. Chevrolet had a Bel Air model that year combining those colors.

So, a Penguin veranda game each night was to count how many pink and charcoal Chevys drove by, with double credit for a convertible.

Being there less than twenty-four hours, Miami Beach was becoming my personal version of paradise. The only down-side on this first evening was the predictable sunburn. The Stertmeyers were overcooked and agony reigned that Sunday night in Room 301 of The Penguin.

It seemed that our two-week vacation in this new-found paradise flew by in the blink of an eye. Hoffman's breakfast and The White House lunch were almost an everyday occurrence. Porge and Dor had a regular rotation of dinner spots that they loved.

Among the best included Pumpernik's, which was similar to Wolfie's with a broader menu and the Rascal House, yet another deli, way north on Collins Avenue in an area known as "Motel Row." Both required that we drive rather than walk.

In the "walk-to" category was Joe's Crab (now nationally famous for their huge crab claws served on ice, but at the time just a little crab shack) that sat at the south end of Miami Beach. We had to go there our first week on the beach as Joe's closed in late June because their big juicy crabs were not readily available in the warmth of summer.

Then there was the M&M Cafeteria in Miami. We got there by walking a few blocks to Collins Avenue and 12th Street where we caught a windowless contraption known as the Jitney. They sat in a long line waiting to take parties of six or less across the McArthur Causeway to the City of Miami where they would deposit you at Pier 5, the home of Miami's first fishing fleet. There, before sojourning six more blocks to the M&M, we would stroll the pier checking out the day's catch. The inviting entrance to the pier featured a large neon sailfish over a sign that said "World's Finest Fishing Fleet."

Another Uncle George spot was the Concord Cafeteria at 19th Street, an easy walk from the Penguin. It featured roast beef and fish dinners at a very reasonable price (always important to good old Porge). An interesting footnote about the Concord is that it was fire-bombed late one night in 1973 and burned to the ground, killing three patrons and injuring an additional 131.

And there were only a few swerves away from the George and Dorothy's around-the-horn routine of less than gourmet cuisine.

The first of two side shows in pursuit of sustenance from somewhere else, took place a mile or two north of the Penguin. Twice we drove up to Miami Beach's new colossus, the Fontainebleau Hotel. Built just the year before on the site of the old Firestone Mansion in an area called "Millionaire's Row."

A hotelier chap named Ben Novak had purchased the land in 1952 from Harvey Firestone whose fortune had been made in the rubber business, mostly selling automobile tires.

Novak quickly employed the talents of Morris Lapidus, an architect known for his minimalist designs, yet with a flair for the dramatic. When the hotel opened in in 1954, it was the largest and most luxurious hotel in South Florida.

It's quadrant shape quickly became iconic. The Fontainebleau's signature features included a 17,000-square-foot lobby with a legendary "Stairway to Nowhere," six acres of formal gardens designed to replicate Versailles that included a meandering swimming pool, and a small fortune in antique furnishings to authenticate the hotel's French period theme.

A more modest part of the Fontainebleau was its coffee shop, located in the basement level looking out onto the formal gardens and pool. It was to this massive eatery that Uncle George brought us twice, so that we might experience the rather leviathan environment from a humbler approach than those sleeping in the rooms above.

Let me be clear. Breakfast with a view of the Venetian garden came at a higher price than pancakes at Hoffman's. This place had real silverware, linen napkins, smartly dressed waiters, a huge menu and individual delicate sterling coffee pots for those so imbibing. For me, the highlight, or the piece de resistance, if you will, was the huge basket of assorted rolls and pastries. I loved it for its contents of biscuits, soft rolls, hard rolls, matzo, egg bagels, onion rolls, and the fruit and cheese pastries. My mother loved it for its cost... nothing... just part of the deal. It was free!! My father explained the $2.50 omelets made up for the free rolls and sweets. He was a banker, you know, and understood such things. All I knew was that basket was going to require a lot of free butter.

The second time we went back, my mother was not too happy. The place was outside the budget constraints she had set for our sojourn south. But she was outnumbered and the basket beckoned.

As stated, there were two places where Uncle George went off script when it came to food. The second was another basement coffee shop, this one at the Saxony Hotel just a few blocks south of the Fontainebleau. And this place served the opposite end of the day… dessert! The shop was called the *Ye Noshery* as in the Yiddish word meaning "to snack.". And its specialty was ice cream sundaes larger than the Fontainebleau bread basket.

Ye Noshery just tickled the hell out of Dor and Porge. They simply could not get over the size of the servings. The night we visited Ye Noshery had been set up by over a week of advance work by Uncle George.

As we sat out each night on the Penguin front veranda watching the crowd move by, he would say to me things like, "Ran, we are going to take you to ice cream heaven. You haven't seen anything like this, son. The sundaes are too big to carry. They have to roll their biggest sundae out on a cart. It's called the Skyscraper. Just wait. You'll see. I have never seen a single serving of anything this big."

So, I waited and waited until the night preordained for this dessert extravaganza finally came. It was the second Tuesday of our vacation, and my severe sunburn had finally turned to a golden All-American tan. I had been warned to go easy on dinner. This was the classic, *save room for dessert* proclamation. And so, I did. I went light at dinner at Wolfie's, settling for a bowl of matzo ball soup, not realizing I was about to see scoops of ice cream about the size of the huge matzo balls.

After touring the lobbies of a few of the luxury hotels along Collins Avenue, each requiring Uncle George, Dad and me to wear a sport coat (mine was charcoal with pink flecks, strictly ultra nouveau) between dinner and The Skyscraper, we finally made our way into the Saxony Hotel and down the spiral stairs that led to ice cream nirvana.

And low and behold, though I had not believed uncle George's description of grown men conveying ice cream by trolley cart, sure enough, there it was before my own eyes. Waiters dressed in smart all-white uniforms including small white garrison caps pushing carts with piles of ice cream, fruit, chocolate, mountains of whipped cream, heaps marshmallow topping and the ever-present cherry. This time he had not exaggerated.

My mother unwillingly allowed me to order a *Skyscraper.* Then Uncle George insisted that I must have the *Skyscraper Supreme,* which included a scoop of chocolate, a scoop of strawberry and two scoops of vanilla ice cream, plus a split banana, strawberries, pineapple and chocolate syrup, and, it would be on him, he proclaimed, because I could not be denied going big.

Mom also grimaced when my father ordered the *Pride of the South* (a mini-Skyscraper with only two scoops of vanilla and a passel of strawberries, small enough for a white clad waiter to convey single-handedly from soda fountain to table.

Aunt Dorothy ordered a single dip (they were about the size of a baseball) of vanilla with hot fudge only, bringing a frown to our server. To further add to the waiter's potential tip dismay, Uncle George only ordered coffee and my mother tea.

The screams and laughter that came with the arrival of every *New Yorker, Chicagoan, Lone Star, Georgia Peach* and, and of course, the *Skyscraper,* to the tables around us was continuous and infectious. Who knew that ice cream could be so much fun?

That was one high calorie night that tipped the fun meter far to the right.

But by then, all of the fun I was having had been infected by a corresponding guilt of thinking about Cleveland sweltering in the Miami heat in some ghetto across Biscayne Bay. The injustice of obtuse racism was starting to resonate with me in a way it never had in Cincinnati.

A week before my Skyscraping event, on our first Tuesday in Miami, Beau and Mitzie Jones arrived at the Penguin. They had befriended Uncle George and Aunt Dorothy a couple of years earlier. Beau was a former

University of Kentucky football standout in the war years. Mitzie was a former beauty Queen. Nothing big like Miss America or even Miss Kentucky. Mitzie's beauty accomplishments were along the lines of more nebulous crowns like Miss Harlan County or Miss White Burley Tobacco. But she was certainly what my dad would call *A Looker*.

My father bonded immediately with Beau. First, Dad was a huge Kentucky Football fan. In the late 1940s, he had befriended Bernie Shively, the Athletic Director at UK, as a result of working as a football ticket-taking Pinkerton on fall Saturdays in Lexington. As it were, Shively had been the head football coach at Kentucky in 1945, Beau Jones' Junior year. More note-worthy is the fact that Beau played his senior year for the future college coaching legend, Paul "Bear" Bryant.

The other thing Beau and Dad shared was their abiding love of bourbon and beer.

Then there was my mother and Mitzie. Let's just say it straight out… they had absolutely nothing in common. I can safely state that the arrival of the Joneses enhanced my father's vacation joy, while rendering my mother's trip south mostly painful.

Beau and Mitzie were from Kentucky, making them, in their own words, "true confederates."

This was immediately apparent in witnessing their treatment of my new pal, Cleveland. From dawn to dusk, Beau and Mitzie acted as if he was their personal slave, with Beau behaving as a *Master* treating Cleveland as his *Boy*.

Yet, because Beau was hysterically funny and Mitzie was outrageously ravaging, no one seemed to notice their bad behavior in the way that I did. But, in reality, their attitude was nothing more than the norm in the South in 1955, and it seemed that nobody was more aware and accepting of that fact than Cleveland. Today, some would insist that he was an *Uncle Tom*. But I would argue that he was not. He was just a victim. What choice did he have? So, he seemed happy to respond to the constant demands from the Joneses with a polite, "Yes, sir, Mr. Beau," or, "Yes indeedy, Miss Mitzie, Ise gets right on dat for ya all."

In the meantime, Cleveland and I continued to bond. Most days after spending the morning and early afternoon hours on the sun-bleached beach, with some White House potato soup squeezed in between, I would catch up with Cleveland for his afternoon break in the alley behind the Penguin.

He delighted in my baseball skills, rewarding me with great tales of his days in the Negro League introducing me to names like *Biz* Mackey, *Gentleman Dave* Malarcher, Ted *Double Duty* Radcliffe, *Mule* Suttles, Mamie *Peanut* Johnson, *Cool Papa* Bell, Judd *Boojum* Wilson and, of course, the renowned Leroy *Satchel* Paige who did make it to the major leagues after Jackie Robinson famously broke "the color line' in Brooklyn in 1947.

Cleveland reveled in telling me about his short Negro League career, while I relished every word. He was particular fond of Satchel Paige. They had played together for the Cleveland Cubs for part of a season in 1931.

Listening to Cleveland describe Paige was priceless.

"Mr. Randy, lets me tell youse about ole Satch. He has more pitches den any five guys youse ever met. He hads da jumb ball, da screw ball, and da whipsey-dippsey-do. Ands if dat ain't be enough, he could gives ya da ole blooper, da looper and or da dropper. Satch calls his fastball da 'hurry-up' pitch. Ise telling ya, ole Satch could make dat ball do lots a tings."

I tried to envision all of those magical pitches while watching ole Cleveland bent over in baseball glee back in our little alley.

By our second week at the beach, I had figured out why Cleveland had warned me about Allen Rone. That kid was trouble. The short list of mischief included taking the hotel's sole elevator up to the roof and then turning it off so guests were force to take the steps until poor Cleveland went up to the rooftop to turn it back on. There was also a timer on the lobby and veranda lights which he had set to shut off around 9:00 o'clock, or four hours to early one night.

Allen's parents were so busy running two hotels that they seemed to leave it to his sister Patty to reel him in. While she was determined, she wasn't very effective.

The stunt that finally ended it for me occurred two days after Beau and Mitzie arrived. The Penguin had something called a solarium on its rooftop. This amounted to nothing more than two open-topped canvass surrounded rooms about fifteen feet square. They contained several lounge chairs. One room was for men and one for women. It was a popular venue for the true sun worshippers as you could sunbathe nude in the solarium.

Now, Allen had innocently showed these to me as part of his day-one tour of the Penguin. It looked to me like the solarium didn't get much use, but Allen told me he was a regular customer. So be it, I thought. It was not for me.

Then I learned too late from Allen that Mitzie was a regular patron. The day in question, not knowing Mitzie was partaking in this solar sanctuary, Allen lured me up to the Penguin roof on the pretense that he had forgotten to show me the view from the top of the elevator shaft, so up the ladder I nervously went. You guessed it. The view from atop the shaft was Mitzie. The minute I realized this, I scampered my young butt down the shaft and down the four floors to the lobby where I found Patty behind the desk and Cleveland on ashtray duty.

Patty sensed nothing. But Cleveland seemed to suspect something.

"What's wrongs wit ya, son? Youse looks like you done seen a ghost."

Then, somehow, he knew that it wasn't a ghost that I had seen.

He pointed upward and asked, "Allen?"

Still shaking, I nodded, as Cleveland quietly swore for the only time of our two-year relationship. He disappeared up the stairs behind the elevator. A few minutes later he returned with Allen in tow who was wearing a look of great satisfaction.

"What's going on?" Patty asked.

"Nothing, Miss Patty," Cleveland responded.

It was immediately clear to me that, while poor Cleveland was faithfully determined to keep Allen out of trouble, there was no way he would dare to turn "state's evidence" on the kid. Allen was the boss' son and Cleveland needed his job.

Cleveland went back to ash tray cleaning while Allen dragged me out onto the empty veranda and said to me, "What's wrong with you? Where did you go, you scaredy cat? That Mitzie has some really nice tits, doesn't she?"

I just looked at him and did not say a word. The cat had the tongue of the scaredy cat. But after that, I steered clear of Allen Rone. Cleveland never mentioned the incident. Fortunately, Mitzie was unaware that I had a snapshot of her beauty queen body in my mind's eye.

One thing I was sure of is that had Beau Jones found out, he would have killed me and then taken Miss Harlan County out to dinner without a second thought about my funeral.

I didn't really need Allen Rone to account for my entertainment. On our second Monday, we all piled into Beau's Cadillac early in the morning and drove to Pier 5 in Miami, where we boarded a very fancy fishing boat that Beau had booked for the day.

The boat had a crew of three very buff, shirtless young guys plus a captain that could have been out of a Hemingway novel.

Out to sea we went. Within the first half hour my mother was already seasick, while Dad and I were happily perched on the upper deck with two huge poles holstered in between our legs.

Our goal was to land a tarpon or a sailfish. That didn't happen. But Dad and Beau both caught several King Fish and one Grouper each. As for me, I had a photo taken with one mean looking Barracuda. The teeth on that baby were small, abundant and razor sharp. Our bait were fish bigger than anything I had caught up to that time.

It was a great day with Mitzie guzzling one bloody Mary after another while Dad and Beau polished off a bottle of Jamaican Rum. My mother finally came up from the boat's head about two hours into our journey, had two bites of a turkey sandwich that Mitzie had packed and then quickly deposited it over the starboard side of the boat. She spent the rest of the day in a berth below deck.

At 3:30 we returned to the dock at Pier 5 where the captain had one of his crew clean my Barracuda, one of the King Fish and one of the Groupers. They then wrapped those in craft paper, put them in a foam cooler with a shovel-full of ice and sent us on our way. I learned from Beau that they would sell the rest of our catch to any number of Miami restaurants for a handsome price.

Needless to say, my mother never went deep sea fishing again.

We did take two other little journeys that my mother enjoyed thoroughly. The first was to Hialeah Racetrack, famous for its abundant flock of flamingos in the track's infield.

The second was a drive up to Ft. Lauderdale, a beautiful little town in 1955 that sat on the Atlantic and featured a series of canals running between the ocean and the inland waterway. The highlight for my mother and Aunt Dorothy was seeing all of the luxurious homes that dotted many of the canals.

One stark vision I have carried with me from that first trip to Miami Beach was the view of Cleveland's back as he headed south down Ocean Drive at 5:30 most afternoons to assure his unwanted ass was off of the beach at the allotted time. A great guy facing a great injustice.

We were scheduled to fly back to Cincinnati with Aunt Dorothy and Uncle George as well as Mr. and Mrs. Freeman on Saturday, June 26th. As always, the day started with pancakes at Hoffman's where Mr. Freeman was still plundering prunes.

After breakfast, Beau and Mitzie packed up their big blue Caddy, gave everybody hugs and headed north honking their horn in farewell. We went across the street to the beach where Porge and Dor slathered on the last of their iodine and olive oil concoction. Of course, we had one last bowl of potato soup at the White House.

That afternoon, I got together with Patty and Allen (the first time with Allen since the nude Mitzie incident) and walked up Collins Avenue for a round of miniature golf. Patty was still flirting, but she was Allen's sister and that killed that deal for me.

Dinner was at Wolfie's.

At 9:00, the airport shuttle pulled in front of the Penguin. The seven of us provided a full house for the shuttle and off we went to the Miami Airport.

Our flight on another DC-6 was scheduled to depart at 11:30 and was right on time. The return trip only had one stop in Atlanta. Against my hope, the damned engine was still on fire, but we landed safely in Cincinnati at 5:45 in the morning to be met by my Aunt Win, Dorothy's sister Shirley and her new husband Ken Eppertt, as well as the Freemans' son, Marty. To my delight, he had Margie with him. Yes, I was still in love, but she hardly seemed to notice me. The group broke into three directions and off to home we went.

My mother and father never returned to the Penguin nor to Miami Beach until a family trip in 1966. They also attended the Orange Bowl Parade and football game in the mid-70s as part of a cruise and tour.

As for me, I took two more two-week trips to Miami Beach in 1956 and 1957, both with Aunt Win. Unlike my mother, she loved the place. Each year we shared the same room 301 at the Penguin in which I had stayed with my parents.

In 1956, Porge and Dor decided to give up on Delta and drive as they had with most of their early trips to Miami Beach.

Aunt Win and I flew down on a flame-infested Delta D-6 and then drove back home with George and Dorothy. In 1956, Beau and Mitzie returned but stayed two doors south at the Edgewater Beach Hotel.

In 1956, my good friend Sandy Schwartz was in Miami Beach the same two weeks as we were. The first week his family stayed at the Sea Gull Hotel a few blocks north of Wolfie's. The Sea Gull had a beautiful pool. Sandy and I spent most days together on the beach across from the Penguin or at the pool at the Sea Gull. Sandy did meet both Patty and Allen Rone. He immediately fell in love with Patty and in lust with Mitzie. Allen explained the solarium to Sandy, but we never explored the one at the Edgewater Beach, though Sandy was not opposed to the idea.

The second week that year, the Schwartzes moved way north to the Sahara Motel in the area known as Motel Row. Uncle George had driven his brand-new charcoal Oldsmobile Eighty-Eight and did drive me up to visit Sandy one evening.

One of the highlights of my two trips to Miami Beach with my aunt stands out because it was so antithetical to who she was.

There were no more honest, law abiding citizens in my world than my mother and her sisters, Aunt Lois and Aunt Win, especially Aunt Win. She was constantly lecturing me on good behavior.

Yet, in Miami Beach, she became a thief, as did I. On several afternoons, after burning our skin sufficiently, we would stroll up Collins Avenue where we would walk into some of the more luxurious hotel lobbies.

Our list included The Di Lido, the Delano, the Sans Susie, the Shellborne, the Neptune, the Algiers, the Roney Plaza (a spectacular pink colossus), and the Sagamore, just to name a few.

Once inside the lobby of the hotel-of-the-day, Aunt Win would find a clean ashtray, take a seat placing the first ashtray over a second clean ashtray and light up a Viceroy filter tip. After a relaxing smoke, she would snub out the Viceroy in the top tray and with her best sly-of-hand slip the still clean bottom tray into her open purse (or pocketbook as she called it).

That's right… righteous Aunt Win became a habitual thief in Miami Beach, and I was her willing accomplice. This became an almost daily game of suspense and intrigue worthy of an episode of the popular TV series of the day, Dragnet. I could envision Joe Friday saying to me, "Just the facts, son. Just the facts."

What possessed Aunt Win to go off the rails, I cannot say. But I can report we went undetected and unprosecuted. Over sixty years later, I am still in possession of more than a dozen of these small hotel logo gems along with a clear vision of executing the crimes with my otherwise highly-principled aunt. I have a warm connection to each ashtray in my collection. She took the secret of her crime to her grave. I think, for me, the statute of limitations has expired.

In many ways, I enjoyed my trips in 1956 and 1957 far more than the first one with my parents. Aunt Win was just a lot more fun than my bickering parents.

And, in 1956, Cleveland was again the highlight of my vacation, including three-way alley tosses with Sandy and me and more great stories of his days in the Negro League.

When Aunt Win and I returned to the Penguin in 1957 Cleveland was gone. All I could learn from any of the Rones was simply that… he was gone. No forwarding address. Gone without a trace.

But this gentle, humble and seemingly happy man had touched me in a very special way. He lives on in my memory and in my conscience. He never knew what an impact he had on me. But I know.

The Penguin Hotel

Hoffman's Cafeteria

Wolfie's Sandwich Shop.

Wolfie's Interior

Stone Wall on Ocean Drive Public Beach
Circa 1955

The White House Hotel
(Great Potato Soup)

1955 Pink & Charcoal Chevrolet Bel Air

In front of Penguin: L to R; Me, Aunt Dorothy, Uncle George, Mrs. Freeman, Mom, Mr. Freeman & Dad

My Barracuda – Deep Sea Fishing

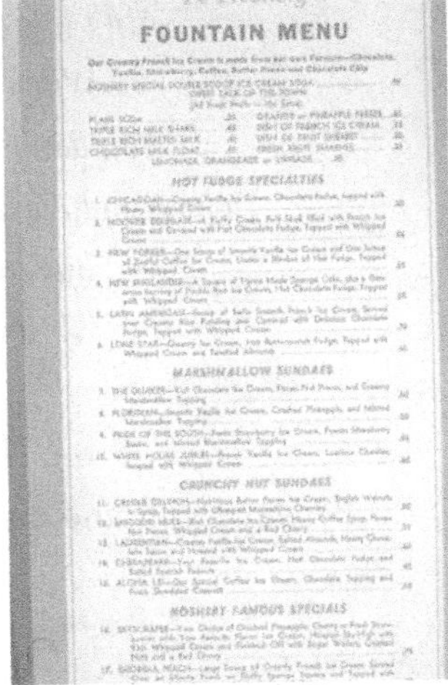

FOUNTAIN MENU

[illegible]

HOT FUDGE SPECIALTIES

[illegible]

MARSHMALLOW SUNDAES

[illegible]

CRUNCHY NUT SUNDAES

[illegible]

NOSHERY FAMOUS SPECIALS

[illegible]

Fountain Ice Cream Menu
The Ye Noshery at the Saxony Hotel

Dad & Me in front of the Fontainebleau Hotel
June 1955

Hialeah Race Trac
Front row: Beau Jones, Aunt Dorothy, Mitzie Jones
Back row: Dad, Uncle George, Me

1955

Ain't it great to have a gal so fat
When you go to hug her
You don't know where you're at
Ya have to take a piece of chalk in your hand
And hug away and make a mark
To see where ya began.

From *Huggin' and Chalkin*
By Kay Kyser and his Kollege of Musical Knowledge

EXPRESS MAIL

It had to be done. There simply was no choice. The Black Shirt Gang sat in my living room and plotted the details.

Freddie said, "We've taken enough abuse from the Fat Lady. It's time to strike back."

"Darn right" we all echoed.

Our heroes on TV bolstered us. Every weekday at 4:00 on Channel 9, the String Bean and his gang, who not coincidentally were dressed just like us, provided inspiration for our silly mini-fraternity of goof-offs. Blue jeans with cuffs double-rolled (as narrowly as possible), Converse high tops, and, of course, black tee shirts with the sleeves-double rolled and a cigarette pocket over the heart - this constituted our official uniform.

As the String Bean sang, "Monday chicken and string beans, Tuesday hamburger and string beans, Wednesday ham and string beans" and so on, we turned our focus away from the screen and to the greater issue of getting back at Fat Ass Bertha Schwartz.

After all, the little patch of grass she called her front yard, pristine though it might have been, was by volume only equal to approximately three times the square footage of her bovine butt.

Yet she would yell at, scream at, and sometimes threaten to shoot with her husband's gun, anyone who dared to attempt to retrieve a baseball from her postage stamp size putting green. And when she screamed, it was with the bravado of an operatic soprano. The sheer intensity of her verbal attacks would often summon the entire neighborhood to see what was causing all of the commotion. Just in the week since school had ended, she had captured two of our baseballs.

As we sat there, Freddie was on a roll. He had us in stitches.

"We can't walk on her lawn, but she can go out and drop her 400 pounds right in the middle of it. She's so big, the next time we play hide-n-seek, I'm going to hide behind her. No one will ever find me. Heck, she weighs more than my whole family, and I'm including the dog. Poor old man Schwartz. Can you imagine trying to hug her? Why, that's like trying to get your arms around the Carew Tower. The next time she sits on her lawn, I'm going to put a *For Sale* sign in front of her. If you drive by fast enough, she looks like a two-bedroom house. You better not let the bread man stop at her house first. When she goes to the butcher shop, she doesn't buy some steaks, she buys a herd of cattle."

"Stop already", Wally pleaded as he rolled on the floor in hysterics.

"OK, OK," Carl said. "We all agree. It's time for action."

Fred wasn't finished. "I could sneak up behind her and stick a pin in her. But it would be a suicide mission. Can you imagine the explosion? It would level half of Bond Hill. Hey, there's a thought. We could drop her on Moscow - The great American secret weapon. Or, we could enter her as a float in the Macy's Day Parade, but I don't think she'd fit between the buildings."

Wally got up from the floor and playfully punched Fred in the arm. "Stop!"

As I wiped the tears from my eyes, I managed to get everyone's attention. "Listen, I hear the ice cream man, and I've been craving a creamsicle all day."

"Anyway," I continued, "I've got an idea that's worthy of the Black Shirt Gang. My cousin Jay, the one who lives in Milford, told me about this. I think it's the perfect revenge. And if we're careful, we can do it without getting caught."

"What's your plan?" Carl asked.

"I'm not sharing anything with any of you knuckle heads without the sweet taste of a creamsicle in my mouth."

The clanging of the bell on the ice cream man's trolley was getting close.

About three houses up, I estimated. As always, Freddie was without funds.

"Hey, can somebody lend me a dime?"

"A dime?" Wally challenged him. "A popsicle only costs a nickel."

"I know, I know. But I can't decide between grape and cherry, so I need to get one of each. C'mon. I'm caddying tomorrow. I'll pay ya back."

Wally and Carl had low tolerance for this side of Freddie, but, he was always good to his word. I knew I'd get my dime back. I ran to my bedroom and dug a dime and a nickel out of my top desk drawer.

We bolted out of the front door just as the refrigerated pushcart rolled past, screaming for the Nick, the ice cream man, to stop. He had to be on commission because he could hear a kid yelling for him to stop a block away.

As always, I asked, "Hey Nick, may I have a tootie frutti popsicle, please?"

And as always, Nick replied as if it was the first time he had heard it, "I don't have any damned tootie frutti." Fred, Wally and Carl stood behind me and snickered.

"OK, I guess I'll settle for a creamsicle then."

Freddie ordered next. "Hey, Nick, how come you never have any tooti frutti?"

"I don't know. I never heard of any damned tootie frutti. I just sell what they give me. What the hell do you want? I'd like to get home before dark."

Freddie ordered his grape and a cherry popsicles. Wally and Carl each asked for a flavor Nick had in stock, and we all retreated back to my front porch.

"OK," said Carl sucking on a fudgesicle. "So, what's the plan?"

"Well, Jay said this was really funny. What you do is you collect a bunch of doggy-do and put it in a paper bag. You roll the top real tight. Then, when it gets dark you post lookouts to be sure no one is walking or driving down the street. Then someone – I figure this a good job for you Ziggy-Fritz, 'cause you seem to hate her the most – sneaks the bag up to her door step and lights it on fire. When it starts to burn, you ring the door bell and then run like you're Jackie Robinson."

"I don't get it," Freddie said." We can't burn her house down."

"No, no," I said. "This is just a small bag of burning dog dirt. Jay says the natural instinct when she opens the door will be to stomp the fire out with her feet. Get it?"

A slow smile came on Freddie's face. He started to dance around the porch like a banshee, a grape popsicle in his mouth, a cherry one in his hand. Carl just looked at Fred and shook his head, then looked at me with a wry grin. Wally, normally our idea-man, and the self-appointed leader of the Black Shirt Gang, displayed an unsure expression.

"I don't know. Starting a fire is serious. What if we get caught?"

"Oh, like blowing up a pumpkin with a cherry bomb last Halloween wasn't serious. You just don't like it because it's not your idea," Fred lashed out at him.

You had to love Freddie. He didn't care what he said or to whom. He had a knack for saying what everybody else wanted to say, but didn't.

Wally reacted in typical fashion. "You're nuts. And quit waving that popsicle around. You get any of that on my jeans and you're going home with a fat lip."

"Oh. Big man," said Fred. "If you're such a big brave cowboy, how about you volunteer to be the guy to do the dirty work this time, and I'll sit up the street to make sure the bad old policemen don't get you and take you off to jail."

"I'm warning you, numb nuts. You better zip it."

Carl brought sense and calm back to the situation. "Hey. I thought we were the Black Shirt Gang here. All for one and one for all, right? The target here is the mean old Fat Lady across the street. Randy's plan is great. And I want a spot where I can get a good view of her tap dancing on the smelly bag.

"Ok," Wally said. "I'm in. When do we do it?"

Carl suggested we go to my basement (the Clubhouse) and draw it up on paper. We charged through the front door, sprinting single file through the living room, the dining room and the kitchen, each of us deftly tossing popsicle sticks in the kitchen trash can before taking the basement steps two at a time.

In the basement, I brushed all of the pool balls into various pockets, leaving the pool table flat, clean and available to develop our plan.

As if it had been his idea, Wally now took charge. Using my Lionel train cars as houses, he re-created the lower third of Grafton Avenue including the slight bend in the road at the Listner's house. He then grabbed some toy streetlights from my train layout and placed them where actual streetlights existed on Grafton. This made apparent our first problem. One of the streetlights was located right in front of the Schwartz' house. In addition, as Wally pointed out, the Schwartz' were the only family on lower Grafton without a tree in front of their house. Thus we had direct light and no cover. Like I said, the mailman would have to run like Jackie Robinson.

As Wally proceeded, I had to admire his leadership and thoroughness. However, we all knew that when the plan was complete, he would have the safest assignment, being the least likely to get caught. He would be in a position to totally disassociate himself from the whole operation. But then, we were followers, and he was our leader. So be it, until someone else challenged him. As long as Fred and I used his dad, Bip, as our surrogate father, we were not about to screw up our friendship by challenging Wally's leadership.

Wally was so thorough that he actually calculated that there had been a full moon three days earlier, so that there would be the least possible moonlight by which to identify any of us in 13 days. Therefore, June 28th was designated as D-Day. Wally would position himself at the bend in front of the Listners', meaning he was already one third of the way home. I would be located in front of the Fischmans', the last house before the Swifton Village apartments. This would allow me to detect cars turning onto Grafton from Langdon Farm Road and afford me a fairly safe escape into the woods behind Swifton.

Carl suggested to Wally that he be allowed to stand in my side yard. Thus he could watch the Gates family through their side living room window. This was important because the Gates were the only family with a direct view of the Schwartz' porch from within their house. More significantly, Carl would have a front row seat for the big event and an easy escape up the hill behind my house to Laconia Avenue.

And, of course, Freddie had been selected as the mailman. When it came to this sort of thing, he had no fear. The plan called for Fred to sprint from the porch, north in the direction of my post. But, after stopping to get a view of the results of his courageous act, he would head through the Taylors' side yard into my Aunt Win's back yard on Newfield Avenue. Newfield offered excellent cover, a safe haven for a criminal such as Fred.

The warning signal to Freddie for any need to abort the mission would be the String Bean Gang whistle. This was accomplished by cupping your hands together and blowing through your thumbs. You could change the note blown by opening and closing your top hand. The result was something akin to a hooting owl. Using this as the signal provided Wally with the perfect argument as to why Fred should be the dog dirt mailman in this operation because poor Freddie had not been able to master the whistle.

This, of course, didn't matter to Fred because he thrived on the excitement of placing himself on the brink. It was the one way he achieved a modicum of respect from Wally and Carl.

Thus, the plan was in place. We agreed that there would be no ball playing in front of my house until after we advanced on the Fat Lady. We reasoned that if we didn't create a stir with her prior to the event, she would be much less likely to suspect any or all of us as the perpetrators.

The next week and a half were filled with the normal summer stuff like baseball practice, Saturday games, swimming at Golf Manor pool, caddying at Macatewa Country Club, evening walks to Pasquale's Pizza for a 15 cent garlic bread or a 25 cent cheese pizza, and afternoons in my room where we would listen to records of Fingers O'Tool playing some of the most outrageous piano to be found. We would then go to my mother's baby grand were Wally and I would bang out simple cords of the latest and easiest rock and roll tunes or drive Carl and Fred nuts with our mechanical versions of *Heart and Soul* and *Chop Sticks*.

Finally, Tuesday, June 28th arrived. With it came the first glitch in our plans. Fred was grounded. Now this was not an unusual occurrence. Had we been more experienced in petty crime, we might have considered this high probability. But we had not. Wally was outraged that Fred could not stay out of trouble.

"He's useless," Wally mused as he swayed back and forth on the front porch glider. "He screws up everything."

"What difference does a day make?" Carl asked.

"That's not the point," Wally yelled coming up from the glider as if he had been thrown off a bucking bull. "He knew we were depending on him. We had the perfect plan. He has no control. He's like those doggone crows, Heckle and Jeckle. He's just out of control, always in trouble. This is a bad omen. Maybe we should just forget about it."

"No way," said Carl. "It's only one day, Bohldini. C'mon, we'll do it tomorrow. What's the big deal?"

We sauntered down the hill in front of my house to wave down Nick the ice cream man. As we did, Wally eyed the Fat Lady's perfectly coiffed front lawn.

"All right, tomorrow, then. But as far as I'm concerned, Fred can walk to our game on Saturday. I'm telling my dad that we're not giving him a ride. He has to learn to be a team player."

Carl and I looked at each other and rolled our eyes. Nick still was out of tootie frutti.

Wally refused to call Fred to let him know our change in plans, and I went in the house and picked up the phone. Our party line was on the phone, so I hung up the receiver. I knew that voice, but I couldn't quite place it. Our party line had recently changed when the Goyerts moved to Amberley Village. They had been a very accommodating polite family with whom to share a telephone line.

I asked Carl to go in and pick up to see if he could recognize the voice. He picked up the receiver and said, "Ok, OK, I'm sorry already."

He placed the receiver back on the cradle and said to me, "I don't recognize the voice, but she sure ain't very nice. She cussed me out good."

We waited fifteen minutes, and I tried again. Same voice, same attitude. I knew the voice, I was sure. But who was it? I politely asked for 60 seconds to make a quick phone call. Her response was curt and rude.

I went back down to the Clubhouse.

"Did you get a hold of the Jackass?" Wally inquired.

"No. The party line is still on the phone."

"How come you don't have a private line yet? Everybody does."

I felt like saying, *because my father's a banker not an engineer*, but instead I just shrugged.

The next time I tried the line, it was free. I dialed Jefferson 5644. The phone rang twice and Fred's brother Herb answered. He shouted for Fred so loudly that I think I heard him in my other ear as well. Fred finally came to the phone.

"Hey, Stert. I'm sorry man. I bet Bohldini's really teed off at me."

"You could say that, but don't worry. We agreed to deliver the mail tomorrow. You are off the hook tomorrow, right?"

"Yea. I have to work at the hardware store until my mom leaves at 5:00. But I'm not grounded anymore."

"Good. Then we'll meet here after dinner. Say about 6:15, 6:30. OK?"

"I'll be there. Tell Carl and Wally I'm sorry"

"Yea. OK. See ya."

"See ya."

I turned to Wally and Carl. "Fred's sorry. We're on for tomorrow."

Wally snickered.

Carl said, "If Freddie gets caught tomorrow, they'll be using that Bar Mitzvah suit of his to bury him in, cause his mother'll kill him."

"If he gets caught, I'll kill him," Wally said.

Wally, Carl and I spent the better part of Wednesday scouring the neighborhood looking for dog dirt. When we found some, Carl would shovel it up with one of his mother's garden spades and deposit it into a lunch bag I brought along. Wally, per usual, supervised, maintaining his distance from our odoriferous treasure. We hid our bag of goodies under a big bush between my house and the Graf's.

We all hurried through dinner. By 6:20, we were in the basement shooting pool and watching the clock. We had determined that it was not pitch dark out until at least 9:30. Fred, Carl and I had all cleared with our parents to sleep over at Wally's that night, on the pretense that we would be playing golf early the following morning at Avon Field. Bip, who left for work at 6:15, would drop us all at the golf course on his way to work. We chose this plan for two reasons. One, it was true and believable. More importantly, should we become suspects in the great Express Mail delivery, Wally's mother was the only one who would likely consider lying for us. We hoped it wouldn't come to that.

We felt we had a good chance on a Wednesday. As hot as it was, my mother never missed *The Medic,* which came on TV at 9:00 and ran for an hour. It was predictable that my father would address the heat by taking two pints of Hudepohl to the Clubhouse, or as he called it, the Rathskeller, and tuning in Waite Hoyt and the Cincinnati Redlegs on his portable radio. This left the coast clear unless the Gates couldn't take the heat. This could mean Mr. and Mrs. Gates would be in their backyard getting themselves seriously around some Hudepohls of their own, affording them a clear view of Carl's escape route.

To check out that possibility, I walked outside and yelled through their kitchen window to Janet Gates who was drying dishes. I asked what her brother Jackie was up too. I knew he was away at camp at Fort Scott, but I hoped I could determine if her father was working that night at their family Pony Keg. She informed me that Jackie was away at Camp. I asked if they'd be listening to the ball game.

"No," she said. Her dad was, indeed, working until midnight, and she and her mom were going to fan themselves and watch *The Millionaire.* They couldn't wait to see who would next benefit from John Beers Ver Tipton's generosity. Perfect! We were looking solid. Look out, Fat Lady, here comes the mail.

With three hours to kill, we walked over to Swifton Shopping Center and made the rounds through Rollman's Department Store at on end down to Murphy's Five and Dime at the other. Along the way we kept our eye out for blondes, brunettes and redheads between the ages of 12 and 15. It was sport of a sort, given our prepubescent state.

We returned to my house at 8:15 to collect my golf clubs and overnight bag. We then stopped at Fred's and Carl's along the way, finally depositing our collection of clubs and clothes at Wally's. We told Bip that we were going to walk up to United Dairy Farmers for an ice cream. We were instructed to be back no later than 10:00.

Instead of heading south toward the UDF, we circled back north. Dusk was now rapidly turning into dark. We collected the bag of mail, checked carefully to be sure we were not being watched, and then positioned ourselves per Wally's original schematic. Since Carl and Fred were centrally positioned in my side yard, it was left to Carl to give the *go* signal, one hoot owl blast of his hand whistle.

I stood just beyond the Fischmans' with the front door of the Schwartz home well in view. I had no wristwatch, so all I could do was wait and sweat, both from the heat and the slowly building fear of getting caught.

Finally, I clearly heard the distinct sound of Carl blowing into his palms through his thumbs. Seconds later, Freddie appeared, bag in hand. After looking both ways, he crossed the street. I knew him well enough to be certain that he was relishing every step of this adventure. Luckily, the Schwartz' had not turned on their front porch light.

Fred moved steadily ahead, up their driveway, left, up the front walk, and on tiptoes now, up the two steps to the front door. He then knelt. Just as he reached for his back-pocket, Wally sounded the warning signal. Fred quickly retreated to the Schwartz' side yard. A car was heading right at me. It was Mr. Fischman in his TV repair truck. He pulled into his driveway as I fell to the ground, hopefully out of his sight. He fiddled around in the back of his truck for what seemed like forever. Finally, he opened the garage door stepped inside and lowered it back down. I heard the lock click.

I waited at least 60 seconds and then gave the all-clear signal, two strong blasts with my palm whistle. Freddie reappeared. Back up onto the Fat Lady's porch he went. He bent over, removed the box of Cat's Eyes wood matches that Wally's dad used to light his pipe. I could see the bright glow of the match. There was only a slight breeze. It was enough to extinguish the first match. Freddie tried again, this time protecting the flame with cupped hands.

When the bag took the flame, it lit up the porch, and Fred became very visible. To his credit, he calmly rose and, rather than ringing the doorbell, he hammered vociferously on the door. The sound of his banging made the hairs on the back of my neck stand up. Using all of the body language I could conjure up, I urged Freddie to get moving. Suddenly he was sprinting like the Winged Victory in my direction.

I took my eyes off Fred when the porch light at the Schwartz' came on. What happened next is truly emblazoned in my memory. There was no Fat Lady. Rather, it was Mr. Schwartz, adorned in shorty pajamas and bedroom slippers, who opened the door.

When he saw the flaming package that lay before him, he did something between a Saint Vitas Day Dance and a Mexican Hat Dance. The bag had practically burned itself out by the time he began to imitate Fred Astaire, but he seemed possessed. The Mexican Hat Dance slowed to an Indian War Dance as he turned in circles raising his feet high in an attempt to determine just what it was, he had stepped in. Then I heard him answer his own question by using the exact word for that which he had all over his slippers. I couldn't tell for sure if he was using it as a noun or a verb or both.

Freddie could not contain his laughter. As I tried to signal him to shut up, he thought I was signaling him to come to my spot. As he pointed at poor enraged Mr. Schwartz, Freddie went into his own dance of laughter as he made his way toward me.

The old man saw him and called after Fred. This sobered us up quickly and we were off in a mad dash, the sound of Mr. Schwartz' expletives fading as we ran. I was certain we had been identified. He had looked right in the direction of Fred and me.

When we finally all hooked up behind Wally's garage, I voiced my concern. But Carl allayed my fears.

"There's no way he saw you. He's blind as a bat. He didn't have his glasses on."

I thought about that for a second. I had no idea. I was transfixed on his dancing feet. But Carl insisted. He had answered the door without the coke bottle thick glasses. Carl confirmed one other thing the rest of us had not seen. Given his vantage point, Carl was the only one who saw the Fat Lady. His description of her standing in the doorway behind her husband doing her Ginger Rodgers to her husband's Astaire had us rolling on the ground.

Though the intended target of our Express Mail was the Fat Lady, we all agreed we had never seen anything, not even Jerry Lewis on a good day, that was as funny as what we had witnessed on that summer evening.

As for me, I could not have realized that I could feel such a combination of guilt and glee as I did on that memorable night. It was a terrible, mean-spirited thing to do, even to a very mean-spirited person. I knew I would always feel badly for suggesting and helping to carry out such a dastardly act. But on that night, the Black Shirt Gang bonded like at no other time. And, Mr. Schwartz, I'm sorry, but thanks for the laugh of my life. He was an innocent man victimized due to his association with an evil woman. Never again would I lay eyes on this poor man without having to repress laughter.

The next afternoon, the Black Shirt Gang, in high spirits, was sitting in my living room watching The String Bean on Channel 9.

My mother came in carrying groceries. After we all helped her take the bags to the kitchen, she went to the phone to give my Aunt Win a call to invite her over for dinner. As the gang settled back in front of the television, we heard my mother slam the phone down.

She walked into the living room and said, "I swear, that Bertha Schwartz is the meanest creature. I feel like picking that phone back up and giving her a piece of my mind. I'm going to call the phone company and insist that they give us a different party line."

She then looked curiously at the four of us as we screamed with laughter.

The Stringbean & Gang.

Nick's Ice Cream Cart-No Tootie Frutti

1956

And there used to be a ballpark
Where the field was warm and green
And the people played their crazy game
With a joy I'd never seen
And, the air was such a wonder
From the hot dogs and the beer
Yes, there used to be a ballpark right here...
Now the children try to find it
And they can't believe their eyes
Cause the old team isn't playing
And the new one hardly tries.
And the sky has got so cloudy
When it used to be so clear
And the summer went so quickly – this year.
Yes, there used to be a ballpark right here.

From *There Used to be a Ballpark*
By Joe Raposo

The Burgerville

There was a piece of music in the late forties and throughout the fifties that was immediately identifiable and captured my complete and total attention no matter what life might find me up to at the time. It cannot be referred to as a little ditty because it was strong and bold and indicated that the Cincinnati Reds and my man Waite Hoyt (brought to you by Burger Beer) were coming on the air.

The minute I heard the strains of the John Philip Sousa march, *El Capitan*, I would rush to the radio. Composed in 1896 for the comic operetta of the same name and based on a book by Charles Kline, Sousa unknowingly had given Cincinnati its most important theme song of the mid-twentieth century.

The fact that *El Capitan* had run for a modest 112 performances at the Broadway Theatre in New York City, and later just 240 more at the Lyric Theatre in London, was of no consequence to me. The vibrant march merely served as an alert that I was in for two to three hours of magic as only Waite Hoyt, the former Yankee pitching great, could describe.

By 1950, Hoyt was in his prime. "Good afternoon, baseball fans," he would start as the engineer lowered the music. "It is a perfect day for baseball here at Crosley Field as the Cincinnati Reds prepare to take on the Pittsburgh Pirates and their All-Star right fielder, Ralph Kiner. Kiner enters today's game leading the National League with thirty-two round-trippers, only two ahead of Chicago's Andy Pafko and six in front of Reds first-baseman, Ted Kluszewski. Big Klu will be flexing those big biceps today, as Pirate Manager Billy Meyer will have right hander Murry

Dickson on the mound. Kluszewski has taken Dickson to the Burgerville twice already this season and the folks in the right-field bleachers will be looking for a souvenir every time the big man comes up today, you can bettcha."

With that, the music would come back up to full crescendo after which Hoyt would begin his first Burger Beer schpiel of the day. Ironically, the reformed alcoholic who had not taken a drink since the Reds were last in the World Series in 1940, extolled the glory of one of Cincinnati's many German beers. Burger, fine lager, was second to none, according to Hoyt. Without saying as much, he conveyed with great conviction that Burger stood head and foam over other local favorites like Hudepohl, Schoenling, Bavarian, Red Top, Felsenbrau and Bruck's Jubilee. To assure that he could slip in a free commercial every so often, Hoyt had anointed the area over the fence where home runs landed as the *Burgerville*.

After some beer pitching, the ex-Yankee pitcher, who replaced the incomparable Red Barber in the Reds' broadcast booth behind home plate in 1942, would come back to baseball.

For example, in 1951, he might say, "Well, fans it's a three team race in the National League on this fourteenth day of August with the Phillies holding a three and one-half game lead over both the Giants and the Dodgers. The Reds find themselves an equal three and one-half games ahead of the basement dwelling Pirates and so far out of first place they couldn't see it with a telescope."

Hoyt would continue something like this, "But it's encouraging for the hometown nine today as the *Whip*, Ewell Blackwell, goes to the mound. The five time All-Star will be looking for his fifteenth win of the season. He enters today's game with an ERA of 2.87 trailing only the Giants' Sal Maglie in that department. Blackwell is also second in the league in strikeouts behind Boston's Warren Spahn."

The happy sing-song ring of Hoyt's voice continued as he would announce, "Here is the starting lineup for the Cincinnati Reds. Leading off and playing second base is Bobby Adams. Batting second is third baseman Grady Hatton. In the third spot is right fielder Johnny Wyrostek, who leads the Reds with a .329 batting average. Of course, as always, in clean-up is first baseman, Big Klu, Ted Kluszewski. Batting fifth is rookie left fielder, Joe Adcock. Center fielder Lloyd Merriman is in the sixth slot and batting seventh is catcher and former Dodger, Dixie Walker, in for the injured Ray Mueller. Walker is followed by shortstop Virgil Stallcup, and pitcher Ewell Blackwell will bat last."

Then Hoyt, who became a professional baseball player at the age of fifteen, earning him the nickname *School Boy,* and was the first player to go from the field to the broadcast booth, would proceed to announce the entire game in past tense. Instead of saying, "and here's the pitch to Baumholtz for a strike," he would announce, "and there was the pitch. Baumholtz took that one for a strike on the outside corner, knee high."

This style of broadcasting may well be due to the fact that until the end of the forties, Hoyt announced all away games, not from the home team's field, but, rather from the studio of WSAI Radio in the basement of the Alms Hotel, reading the ticker tape being transmitted back to Cincinnati from, say, Philadelphia. In the background, you could hear the ticking of the tape machine as the report came over the line, and Hoyt would re-create the action as if he were sitting in the first row at Shibe Park.

In the early years of my life, the Reds stayed stuck in what was known as the second division. There were eight teams in the National League and eight teams in the American League. If you stood in the standings among the top four teams, you were said to be in the first division. And, of course, if you were one of the bottom four teams you resided in the dreaded second division.

From the end of the war until 1956, the Reds were never a contender. In fact, they never recorded even a winning season during that period. Not once did they get beyond June and find themselves in the first division.

But I loved them just the same. I knew every manager, every player, their numbers, their batting averages, their ERA's. In fact, it would be hard for me to believe that there was a bigger baseball fan anywhere in the world than I. I suppose there may have been, but this I could not imagine.

I studied everything I could get my hands on. And, I wasn't alone. Most of my friends were also students of the game. Big fans like me. Well, not like me. To them it was a passion. To me it was a religion.

I didn't pray to Jesus or Yahweh or Buddha. My faith was directed to the real saints in my life. In reality, most were no more than mediocre. Nonetheless, Graddy Hatton, Bobby Adams, Virgil Stallcup, Ray Mueller, Johnny Wyrostek, Jim Greengrass Herm Wiehmeier and Ken Raffensberger were the guys with whom I placed my total faith. And, as it is with religious idols, my heroes never lived up to my hopes and expectations. Yet I never lost faith in them.

Then, finally, in 1956, the Reds, now known as the Redlegs thanks to Joseph McCarthy and the great *Red Scare* of the early '50's, rewarded my dedication. It was no longer acceptable to call them the *Reds*. That term had taken on a very negative connotation in post-war America. The *Red* scourge had drawn a supposed *Iron Curtain* between Communist Eastern Europe plus the Soviet Union and what was then called the *Free World*. To say *Red Sox* and *Redlegs* was fine. But the *Reds* were now the enemy. Meaning no disrespect, to me they had been the Reds and I continued to refer to them as such. So sue me.

At any rate, my Reds were now a contender in the National League. The main man, and only genuine hero of the old Reds, was Big Klu, Ted Kluszewski. And only he remained from those teams of the late forties. Number 18 continued to cut his shirtsleeves to make room for his Neanderthal biceps. And he was still using those massive arms to hit the ball into the right field bleachers – the *Burgerville*.

And this year, joining Klu were a newer and better cast of characters that we were all growing to love. There was shortstop and team MVP that year, Roy McMillan, second baseman, Johnny Temple, third baseman, Ray "Jabo" Jablonski, catcher Ed Bailey, and clearly the best outfield in recent Redleg history. In right field was Ohioan, Wally Post and in center field was the fleet-footed, strong hitting Gus Bell.

But best of all, the Reds finally had an African-American super star. Rookie Frank Robinson, wearing number 20 (his age on opening day), proudly prowled the outfield like a hungry cat. At bat, he crowded the plate, elbows high over the strike zone. His attitude seemed to be, "You better hit me if you don't want me to hit you!"

And hit him they did. Frank Robinson led the league in being hit by a pitch. He got whacked 20 times. The next closest player in that category was Solly Hemus, who was hit a meager eight times throughout the 1956 season.

Yea, Robinson had us all excited. Who other than a blatant racist, and there were plenty of those around, couldn't get excited about Frank Robinson? In 1956, he was honored as Rookie of the Year, voted to the All-Star team, batted .290, led the team with 38 home runs, and played in every one of the Red's 154 games. It was as if we had our very own Jackie Robinson. Many, at first, thought Frank was Jackie's younger brother. He was not. What he was, though, was unbelievable! 38 home runs was a career for many players of that era.

And this team had real character. In fact, it had real characters. If Major League Baseball had staged a street brawl in 1956, the Redlegs would have won handily. Under the category of *hard-nosed,* this team offered up names like Smokey Burgess, Johnny Temple, Joe Nuxhall, Ed Bailey, Ray Jablonski, Alex Grammas and Rocky Bridges. Most were small in stature but full of vinegar and ready for a fight.

And, to stoke the flame, there was fiery manager Birdie Tebbetts. By mid-season, he had the Reds in first place. They stayed in the pennant race until the last day of the season, ending up with a 91-63 record, two games behind the Brooklyn Dodgers. For his efforts, the Baseball Writers of America voted Birdie Tebbetts as the 1956 Manager of the Year.

Thus, as May turned to June, these new *Redlegs* had us glued to WSAI on our radio dial. Every once in a while, they would televise a game, in which case Mark Scott and George Bryson were the commentators. Bryson was new that year, just like the team. For my taste, he was too full of superlatives and too full of other stuff as well. For example, he might report, "The old Smokster (Smoky Burgess) hit a real daisy-cutter - a real blazer that time. And that little white sphere had no problem scooting right through the tunnel that is Eddie Matthews' legs. Burgess never goes to the left side of the ballpark and caught Matthews looking like Rip Van Winkle on that one. Looks like the old Redlegs have a rally percolating at old Crosley Stadium now!"

As it turned out, I would wind up playing high school baseball with Bryson's son, George, Jr. Junior would become known as *Chico* for his dark Mexican-style good looks. He was carefree and happy. A decent ball player and a good guy, he later went to Hollywood and showed up with bit parts in a couple of movies, including *The Courtship of Eddie's Father*. Later he returned to Cincinnati to manage the Playboy Club. The ladies liked Chico.

But, as stated, the senior Bryson was not my cup of tea. So when the *Redlegs* were on TV, we would turn the sound on the TV down and the sound on the radio up and enjoy Waite Hoyt telling us what we were seeing on the small screen.

People really started to take note of the home team after a double-header on Sunday, June 24th. The Reds took the World Champion Brooklyn Dodgers twice that day. They ran off with game one by a score of 10-6 with catcher Ed Bailey hitting three home runs. Then they won a squeaker in the second game 2-1. To polish off the exciting Sunday, eleven of the Reds appeared that evening on the popular television show, *What's My Line?*

Ted Kluszewski acted as spokesman for the group as they signed in as the *mystery guest*. With host John Daly sitting next to Klu and the remaining ten ballplayers standing behind them, the blindfolded panel asked the questions. The panel that night included regulars Dorothy Kilgalin, Bennett Cerf and Arlene Francis along with guest panelist, ventriloquist Paul Winchell.

To me, this was unbelievable - my beloved Reds on National television. But sure enough, there stood Ted Kluszewski, Frank Robinson, Johnny Temple, Ed Bailey, Joe Nuxhall, Roy Mc Millan, Ray Jablonski, Gus Bell, Wally Post, Smokey Burgess and Johnny Klipstein. And the famous journalist, Bennett Cerf was steeping high praise on them. This was great stuff!

But the night the Reds rewarded my years of unrewarded loyalty the most was Saturday, August 18, 1956. On that evening, the Reds hosted the first place Milwaukee Braves. The Braves entered the game with the same number of wins as the Reds, but 3 fewer loses. Thus, they led second place Cincinnati by 1 1/2 games.

At this point in the season, the Reds were on track to set a team record and challenge the league record for most home runs by a team. Entering this Saturday night game, Kluszewski and rookie Frank Robinson had both hit 28 round trippers, while right-fielder Wally Post had 24 in the books.

As the beautiful cords of *El Capitan* blasted from the radio perched on the small bookcase headboard of my bed, I settled in to my favorite place to listen to a game. For some reason, I would often sit on the old cedar toy box in my room with my legs stretched out onto the side of my bed. It never entered my mind to recline on the bed itself. Too much relaxation would not allow me to use the body-English needed to help my team.

Waite Hoyt, as always, came on by stating the importance of this game for the hometown team. It seemed as though you could hear the hope in his voice that night. After so many years of reporting on mediocre ball teams, Hoyt, and all of us, sensed that this could be our year.

Hoyt reported, "Well Cincinnati baseball fans, a win tonight could bring the Redlegs within 1/2 game of the National League lead with just six weeks remaining in this 1956 season. Birdie Tebbetts has Johnny Klippstein on the mound for this important game against first-place Milwaukee, while Braves manager Fred Haney will counter with Ray Crone."

"Birdie will be making two adjustments to his regular line-up tonight, moving Frank Robinson to center field for the injured Gus Bell and inserting Alex Grammas at third base in place of Ray Jablonski. Thus, Big Bob Thurmann will start tonight in left"

After selling some Burger Beer, Hoyt then announce the starting line-ups in his matter-of-fact style.

"And now for the starting line-up for the league-leading Milwaukee

Braves. Leading off and playing second base is Danny O'Connell. Batting second is shortstop, Johnny Logan. In the third slot is centerfielder Hank Aaron, who enters the game hitting .335. At third base and batting clean-up is hard hitting Eddie Matthews. Matthews will be followed by first baseman and former Redleg Joe Adcock, who is flirting with the 300 mark entering this game. Left fielder Bobby Thompson, Center fielder, Bill Burton, catcher Toby Atwell and starting pitcher, Ray Crone round out the Braves line-up."

Then, "Here is your starting line-up tonight for the best Cincinnati team in recent memory. Leading off is feisty second baseman Johnny Temple. Tonight sees Frank Robinson moving from left to center and up one spot in the batting order. Batting third is left-fielder Bob Thurman, getting the start due to the injury to Gus Bell. As always, Big Ted Kluszewski fills the clean-up spot. Batting fifth and playing right field is Wally Post. Catcher Ed Bailey is in the number six slot followed by third baseman, Alex Grammas. Smooth-fielding shortstop Roy McMillan bats eighth and starting pitcher Johnny Klippstein will bat ninth."

Hoyt then announced, "Your umpiring crew for tonight's ballgame will find Frank Dascoli behind the plate, Frank Secory at first base, Bill Engelin at second base, and veteran Larry Goetz calling the line at third."

Hoyt would continue, "This is unfamiliar territory for the Cincinnati nine, who have found themselves squandering in the second division over the past 15 summers. Now, just 1 1/2 games out of the lead and with the ever-present Brooklyn Dodgers lurking right behind, can the line-up patched up this evening by Birdie Tebbetts get the championship momentum going for the Redlegs? Well, we will find out right after this word from Burger Beer."

As I settled in on the less than comfortable toy box, my box seat for the game, I had no idea what a treat I was about to be handed by my team. This would be a memorable night, a night that I would carry with me forever after.

As the national anthem was being played, my father stuck his head in the door, already adorned in blue pajamas and his maroon silk bathrobe.

"They getting ready to start?" he asked.

"Yea, they have Thurmann in for Bell and Grammas in for Jabo," I reported.

"Oh, oh," he said. "That Tebbetts is such a knucklehead. I'll check back later."

With that, he was back to the living room. Unlike many Saturday nights, he seemed to be totally sober. Less drunk for him always meant less stress for me. As much as he loved the Reds, he loved Jackie Gleason even more. So, while I would be glued to the radio, he would be doubled over in hysterical laughter watching Gleason, Art Carney and other guests, while my mother would plead for him to calm down so she could hear.

I loved Gleason too. The show had started as the *Cavalcade of Stars* on the Dumont network in the late 40's. It was first hosted by comedian Jack Carter and then Jerry Lester. When Gleason took over, CBS bought the show from Dumont and renamed it the *Jackie Gleason Show.* Gleason portrayed a number of recurring characters, including a disdainful, mustachioed "playboy" millionaire Reginald Van Gleason III; friendly Joe the Bartender, always with bar towel in hand; loudmouthed braggart Charlie Bratten; mild-mannered Fenwick Babbitt; verbose Rudy the Repairman; and a put-upon character known only as the Poor Soul, whom Gleason always performed in pantomime. In between skits, the June Taylor Dancers would do their leggy Radio City Music Hall Rockettes shtick. I suspected this was a big part of my father's fascination with the show.

But, of course, the big attraction of the show was the Honeymooners. Gleason played the blowhard Brooklyn bus driver Ralph Kramden. Along with his wife played by Audrey Meadows and his dolt of a friend Ed Norton, the sewer-working upstairs neighbor, played by the great Art Carney, Gleason kept America in tearful laughter throughout most of the 1950s. I could always tell when the Honeymooners were on the show, as the decibel level of Dad's laughter went up significantly.

In 1956, there was no way I was trading in the Reds for Gleason. So, as Klippstein hurled the first pitch of the game, I was perched on the toy box and of a single mind. The only thing in the world at that moment was the game!

As I readied myself for a night of baseball, I noticed that my friend Jack Gates and his dad Big Al were seated at their kitchen table next door leaning toward their radio. Predictably, they were hunkered down for the game as well. The Gates and I would enjoy another game separated by only a 15-foot patch of grass and a couple of windows and within ear shot of each other's cheers.

It was a hot August night. The toy box was strategically located between the two open windows in my bedroom. I was hoping for a cross breeze. Our one and only electric fan was providing relief to my parents in the living room.

The game did not get off to a good start. Danny O'Connell hit that first pitch into left center for a double and then moved to third on a single by Logan. Only Robinson's arm kept him from scoring. But after Klippstein got Aaron on strikes, Matthews hit a fly to deep center, O'Connell tagged up at third and the Braves led 1-0.

Being conditioned to years of losing, I had already started to think this was not the Red's night. This thinking was reinforced when Cincinnati went down 1-2-3 in the bottom of the first. Jack Gates yelled through his open kitchen window, "Here we go again."

I stuck my head to the left, peering through the window, and shrugged. It was only the first inning.

The top of second didn't begin any better, as Thompson and Burton started the inning with back-to-back singles. After Ed Bailey corralled a pop foul by Atwell, Thompson and Burton moved over a base on a perfect bunt by Crone. But Klippstein got out of the inning by getting O'Connell to pop up to McMillan at shortstop.

The Reds loaded the bases in the bottom of the second on three straight singles by Kluszewski, Post and Bailey. They then tied the game when Grammas lifted a sacrifice fly to deep leftfield.

After Klippstein set the Braves down 1-2-3 in the top of the third, the game changed from normal to special.

Hoyt reported the fireworks in typical past-tense fashion.

"The Reds bring the top of the batting order up here in the bottom of the third. Temple, after digging in, looked at a curve ball, low and outside. And the pitch was made by Crone, which was a fast ball that caught the inside corner for a strike. Temple stepped out of the batter's box and looked down to the third base coach for the signal. The pitch made by Crone and Johnny lifted a lazy fly ball to center, and Aaron settled under that one with ease."

And then the fun began. In quick fashion, the Reds went up by four runs. Robinson took a 1 ball-1 strike fast ball over the left field fence bouncing it "off the face of the laundry" (the Superior Towel and Linen Building) according to Hoyt. Bob Thurmann then drove a double into left center field. Ted Kluszewski stepped up to the plate.

Hoyt continued with measured enthusiasm, "Well fans, Big Klu took that 2-1 pitch from Crone way up in the Burgerville. He hit that one a country mile. That ball landed near the top of the right field bleachers. Thurman scored ahead of Klu and the Redlegs lead this one 4 to 1."

The Gates and I harmonized a rousing cheer, providing stereo for anyone who might happen to be snooping around in the side yard. Hoyt advised us all that Haney would replace Crone with Bob Buhl on the mound. I ran to the bathroom while Buhl took his allotted six warm-up pitches.

Before I could settle back onto my toy box, Hoyt was now screaming into the Crosley Field microphone, "Can you believe it? Wally Post just slammed the first pitch from Buhl up against the laundry on the far side of the left field wall. That's back-to-back visits to the Burgerville for the Redlegs, and they now lead the first place Braves by a score of 5 to 1."

Hoyt continued, "Wally just missed winning a Kuppenheimer suit with that one. That ball hit less than a foot to the left of the famous sign atop the Superior Towel and Linen Building that says 'hit this sign and win a new Kuppenheimer suit.'"

No suit for Post and no more scoring for the Reds in the bottom of the third. After two weak grounders to Adcock at first base by Bailey and Grammas, the inning came to an end.

While Waite Hoyt was extolling the perfection of Burger Beer between innings, I gave a wave to Jack and then rushed to the living room to report the three homerun third inning to my dad. I found him doubled over with his intense "hee, hee, hee, hee, hee, oh, hee hee, hee, hee (deep gasp) oh, hee, hee, hee" laugh as he listened to Ralph Kramden threaten to send Alice Kramden "to the moon."

As Norton bust through the door on the small screen of our Philco saying "hey, hey hey, Ralphie boy," my dad increased his laugh and waved me off.

The Reds were taking the Braves to the moon and all he wanted to do was watch Ralph Kramden? Oh well, his loss.

Over confidence is a terrible thing in sports. I already had this one in the win column for my Reds as I settled back onto the toy box.

Waite Hoyt was back on the air to continue the fun. "The Braves will bring the number five, six and seven batters in their line-up to face Klippstein here in the top of the fourth."

Immediately the game changed direction.

As Hoyt reported, "There was the first pitch to Adcock. Adcock took a big swing at that one."

He paused a moment then said, "Well that ball cleared the center field fence and is rattling around on Central Avenue. Klippstein would like to have that pitch back. That was number 29 for Joe Adcock, keeping him one ahead of Big Klu on the season"

My confidence swung 180 degrees in a matter of seconds. The Braves were not through.

After Bobby Thompson grounded to Johnny Temple for an easy out, Burton stepped in and quickly struck a doubled down the left field line.

Hoyt continued his play-by-play. "The weak hitting Atwell has stepped in to face Klippstein as Burton has taken a safe lead off second. Atwell was only batting .143 at game time and could be facing a one-way ticket back to the Pony League (Pennsylvania-Ohio-New York) if he doesn't turn it around soon."

No sooner was that out of Waite Hoyt's mouth, than Toby Atwell "turned it around" with a two-run homer, Burton scoring ahead of him.

"Well, they have been flying out of Crosley Field and into the Burgerville tonight," Hoyt said.

I could only wonder how George Bryson might be describing this home run derby, had the game been televised on this hot summer night. Perhaps, "There's another reverse shooting star off the old piece of ash wielded by the diminutive Toby Atwell. Can you beeeelieeeve the fireworks here at the old ballpark? Somebody better order more baseballs for this one. Five round trippers and it's only the top of the fourth. Does anyone around here know what the record is? It's time to back up the walls another twenty feet. Or maybe we should switch to soft balls."

The score was 5-4, and I notice Mr. Gates headed to his icebox for another beer (Schoenling, not Burger). My best way to settle myself down in a situation like this was to go to work with my Duncan Yoyo. I grabbed the new aqua blue wooden yoyo with little gem stones surrounding the circumference, and did a half dozen walk-the-dogs and a couple loop-the-loops while trying to send good karma from by bedroom down to Crosley Field. It worked.

Fortunately, Klippstein was able to stop the bleeding by getting Buhl and O'Conner both to ground outs. But, the Red's run-a-way was back to a one run game.

I took the yoyo string from my middle finger and ran to the kitchen to grab a Barq's cream soda from the icebox, quickly snapping off the bottle cap and heading back to my room. Gleason was over, and I bumped into my dad as he exited the bathroom.

"How they doing?" he asked.

One run game, Reds ahead…bottom of the fourth," I reported.

"I'm gonna listen in bed," dad informed me.

He headed one way; I headed the other.

The bottom of the fourth went quickly with McMillan and Klippstein going down on strikes and Temple grounding out to Logan at second base.

That same Logan started off the 5th inning by driving an easy double into the gap between left and center. I started to sweat. Was it the 95-degree heat or the Milwaukee Braves staging another charge? Whatever it was, Tebbetts had seen enough of Johnny Klippstein. Hoyt described Birdie's slow hike to the mound as he tapped is left wrist indicating he wanted Hal Jeffcoat from the bullpen down the leftfield line. "No win for Klippstein tonight," stated the ex-Yankee hurler.

To help those who did not understand how these things worked, Waite Hoyt explained, "If Jeffcoat can get the Red's out of the fifth, he stands to pick up his 4th win of the season against two loses."

That possibility didn't look promising as Jeffcoat unleashed a wild pitch allowing Logan to move over to third. I jumped back up and grabbed my yoyo.

Always the baseball professor, Hoyt said, "Jeffcoat needs to be throwing that sweeping curve ball of his now in hopes of getting a ground ball, with the always dangerous Hank Aaron at the plate."

As if Hal Jeffcoat was listening to the radio, he threw a curve ball that, according to Hoyt "broke a good two feet, and Aaron grounded weakly to Grammas at third. Alex looked Logan back to the bag and threw to Kluszewski for the first out."

Jeffcoat then got Matthews to hit a hard grounder to Temple at second that kept Logan hugging third base. That was followed by a fly ball off the bat of Joe Adcock to Wally Post in right field and the Reds were coming to bat with a narrow one-run lead.

I heard Jack Gates and his dad cheer from the window and my dad say, "Well, I'll be a son-of-a-buck," from his bedroom. I tried an impossible around-the-world with the Duncan hitting the ceiling.

"What was that?" my father yelled from his bedroom.

"I dropped my yoyo," I lied.

"You better be careful with that damned thing," he commanded.

I went back to walking the dog, a trick I had mastered, and readied myself for the bottom of the fifth inning.

As I sat back down on the toy box, Frank Robinson grounded out with what George Bryson would have described as a *daisy-cutter* to short. Hoyt just called it, "a hard grounder that Logan fielded easily and threw

Robinson out at first with room to spare."

Bob Thurman then stepped to up to the first base side of the plate. I began to fidget with some of my baseball cards, wishing Gus Bell was healthy and Thurman was where he belonged, riding the lumber in the Red's third base dugout. Thurman rewarded my youthful skepticism with a long drive to right field.

Hoyt explained with enthusiasm, "Wel,l that one just snuck over the fence and into the right field bleachers. But it still counted, and the Redlegs lead six to four."

Here we go, I thought, with Big Klu coming up. Ted rewarded my youthful enthusiasm with a weak ground ball to Adcock at first. Then right-handed Wally Post replied with the mirror image of Kluszewksi, hitting an easy ground ball to third and the fifth inning was over.

Jack Gates yelled over from his kitchen window that he wanted to bet a nickel that the Reds would blow this one. I looked through the left-hand window in my room and saw Big Al reach into their ice box for yet another beer (did he think he had to score a Schoenling for every run scored?). I accepted Jack's big-time wager, grabbed my yoyo, walked a couple of dogs, straightened the spinning cord on the Duncan by running the string between my thumbnail and index finger then settled back on the toy box for the 6th inning.

It proved to be an uneventful inning. The only excitement was supplied by Jeffcoat's control, or lack thereof. He walked two guys and snuck a wild pitch in between. But the Braves never got a ball out of the infield, and the Reds came up to bat still leading by two runs. Hoyt sold some Burger, and Big Al improved the stock value of Schoenling with another trip to his dwindling supply of long necks, before Ed Bailey stepped to the plate to start the bottom half of the inning. The Red's produced a groundout, a strikeout, a walk and a weak fly ball, not giving Big Al time to get half way through beer number seven.

So, the seventh inning began with the Reds holding a two-run lead, Big Al Gates holding a half a Schoenling and me clutching my rhinestone covered Duncan yoyo. Jack Gates was sweating over a nickel and probably torn as to whether he wanted to win the nickel or have the Reds win the game.

My father got up from bed and retrieved the fan from the living room and placed it at the front window of the small bedroom he shared with my mother.

Over the next two- and one-half innings, Waite Hoyt did some of the best broadcasting in his career with the exceptions of most rain delays and on the day when he spoke extemporaneously for two hours in August 1948 upon the death of Babe Ruth.

Hoyt had been a pall barer at Ruth's funeral. On that hot August day, Joe Dugan, another Ruth teammate, said to Hoyt, "I'd give a hundred bucks for a ice cold beer right now."

As the story goes, Hoyt looked back at Dugan, nodded and said, "So would the Babe."

At this point in the game, Hoyt, with the nose of a coon dog, had smelled out the possibilities in this home run derby. Without reference books or an army of statisticians, he began to tap into an unbelievable well of baseball knowledge to color his play-by-play of the game.

"As I think back on the history of this great game of baseball, I cannot help but wonder if the Redlegs might be on the verge of real greatness tonight. With 5 trips to the Burgerville in the books, they are getting close. Many teams have hit six homers in a game, very few have hit seven and only the 1939 Yankees and the 1953 Milwaukee Braves, fresh from their move from Boston, have hit eight. Not a single team has ever hit nine," Hoyt reported matter-of-factly.

"Well, we just have to wait and see. But let's keep in mind Cincinnati only leads a very good Milwaukee team by two as we begin inning number seven."

I processed what Hoyt had just told me, as I heard my father say some intelligible comment about the 1927 Yankees. He mumbled a lot in bed.

Suddenly, I had more to root for than just a win. Now I was rooting for homers as well. Jack Gates must have taken an extra ten seconds to digest what Hoyt had said, because he yelled across the yard, "I got another nickel that says they won't hit nine."

I fired back, "Make it eight and you have a bet."

"You're on," he replied.

My mother weighed in, yelling from her bedroom, "I better not see you wasting good money betting on baseball, young man."

Then to my father, "See what you are teaching him?"

He answered with a couple of his patented "Hee, hees," followed by, "please pipe down, I'm trying to listen to the ballgame."

I turned my attention away from my parent's bedroom and back to my little Crosley radio perched on the headboard of my bed.

Waite Hoyt reminded his listeners that "Milwaukee will bring the meat of their order to the plate here in the top of the seventh."

Jeffcoat quickly retired Logan and Aaron, making them look like hamburger rather than steak. But then Eddy Matthews slashed a double into the gap between left and center. When Adcock hit a ground ball to McMillan at short, I knew we were out of the inning before Hoyt confirmed that the throw over to Kluszewski was there in time to get Adcock. McMillan was the smoothest fielding shortstop in baseball. He was as graceful at short as Johnny Temple was rough at second. I loved them both.

My father mumbled, "They'll blow this thing… just wait."

I snuck a peak over to the Gates' kitchen and saw Big Al disappear down the basement steps. Time to get another case of Schoenling on ice, I was guessing.

Over the airwaves, I could hear the strains of *The Mexican Hat Dance* coming from the Crosley Field organist, a reminder that this game had reached the middle of the seventh, or as it was known, "stretch inning." I visualized all of the fans on their feet stomping those same feet on the appropriate beat of the music – a Crosley Field stretch inning tradition.

The bottom of the seventh inning started with the Reds sending up the top of their order. I moved forward to the edge of the toy box as feisty second baseman, Johnny Temple came to the plate. He quickly attacked the first pitch.

"That was a sharp liner to center. Unfortunately, it was right at Burton, and the Redlegs have one down here in the bottom of the seventh," reported Waite Hoyt.

In my mind's ear, I heard George Bryson saying, "Little but mighty Johnny Temple lines an absolute rope to straight away centerfield that is corralled by the fleet-footed Bruton. That ball got out there fast, almost handcuffing Billy Boy. It was like Temple was shooting at a target and hit the bull's eye with that one."

Hoyt advised his listeners that Frank Robinson was coming to the plate, turning my attention back to the real game versus the one I was hearing in my imagination.

Conley, obviously respecting Robinson's power, was a little too careful and dealt Robbie a base on balls.

Hoyt reported to his listeners that Bob Thurman had stepped into the batter's box.

"Well, fans, Thurman took Buhl to the Burgerville his last time up. Let's see what he can do against Gene Conley here in the bottom of the seventh. Robinson has taken his lead off first, always a threat to steal a base."

Hoyt continued, "The first pitch from Conley was a sweeping curve ball low and away. Gene is having a hard time finding the strike zone here in the seventh inning.

On the next pitch, Conley found the strike zone and, on this night, Bob Thurman owned the strike zone. The roar of the crowd announced, before Hoyt could, that Bob Thurman had hit his second home run of the night. The Reds lead by four.

I took a quick peak to see how Big Al was coming with beer number seven and if Jack might be hiding his money. They were both dancing around the kitchen. My father let go with a lengthy string of "hee hees."

Just as he had done with Thurman, Conley started the Red's next batter, Ted Kluszewski with a breaking ball that was too low. Hoyt then painted a verbal picture of a nervous Gene Conley fidgeting with the rosin bag behind the pitching rubber.

Before Hoyt could get the past tense description out, I heard the crack of Big Klu's finely milled ash, Louisville Slugger, making contact with Conley's fastball. The crack of the bat and the roar of the crowd melded into a single sound, lifting me off the toy box.

"Well, there was no doubt about that one," Hoyt reported. "Big Klu took that high fastball way up into the moon deck, and the Redlegs have increased their lead to a five run margin."

At that point, Waite Hoyt, Jack Gates and I were all working on the math.

Let's see, I thought. When the inning started, the Reds had four. Now they had six.

Jack weighed in from his kitchen window. He shouted across our side yard, "They will never get two more. They have the weak part of the batting order coming up."

Hoyt seemed more optimistic as he tapped into his wealth of baseball knowledge.

"Well, Redlegs fans, that was Big Klu's second round-tripper of the game, giving the home team six so far in this exciting ball game," Hoyt reported.

I do not know if he was getting help or if he had all of the facts in his head. In either case, he continued with a litany of statistics.

In a matter-of-fact fashion, he reported, "While the 7-homer trick was turned as far back as 1886, the 1939 Yankees were the first team to have 8 home runs in one game. As I recall, on June 28th, 1939, Joe DiMaggio and Babe Dahlgren connected twice in the first game of a doubleheader and 4 other players hit one apiece. Not only that, but the Yankees hit 5 more homers in the 2nd game, posting 23-2 and 10-0 wins and setting the doubleheader record of 13 homers. The Yankees, in the first game, became one of 6 teams to hit as many as 7 homers and score 20 or more runs in the same game. The only other team to achieve the 8-homer mark was the 1953 Milwaukee Braves. Jim Pendleton had 3 round-tippers that day."

Before going back to the game, Hoyt posed the obvious question. "Is it in the cards tonight here at Crosley Field for the Redlegs to become the ninth team to hit seven, the third team to hit a record eight, or could they even set a new major league record with nine? Well, they have at least an inning and two-thirds left to try."

I settled back on the edge of my bedroom box seat squeezing my Duncan Yoyo so hard it hurt. *Come on,* I prayed, *just three more homers.* The hope quickly vanished when Wally Post, always a threat to go long, hit a "lazy fly ball for an easy out" to right field and Ed Bailey hit a hard liner, also, to Hank Aaron in right field, for the third out of the inning.

Just like that, the hope seemed to evaporate. While Hoyt usually reported games objectively, on this night he had made his affection and hope for my Reds apparent. His disappointment was clear as he reported, "With the Redlegs leading 9-4 after seven innings, it is likely they will only have one more at-bat to get the home runs needed to tie or break the record. But let's keep in mind that they lead the league front-runners by 5 runs and a win tonight will get them to within 1/2 game of the Braves. And now, a word from the Burger Brewing Company."

Everybody in my life was pacing at this point, with the exception of my mother. My father was in the bathroom. Jack Gates kept yelling across the side yard, first pulling for the Reds and then worrying about our bet. I half expected to see Big Al with a Schoenling in each hand, but he only had one (his 8th by my count).

Jack finally yelled to me, "Jiminy Crickets, this is killing me. I want them to break the record, but we have that darn bet."

I responded, "Holy mackerel, Jackie, forget the doggone bet. Let's root for the Reds."

Relieved, he smiled his thanks and then hunkered down next to their kitchen radio. I gave my Duncan a whirl, failing miserably to walk the dog. Too nervous for yoyo tricks, I sat down, cursed Burger Beer for interrupting the game and started to pray again.

Finally, the voice of Waite Hoyt brought us all back to the game. My father, decked out in his powder blue pajamas and his maroon silk bathrobe, came into my room and sat down on my bed. He rolled his eyes pointing to his bedroom. The message was that my mother just didn't get it.

There was tension in Hoyt's voice as he announced, "The Braves will bring Thomson, Bruton and Atwell to the plate here in the top of the eighth inning. Thomson has stepped into the batter's box as Jeffcoat went to his windup. Thompson took that slow breaking curve on the outside corner that Frank Dascoli called a strike. Thompson didn't like that call as he stepped out of the box and took a long look at Dascoli."

Three pitches later, the hero of the 1951 National League play-off game between the Giants and the Dodgers, was called out on strikes. Hoyt reported, "Well, that was a high fastball, a dangerous pitch to throw to Bobby Thomson. But he took that one and Dascoli called it strike three. Thomson had a few words with the umpire on that call before heading back to the dugout."

"That's a big one," my father said.

Apparently Bruton was thinking Dascoli was calling a big strike zone because Waite Hoyt advised us, "Bruton chased a breaking ball way outside and grounded a squibbler off the end of his bat right to Johnny Temple at second base. Temple made the easy throw over to Kluszewski for out number two."

Hoyt continued, "Toby Atwell, the number eight man in the Braves line-up has stepped into the batter's box. Now for those of you anticipating the Redlegs' half of this eighth inning, and I suspect you all are, the Redlegs will bring up the bottom of the order. That would be Alex Grammas, Roy McMillan and the pitcher Hal Jeffcoat. Needless to say, there is not a great deal of home run power in that group."

"After digging in, Atwell looked at a sweeping curve from Jeffcoat, way outside for ball one. Bailey fired the ball back to Jeffcoat as if to say, 'come-on, bear down out there.'"

"The next pitch from Jeffcoat was a fastball which Atwell lined right at Post in right field for out number three. That one was a can of corn for Wally. After this word from Burger Beer ,we will see what the bottom of the Redlegs order can generate in the bottom of the eighth."

I grabbed my yoyo. My father, seeing Big Al with his big paw on a Schoenling, decided he needed a Hudapohl. So off to the kitchen he ran, returning with a full glass of beer.

My mother yelled from her bedroom, "Harold, are you having another beer? You don't need any more beer tonight."

"Oh, pipe down in there. The kid and me are trying to listen to the ball game," he responded.

"Well you make that the last one, or you can sleep on the porch," she advised.

Ignoring her, I reasoned the obvious logic. That is exactly what my father did, saying to me, "They don't stand a chance with Grammas and McMillan coming up. Do they even have a homerun between them this year? And Tebbitts is such a knucklehead, he won't pinch hit for Jeffcoat. Oh, well."

I knew he was right. Yet there did seem to be a sense of destiny in the air on this special Saturday night.

Waite Hoyt came back on the air to report that Alex Grammas had come to the plate. Before you could say "Mighty Casey has struck out," Grammas hit what Hoyt described as a sharp groundball to Johnny Logan at shortstop.

"Well", Hoyt explained, "that one just handcuffed Logan, and the Redlegs have their leadoff man on first base and give an error to Johnny Logan."

This was a great sign, I reasoned, now expecting the weak-hitting McMillan to hit a homer. He did not. But the excitement in Hoyt's voice filled my room and the Gates' kitchen when he reported, "McMillan hit a line-drive single to right on the first pitch. Grammas wisely chose not to test Aaron's strong arm and stopped at second. The Redlegs have two on with no outs here in the bottom of the eighth, and that will bring pitcher Hal Jeffcoat to the plate, with everybody in the ballpark looking for a sacrifice bunt."

Hoyt continued, "Well, fans, the play here is to lay one down the third base line, if Jeffcoat can. That would force Matthews in. Jeffcoat did square to bunt, but took a fastball high for ball one. "After looking down to third for the signal Jeffcoat turned again to bunt. And, sure enough, he laid down the perfect bunt that hugged the third base line. A charging Eddie Matthews fielded the ball cleanly and threw Jeffcoat out at first. But

Grammas has moved over to third, while McMillan is now standing on second base," Hoyt reported.

My father polished off his beer, moving closer to the radio, while I inched nearer to the edge of the toy box. Dad said, "Temple has to get on. That will get Robinson and Klu up. Then there would be an outside chance for another homer."

The Reds feisty second baseman would battle to get on. I was sure of that.

Waite Hoyt described the action.

"The first pitch to Temple was low and away for a ball. Johnny added a little rosin to his bat and has stepped back in. The next pitch was on the inside corner for a strike. Now it is Conley's turn to play with the rosin bag behind the mound. The next pitch was made to Temple and he hit a hard liner to right, but Aaron was there and made the catch for out number two. Grammas, again, wisely chose not to test Aaron's arm."

Now my father and I were walking around my small bedroom trying not to bump into one another. The Gates were on their feet in their kitchen.

As Frank Robinson came to the plate, I turned my back to the radio. It was like being unwilling to watch the obvious. If Robinson made an out, this would turn into just another game, rather than something very special. I fully expected him to strike out. I was resigned. This was the Reds, after all. Great fun, but in the end, they always let me down.

I could visualize Robby dangling is bony elbows into the strike-zone as Connelly readied to make the first pitch. Then just like that, I heard Waite Hoyt scream in present tense, along with the crack of the bat, "That ball is tagged, and the Redlegs have home run number seven of this game. Well, Robinson took that one high up off the laundry beyond the left field fence for a three-run homer, his second of the night."

My father and I were screaming so loud my mother came in to digest all the commotion. However, when she saw the Gates waving from their kitchen window, she took a quick exit. Above all else, my mother was modest. Jack and Big Al were not supposed to see her in her night gown.

As the excitement settled a bit, Hoyt announce that Bob Thurman was coming to the plate.

"Well, the Redlegs now have twelve runs and seven round trippers on the evening as Bob Thurman steps to the plate. Normally relegated to pinch hitting, Thurman already has two homers this evening. Can he make it three? If so, the Redlegs would tie the modern-day record for home runs in a game."

Then Hoyt advised, "Fred Haney has decided to stick with Conley, although there is action in the Braves' bullpen down the right field line."

Could Thurman do it again, I wondered. Or if he just got on base that would give Big Klu a chance. That was our best hope.

Before Thurman got his chance, Hoyt ran another baseball factoid passed us. "With less than six weeks left in this season, I am reminded of the second to last game of the 1947 season for the New York Giants. On that day, Smokey Burgess, now with the Redlegs, hit a pinch hit homerun off the Cub's Sad Sam Jones, giving the Giants 221 homers for the season which stands as the major league record. Robinson's homerun was number 200 for the Redlegs this season. Could they be staring down another record?"

Then Hoyt went back to the action at Crosley Field. "The homer by Robinson cleared the bases with Grammas and McMillan scoring two unearned runs ahead of Robby. So, Conley will deliver to Thurman from a full wind-up. The first pitch was low for a ball. Conley has gone behind the mound to dust off with the rosin bag, as Thurman has stepped back in. Another bad pitch from Conley was taken outside for ball two."

My father weighed in, "Conley is one stupid son-of-a-buck, not pitching to Thurman. Can't he see Kluszewski in the on-deck circle?"

Conley must have been clued into my dad's logic because on the next pitch there was a deafening roar from the crowd. Hoyt let the 21,147 fans, assembled at Crosley Field that night, do the talking on this one. There was plenty of good old fashion hollering coming from the Stertmeyer and Gates households as well. As we continued to dance around my room, Hoyt remained quiet, the only sound coming from the radio was that of the cheering crowd.

Finally, Hoyt quietly stated, "Well ,the Cincinnati Redlegs have just tied the major league record for homeruns in a game. It came off of Big Bob Thurman's third round tripper of the game. And the Braves now must face Ted Kluszewski at the plate. Ted will have the opportunity to set a new record. But it will not come off of Gene Conley. Haney has headed to the mound tapping his left hand, and will be bringing in left-hander Dave Jolly to face Kluszewski."

After a quick reference to *10 visits the Burgerville* (8 by Cincinnati and 2 by Milwaukee), Hoyt went back to the action on the field.

"Dave Jolly has completed his six allotted warm-up pitches and will try to end the misery for Milwaukee. But you can betcha that Klu will be eyeing the right field bleachers."

That didn't happen, as Jolly threw four straight balls to Kluszewski. Hoyt laughed at the resounding boos that followed "ball four." Kluszewski trotted down to first base.

Hoyt's analyzed the action. "Well, I know Kluszewski is one of the most intimidating batters in this or any other league. But Wally Post will now come to the plate. The left-hander Jolly gave a free pass to the left-handed Kluszewski and now has to stare down the powerful right hand hitting Post. No bargain there." I was a big fan of Wally Post. He was an Ohio boy from the little town of Coldwater. I had played in a knothole all-star game there the previous summer and still remembered the sign on the edge of town that read:

Welcome to Coldwater Ohio
The Home of Wally Post
And
The Only Place in the World
Where
You Can Boil Eggs in Cold Water

So, as Post came to the plate, I was confident that he could deliver number nine and the record. I visualized the scene as Waite Hoyt reported the obvious. "There are more than 20,000 fans here at Crosley field and every one of them has been on their feet since this half of the 8th inning began."

You could definitely hear the din from the fans over the radio as Hoyt stated, "The first pitch to Post was high and inside for a ball. Atwell has given the signal to Jolly."

The next sound that came over the airways was a huge "OOOOH."

Hoyt reported, "Post took a big cut at that fast ball from Jolly, but missed. If he had connected with that one, it might have wound up somewhere downtown. Post has stepped out of the batter's box, but did not bother to look for a signal. He knows that Birdie wants him to take one long if he can."

We awaited Waite Hoyt's report on the next pitch.

"Well, Wally struck that one solidly for a line-drive single to centerfield. Kluszewski stopped at second. That will bring lefty, Ed Bailey to the plate."

So, the record came down to the Reds' catcher from Strawberry Plains, Tennessee. His down-home manner and solid hitting made him a fan favorite.

The anticipation was overwhelming. I stood there in my small bedroom with my father trying to will Bailey into a homerun swing. The whole evening came down to this. Could he do it?

My attention turn backed to the radio. Hoyt calmly reported the action repeating the question that lingered in my mind, "Can Ed Baily do the seemingly impossible here in the bottom of the 8th? The Redlegs have two out and two on as Bailey has stepped into batter's box. The first pitch was inside, but caught the corner for strike one. Bailey after stepping out and stretching has stepped back in eyeing the next pitch from Jolly."

"Do it, Ed, do it," I screamed at the radio.

And then, just like that, it was over as Hoyt announce. "Unfortunately, Ed may have been a bit too anxious on that one as he lifted a lazy pop fly just outside the third base line that Matthews easily settled under for the third out. So, after eight innings, the Redlegs lead by a score of 13 to 4. Sadly, I am afraid that the Burgerville is now closed for the evening. But the hometown nine has tied the major league record for homeruns in a game. Not so bad. And, now a message from Burger Beer."

The air kind of went out of the room at that point. I looked through my bedroom window to see a dismayed Jackie Gates and an angry Big Al Gates pop the top off another Schoenling. I had lost count but was sure Mr. Gates had scored more Schoenlings then the Reds had home runs. For a second, I thought about rooting for a Milwaukee comeback in the top of the ninth, so that the Reds could get another turn at bat. But that was ludicrous.

My dad said, "Well, they tied the record. I'm headed to dreamland kiddo."

Disappointed, I listened as Hal Jeffcoat set the Braves down 1-2-3 in the top of the ninth. The game was over. But as I listened to Waite Hoyt recap the action, I realized what an amazing gift my Reds and *School Boy* Waite Hoyt had given me that night. After running through the game's statistics, he reminded me, and all listening, what an extraordinary game we had just witnessed through his words.

Hoyt ended the broadcast by saying, "For the 22,141 fans here at Crosley Field and all of you listening here on Redlegs Radio, you have been treated to a very special game of baseball. The 1956 Cincinnati Redlegs stand just 1/2 game behind the Milwaukee Braves and have put in the books a game that may rank up there with the back-to-back no-hitters pitched by Johnny Vander Meer on June 11th and June 15th way back in 1938, in the annals of Cincinnati baseball."

Hoyt continued, "Tonight the Redlegs showed they have the stuff that could lead to their first National League Pennant since 1940. It was a magical evening. I hope you all enjoyed it as much as I did. And we will do it again tomorrow afternoon as the Redlegs take on these same Milwaukee Braves. This is Waite Hoyt wishing you a good night from Burger Beer."

With that, the strains of El Capitan lulled me into a deep and satisfying sleep.

The Crosley Radio

Waite Hoyt at the Mic

Jewel-studded Duncan Yo-Yo

The 1956 Reds

1956

For it's one, two, three strikes, you're out,
At the old ball game!

From *Take Me Out to the Ball Game*
By Jack Norworth (1908)

DON PERFECT

'Twas the fall of Fifty-six
The leaves were turning brown.
And for the fourth time in five years,
The Series would be held in a single town.

Now the Dodgers had finally won one
In Nineteen-fifty-five.
And with the way they were playing
Seemed fate, again, was on their side.

'cause Sal "The Barber" Maglie
Had tossed a no-hitter the week before.
And Da Bums had the same team from Fifty-five,
And were itchin' to win one more.

Sure enough, Game One went to the Dodgers,
The Barber was throwing darts.
He beat Ford and the pinstriped Yankees,
An early knife, right in their heart.

In Game Two, it just got better,
The Dodgers proving, they were no longer Bums
They bombed the damn Bronx Bombers,
And now had two games while the Yankees still had none.

Don Larsen lasted less than two innings,
He'd been unbeatable the month before.
Furillo, Reece and Snider were looking happy,
Brooklyn fans' hopes began to soar.

But, alas, it was Casey Stengle's Yanks
Against the Brooklyn Blue.
He still had some tricks up his sleeve,
His Yankees – they weren't through.

Game Three was at the *House that Ruth built*
And the Yankees proved their mettle.
'cause you just don't beat the Bombers two straight,
And they had a score to settle.

With Yogi, Billy, Gil and Mick,
The Yanks were tough up the middle.
And with Whitey back tossing the pill,
They finally solved the Dodger riddle.

For Game Four Smokey tried to get his guys smokin'
But at the Stadium, there's no place to hide,
Hank and Mick homered,
And, now the Series was tied.

Out in deep center field, as a stark reminder
Stood the monuments to Babe, Miller and Lou.
And as Mel Allen was quick to explain,
"After four, this here Series is brand new."

So, Dodger fan Mr. Bigler brought a TV
To school on this perfect October Monday.
'cause he knew his Bums would win Game Five,

And he wanted us to see each and every play.

It was hard to doubt their chances,
With "The Barber" back on the mound.
And he looked real sharp early,
Setting the first eleven Yankees down.

But Larsen, so bad in Game One,
Was out there throwing bullets as well.
And his control sure seemed laser sharp,
As Mel Allen was pleased to tell.

Yet, in the second inning,
Robinson lined a hard one down the third base side.
Off Carey's glove right to shortstop McDougal,
Whose throw beat Jackie by a stride.

In the bottom of the fourth,
Mickey came up to the roar of 64,000 fans.
And he rewarded their appreciation,
By hammering the second pitch into the right field stands.

With one out in the fifth,
Hodges hit an absolute rope.
But he hit it to the wrong place,
Mickey's backhanded grab ended the Dodgers' hope.

By the seventh with the shadow now in front of the plate,
And the autumn sky displaying an eerie hue.
Larsen had still given up no hits,
And Maglie only two.

But those two hits had led to two runs,

And now the fans would scream and shout
With each pitch Larsen made,
And, especially, every Dodger out.

The ninth started with Furillo up and Yogi said,
"This guy's got good stuff today."
Carl replied by going deep to right,
But Bauer was camping there and made the play.

Then a grinning Campy stepped in,
Not knowing his career was almost through.
He grounded weakly to Martin,
A quick toss to Collins, and that was two.

Smokey now called back Maglie,
Sending Darrell Mitchell to the plate.
The six of us transfixed on Bigler's TV,
So anxious we could hardly wait.

We watched in disbelief
As Mitchell took strike one.
He swung and missed the next pitch.
Now, this was really fun.

Larsen went to the resin bag,
Then rubbed his hand on his thigh.
Mitchell fouled one off,
That was just a little high.

We shifted and fidgeted and squinted
This was something we all wanted to see.
It was a fastball on the outside corner,
Babe Pinelli cried, "Strike Three!"

Yogi threw his mask into the air,
And dashed to the mound.
He jumped on a stunned Don Larsen,
As the crowd made a deafening sound.

Even old man Bigler
Cheered the sight on TV.
While Freddie and I danced around the room
In unadulterated glee.

The Dodgers came back the next day,
Winning by one in ten.
But the Yanks took Game Seven,
And were champs yet once again.

Yes, it was a perfect bright October day,
With Don Larsen on the mound.
And we all watched his perfect pitching miracle,
Worthy of a place in Cooperstown.

And as always is the case in fall,
October faded to November.
For those of us who saw that Series,
Don Larsen's all we'll remember.

Don Larsen Delivers - October 8, 1956

Don and Yogi Celebrate

1957

Knocked once
Tried to tell them I'd been there
Door slammed
Hospitality's been there
Wonder,
Just what's going on in there?

From *Green Door*
By Bob Davie and Marvin Moore

THE PEEK

I had finally reached the age where the walk home from anywhere in the dark of night had ceased to be spooky and frightening.

On this night, the crowd at the Cincinnati Gardens Ice Rink had been sparse, allowing me to *hot dog* with my few good high-speed hockey moves and great ice shaving stops. Proud as ever of the honor of wearing my *Ice Patrol* sweater, I was one of three *enforcers* on the ice. With me out there, no one dared to skate clockwise. All pranksters would have to deal with me. Yes, in my own mind, I was important.

Because being a new member of the ice police was such an ego boost, I usually left the Gardens after the 8:00-10:00 skate feeling fairly full of myself. Normally Wally and Carl worked the Friday night shift with me. Not so on this night. Actually, I was glad I was on my own. Without the two clearly better skaters, I was the kingpin for the evening, and therefore, feeling better than usual.

I exited the Gardens bundled against the harsh winter's chill not worrying about ghosts or evildoers, but rather, pondering the fact that the weekend lie ahead. With my gloved hands jammed deep in my coat pockets, I tried to get that silly Georgia Gibb song, *Dance with Me Henry,* out of my mind. It was one of the favorites of Tom Byron, the disc jockey who spun the 45's at the Gardens. It had long ago been decreed that skating was not fun without music. Generally, I subscribed to that theory, excepting Miss Gibbs and *Henry*. I finally gave in and began to whistle the despicable melody.

With the temperature in the mid-teens I opted for the most direct route home, that being through the upper and lower parking lots and then a quick dash behind the Swifton Village Apartments on Langdon Farm Road. This choice also took me past the south side of the Tremont residence, just four doors down the street from my house. Serendipitously, as I continued to whistle *Dance with Me Henry,* I turned my attention to the bedroom window of Anne and Susan Tremont. Just as I did the light went on.

Now understand, I was deep in the throes of advanced puberty and all that is implied with such a condition. Anne Tremont was two years older than I. Susan was two years older than her sister, meaning they were both pretty well developed. Curiosity got the better of me.

Instead of staying the course and heading directly home, I veered left toward the illuminated window. As I peeked through the half-inch space between the bottom of the Venetian blind and the window-sill I saw Susan Tremont only a few feet away.

Though I had seen her flirt with some of the older boys at school, what appeared before me now was a Susan Tremont with whom I was not familiar. She was in the midst of an exotic dance to the sounds of the current musical hit, *The Green Door.* Suddenly, *Henry* was no longer dancing in my head. Instead, Susan Tremont was dancing a very provocative striptease. Each button on her blouse that she unbuttoned evoked a growing response in me.

Why she was performing in such a manner, I could not say. What I do know is that I was getting a clear glimpse through a tiny opening in the forbidden *Green Door.* As she continued, it was as if she knew I was watching. But, of course, she didn't.

Before I knew it, she had removed every stitch of clothing, proving, as I had always suspected, that she was a true redhead. She seemed quite pleased with her performance, showing no propensity to stop until the music did. This was just fine with me.

Suddenly her act was ended by a determined knock on her bedroom door. As she grabbed for something to hold in front of her, she turned toward the door, as it swung open, giving me a perfect view of her perfect posterior. It also gave me a view of Mrs. Tremont coming through the door, as she demanded that Susan "turn down that terrible music."

The sight of Mrs. Tremont converted my teenage arousal into cold freight. I instantly did my imitation of Crazy Legs Hirsch, with the sound of Susan screaming at her mother fading with each step. A vision of doing jail time pushed me on as I took our front steps three at a time, my ice skates banging painfully off my right shoulder into my right ear.

I catapulted through the front door, scaring my poor Mother half to death, diverting her attention from the half-completed jigsaw puzzle spread out on the folding card table

"Randy, what in God's name are you doing? Are you trying to give me a heart attack? You're sweating like it's the middle of July. Did you run all the way home? Where do you get all of the energy?"

That was way too many questions to answer, so I just shrugged and headed to my room. After several minutes, I had calmed myself somewhat. I went to the kitchen, took a Barq's root beer from the icebox and popped the bottle cap with the opener Dad and I had recently attached to the side of the kitchen cabinet. Doing a 180-degree spin I attempted to catch the bottle cap behind my back before it dropped to the linoleum floor. This was a move I had been practicing with no success to date. When I felt the cap hit my left palm dead center, I squeezed. Success! The satisfaction of this small triumph over a Barq's root beer bottle cap helped to relieve the tension further.

I finally fell asleep that night with mixed visions of Susan Tremont's very naked body and my picture on the wall of the post office...*Crazed teen wanted in connection with peeping Tom incident.*

I awoke on Saturday morning with the feeling that I needed another opinion about what I had done. I reasoned that Carl Schiele, being the most levelheaded of my friends, would give me an objective opinion. More importantly, he could be trusted to keep his big trap shut.

I rushed through a breakfast of French toast sprinkled with sugar, noting as I gazed out the kitchen window that there had been a significant snowfall over night. Knowing my Mother had dental radar, I quickly brushed my teeth, pulled on my rubber boots and bundled up in my Pea jacket, wool gloves and cap. My Father was out front shoveling snow, which he actually enjoyed. Thankful for this flaw in his character, I asked if I could help. Laughing at my insincerity, he declined my offer and kept pitching shovelfuls of snow toward the curb.

When I described to him my victory over the falling bottle cap, my father replied, "Das ist gut," while giving me an encouraging slap on the back. Pleased with both the accomplishment and the paternal compliment, I headed toward the Schieles'.

The trek up to Carl's house took more effort than normal, given the six inches, or so, of snow combined with the up-hill grade of Grafton Avenue.

Sadly, for Carl, his father was not a snow worshipper. Thus, I discovered Carl was half way through his snow removal duties. Carl had great instincts, and recognized immediately that I was not there to help with the snow.

"So, what's on your mind?" he asked.

"Whadda mean?" I countered.

"Stert, something's up. I know you. What is it?"

It was time for true confessions. I knew I could trust Carl, so I swallowed the tiny bit of guilt I was feeling and spilled the beans.

"Well, you ain't gonna believe this, but on my way home from the Gardens last night I was walking by the Tremont's and the light to Anne's and Susan's bedroom came on and well..."

Carl was no longer working the shovel. He was all ears, and he clearly knew what was coming next. His eyes said, *Give me all of the gory details.*

"Jeepers Carl, I don't know what it was, but I just knew something was going on behind that window. I took a quick peak, and well, there she was doing this strip dance to *The Green Door.* I mean there's Jimmy Lowe singing and there's Susan, responding one button at a time. And the next thing I know there she was in her birthday suite. And I gotta tell ya, it's some fine suit. And then her Mom comes in the room, and I got the heck out of there. Man, I thought I was going to jail for sure. And..."

"Jeez, Stert slow down. You're leaving out all the good details. What did she look like? Does she have great knockers?"

"Yea, I guess so. I don't know. They looked great to me. And then I couldn't take my eyes off that red patch of hair."

"Well of course it's red, you knuckle-head. She's a redhead, ain't she?"

He pondered it all for a moment, "*The Green Door,* huh? Holly cow, do ya think she does that every night?"

"How the heck do I know? You think all I do is peek in windows?"

"Have you told anyone else?"

"Heck no!"

"Good. You can't tell Wally or Fred. They can't be trusted. When we go back..."

"Whata ya mean go back? I'm lucky Mrs. Tremont didn't see me last night. I'm not going anywhere near that house."

"Sure, we are. The fact she didn't see you just shows how safe it is. The light inside reflects off the window. There's no way they could see you. You've discovered gold, and we're going to mine some more of it."

I was beginning to think that I had made a huge mistake telling Carl about this. I could see that look of determination on his face. He would not be satisfied until he, too, carried a vision of a naked Susan Tremont in his mine's eye.

"Anne shares a room with Susan, doesn't she?" he asked. "I think she's even keener looking than Susan. Man, this is going to be great. We'll have to wait until all of this doggoned snow melts. Can't be leaving foot prints in the snow."

For the next two weeks, the only thing keeping me out of jail was the snow. Thankfully, it kept falling and falling. On the Monday and Tuesday following my secret glimpse of Susan Tremont in all her glory, school was cancelled for the first time in two years. Just as the snow began to melt, Tony Sands was reporting the probability of a weekend blizzard. Though he never got the weather right, this time the beak-nosed Channel 5 weatherman was right on target. I awoke on the next Saturday morning to discover the snow blowing sideways. While the adolescent in me craved another peek at Susan, I was thrilled with Mr. Sand's accuracy.

Carl, on the other hand, was as upset with the snow as any adult faced with driving in it. While the weekend was filled with the construction of snow forts, snowmen and snowballs, not to mention some of the best sled riding in recent memory, Carl was abnormally cranky. Only I knew the reason. He remained obsessed with Susan Tremont while Fred and Wally remained in the dark.

Three days later the snow stopped, but it remained frigid. Tony Sands advised that the bitter cold would last for several days. He proved to be uncharacteristically correct again. I'm sure Mr. and Mrs. Schiele must have become suspicious with Carl's recent obsession with the evening weather report. I knew this, because my parents began to wonder why he called every evening at 6:15, right after the local news and just as John Cameron Swasey was coming on the air with the national news. Interrupting John Cameron was something Harold Herbert Henry Joseph Stertmeyer would not tolerate.

As is always the case in Cincinnati, the weather inevitably changes and when it does so, it happens quickly. Thus, on the first Tuesday in February a warming trend began. By Wednesday afternoon the temperature had risen to near 60 degrees. By Thursday afternoon the only snow remaining was a miniature of the piles that had once stood at the curb. Carl was thrilled. I was as nervous as a knothole kid facing a Don Newcomb fastball.

Predictably, Carl had a plan. He reasoned that with us working the Ice Patrol on Friday night, the chances of catching the Susan and Anne Show between 10:00 (when we left Cincinnati Gardens) and 11:00 (our curfew time) was remote. Therefore, Saturday presented a higher probability of success. But we would need an excuse to ditch Wally and Freddy, especially if Wally's dad Bip offered to take us all to a movie.

Actually, I had an excuse. We were celebrating my Aunt Win's Birthday that night. Although we would be finished with dinner by 6:30, I did not have to point this fact out to Wally and Fred. Carl decided he would be grounded for talking back to his mother. Now, Carl never talked back to his mother. But that was to be the excuse he would give to Wally and Fred.

Having devised excuses for our friends, we still had to tell our parents where we were headed on a cold winter's night. The obvious thing was to tell them that Bip was taking us all to the movies, so we did. The plan was far from perfect, but lacking any better ideas we settled on this course. We could only hope that none of our friends or parents had any communication prior to, or soon after, the big event.

Saturday came, and with it returned the winter chill. We did catch one good break. Fred and Wally were indeed going to the Twentieth Century Theatre for a double feature. They were gone for the night. Thanks, Bip!

Carl's plan called for us to meet at Pasquale's at 6:40. We would circle back to Swifton Village where we would crouch down behind the garages adjacent to the Tremont's. There we could observe the bedroom windows of Susan and Anne Tremont. When a light came on, we would quietly scale the split rail fence and peek through the back window rather than the side window where this adventure had started weeks earlier. According to Carl, the back window provided much better cover from the street and the apartments next to the Tremont's' house.

I knew early into this that I had under dressed. Outfitted in only a long-sleeved shirt and my winter jacket I was freezing. Carl was so excited he didn't seem to notice that we were developing frostbite.

After about twenty minutes the light we were awaiting came on. My heartbeat seemed to double instantly. We moved into action, quietly taking a position beneath the window. As if by plan, the venetian blind had been left about one inch from the sill, offering an abundant view. As we rose in unison, we were rewarded with a view of Anne draped in a bathrobe and her hair wrapped in a towel. No sooner had we locked our gaze onto her, than she took off the robe to reveal, without question, that she was not a redhead.

I glanced at Carl. For the first time in my life I understood the phrase, *his eyes were popping out of his head*. I returned my attention to the action inside. Anne was a very attractive girl; even more so than her older sister. And for that matter more likeable. The latter fact was causing me to feel a great deal of guilt.

Unlike Susan, Anne did not provide a dance. Rather, she methodically went through the drawers of her dresser, selecting items of clothing, laying each selection neatly on the bed. When she had completed this process, she sat down and slowly positioned her bra in place, securing it somehow from behind. This was a process with which I had no familiarity. She then slid into her panties. This was followed by the positioning of some contraption that she put around her waist. I quickly discovered the purpose of this gadget. She pulled on nylons, the top of which she attached to the gismo around her waist. I was getting quite a view and quite an education.

Finally, she put on a blouse and skirt. She finished with an argyle sweater. There was more to come in the beautification of Anne Tremont and the education of Carl and Randy. Anne spent the next half an hour applying make-up, lipstick and fooling at great length with her hair. While I was intrigued with this process, I was also freezing.

I was just about to nudge Carl to suggest we go find some warmth, when Susan entered the room. Though a bit muffled, we could hear their conversation.

"Jimmy's here," Susan informed her sister.

I knew that *Jimmy* was Jimmy Goldblatt, a senior guard on the football team and Anne's boyfriend. In the parlance of Woodward High School, they were *pinned.* This meant that Anne wore Jimmy's Phi Epsilon pin on her abundant chest while Jimmy attached her Chi Sigma Delta pin to his shirt. It was kinda like being engaged to be engaged. And it clearly meant there would be some serious snoofing in Goldblatt's car later in the evening. Jimmy was one lucky guy I thought. And he would likely kill me if he had any idea what was going on in the Tremont backyard.

"Tell him I'll be right there, please," Anne asked Susan.

"Go tell him yourself! I have to get ready. Bob will be here any minute and I haven't even showered yet."

Bob would be Bobby Baldwin, Susan's steady boyfriend for the past two years. Bobby was a senior at Walnut Hills High School. He had been around the neighborhood a lot since he began dating Susan and had taken a liking to me, providing more guilt for me to digest as Carl and I continued to snoop.

Anne dashed from the room and Susan pulled the door closed behind her. We watched her walk over to her high-fi and place a 45-rpm record on the turntable. When I heard the strains of *Green Door,* I nudged Carl. However, Susan apparently did not have time for a strip tease this night. Instead she proceeded to rip her clothes off faster than you could say Gypsy Rose Lee. She then threw on a robe and disappeared out the door.

No longer able to feel my fingers or toes, I turned to Carl and said, "Let's get out of here while the getting's good."

"Not a chance Poncho! She's in the shower and she's coming back. If you don't want to stay for the finale, you can hit the trail and old Cisco here will fill you in back at the ranch."

"Ok, Ok. But I think we're pushing our luck."

As we awaited her return the window began to steam up. The available viewing space became smaller and smaller until it had been reduced to about a space of one-inch square, meaning we would have to take turns. Finally, during my turn, Susan came back into the room. She quickly dropped the robe. Her routine was less organized than that of her sister. She was a panties first girl.

Carl was getting impatient. He began to lean into me to push me aside, whispering a little too loudly, "Let me see will ya?"

With that, Susan turned toward the window. Seeing her attention headed our way, I quickly ducked beneath the window. Carl, thinking I was making room for him, pressed his eyeball to the viewfinder.

Suddenly I heard the shriek from Susan screaming, "Aha!!! Mother!!!" And I just about came out of my skin.

I bolted south clearing the fence in full stride as I caught a peripheral view of Carl scrambling up the rock garden in the back of the yard. I finally stopped running when I reached Murphy's at the far end of Swifton Shopping Center. I had no idea what Susan had seen or where Carl was. Certain only that there must be an all-points bulletin out on me, I tried to prepare for the inevitable interrogation by a Cincinnati version of Joe Friday. What would I say when he asked for "Just the facts?" I was doomed, all for a cheap thrill and my willingness to be a follower and not a leader.

I wondered around the shopping center until nine o'clock when the stores closed. My only choice now was to wonder down stairs to Pasquale's for a small $ .25 cheese pizza or a $ .15 garlic bread. I walked into our favorite Pizza Parlor to find a grinning Carl Schiele polishing off a $ .35 pepperoni pizza.

"Jeez, we're in big trouble," I said.

"The heck we are," said Carl. "I hung around up in the bushes in old man Graf's yards. They came out with a flashlight and looked around. Mr. Tremont kept asking Susan if she was sure she saw someone. He finally convinced her it was just her imagination. She took off with Bobby Baldwin a half an hour ago."

"Are you sure? I asked.

"Yea, no sweat. Man, those Tremont girls have great knockers, don't they?"

"Well I'm never going to lay eyes on them again. I'm out of the peeping business"

"Yea, we better lay low for a while. I wonder if the Wilkins twins leave their blind up like that."

"I don't know and I don't care," I assured Carl.

"Well, maybe you're right," he conceded. "We could get in a mess of trouble if we got caught."

When we left Pasquale's, we headed up Reading Road all the way to Dale Road and then back to Carl's house to avoid passing near the Tremont's.

Finally, I made it home. I had calmed down some, realizing I wasn't headed to jail. Yet, I was not feeling any real sense of relief. There remained a very uneasy feeling in me as I climbed into bed that night. As I lie in bed, I looked toward the two windows in my bedroom. I was in my little private space. Yes, *my private space*.

As Jimmy Lowe sings the song, "Door slammed, hospitality's been there."

Well, I no longer wondered, "Just what's going on in there?"

I learned a good bit that night. And it was more than a lesson in the female anatomy. What I really learned is that there are certain doors that you just shouldn't knock on. It was lesson about respect and what happens when you set that aside. Never again did I knock.

"The Green Door" by Jimmy Lowe

1957

Indoor fireworks
Can still burn your fingers
We swore we were safe as house
They're not so spectacular
They don't burn up in the sky
But they can dazzle or delight
Or, bring a tear when the smoke gets in your eyes

From Indoor Fireworks
by Elvis Costello

THE CONTEST

I hesitate to tell this story, given what is going on in the world at the moment. Yet, more than six decades after the fact, it is a yarn of an event in my life that provided a valuable lesson that has benefited me since. Thus, it should be told.

From the beginning, this was a deal that could only lead to trouble, but there was no denying its eventuality. The original scheme should be credited to my friend Wally Bohl. But it became Freddie Zigler's passion. It was never about doing damage. Rather, it was a simple reflection of the ongoing competitiveness that resides in normal teenage boys… and I guess we were all fairly normal. It was no different than contesting who could throw or kick a football further, or could run faster, or, for that matter, who could garner the interest of the prettiest girl. Naïve as it was, it was merely about winning.

Thanks to Wally Bohl and the fourth hombre in or little gang, Carl Schiele, we discovered early in the summer of 1957, how to make gun powder. Yes, gun powder. It was quite easy, as it turned out. Just the right mix of ground charcoal, abundantly available at the time due to the recent popularity of the charcoal grill, added to precise measurements of sulfur and saltpeter, and, voilà; gun powder. The latter two items, sold in medium size jars, were obtained by a mere five-block jaunt up to Lowenthal's Drug Store at the corner of Reading Road and California Avenue. If they were out of either ingredient, we would simply backtrack down Reading Road to Discepoli's Pharmacy at the corner of Dale Road, where, sadly, we would pay a little more and be tempted to drop a dime for a cherry coke at their soda fountain.

At first, Wally and Carl kept the newfound secret they had gleaned from the pages of "Popular Science Magazine," to themselves. But ultimately they needed a testing ground. The only choice for that was our little laboratory of mischief behind Freddie's garage, the scene of many past tests with 2 inchers (firecrackers) and Cherry Bombs (red, round, and considerably louder than firecrackers). Both Mr. and Mrs. Zigler worked at their hardware store in Northside, leaving the Zigler domain totally unsupervised Monday through Friday from 8:15 in the morning until at least 5:45 every afternoon, not to mention most Saturdays. So, needing a venue for this new tomfoolery, Wally and Carl decided to cut Freddie and me in.

As their first step, they brought the copy of "Popular Science" to the Gang's Club House. If Fred's backyard was our laboratory, my basement was our Club House. It had been designated as The Club House the previous summer due to the presence of my pool table, shuffle board table, good radio for listening to ballgames and my extensive Lionel train set up. Plus, it was always cool down there, even on the hottest days of summer.

And, as a gang, we were inspired by popular Cincinnati TV personality, Bud Chase, or "The Bean" as he was known to afternoon television fans. Our little foursome was modeled, in large part, after The String Bean and his gang, who, in turn, were fashioned in the manner of the old "Our Gang" of the silent movie days. String Bean's gang had a subterranean clubhouse just like my basement.

The Bean's Clubhouse was always a hoot. Our band of hooligans tuned in regularly at 4:00 in the afternoon on Channel 9. The Bean's principal cohort was an overweight Channel 9 studio staffer named Lee Fogel, who played a wound-tight kid named Louie Swoboda, aka Louie the Louse.

When The Bean wasn't making fun of the rest of the world, delivering commercials for items that were bad for kids or answering fan mail, he ran Laurel and Hardy shorts, or *Crusader Rabbit* and *Jim and Judy in Teleland* cartoons, as well as a weird series called *The Chimps* that featured monkeys in Sherlock Holmes-type costumes.

Bud Chase closed each show at an upright piano playing *That Old Gang of Mine,* in the style of the great Fingers O'Toole. We too had a piano, my mother's Baldwin baby grand, which held a prominent spot in our living room. Wally and I often sat at its ivory keys and banged out elementary tunes, including a duet of *Heart and Soul.*

Thus, it was to our gang's cool, below grade clubhouse that we assembled on a hot July day to learn about gun powder. We all peered over Wally's shoulder as he read from the magazine.

"Gunpowder is an explosive mixture. Its most common formula, called 'black powder,' is a combination of saltpeter, sulfur, and carbon in the form of charcoal. While the relative amounts of the components can vary, an increase in the percentage of saltpeter (potassium nitrate) quickens the speed of combustion. The most common formulation uses 1 part sulfur, 1 part saltpeter and two parts finely ground charcoal."

Wally continued, "In the past, gun powder was widely used for blasting and for propelling bullets from guns but it has been largely replaced by more powerful explosives. Another form of powder containing potassium chlorate instead of the nitrate that is commonly used in fireworks and in matches. The origin of gun powder was probably Chinese, for it seems to have been known in China at least as early as the 9th century where it was used for making firecrackers."

"Every damned thing in the world is either made in China or Japan," Fred butted in.

Wally and Carl both struck looks at Freddie that said, *shut up and listen.*

Wally went back to the magazine. "There is some evidence suggesting that gun powder first came to Europe through the Arabs. Roger Bacon was long credited with inventing it because a formula for making it is given in a work attributed to him. Yet, some German scholars have attributed its invention to the alchemist-monk Berthold Schwarz. However, it is now generally agreed that gun powder was introduced and not invented in Europe in the 14th century. Its use revolutionized warfare and ultimately played a large part in the alteration of European patterns of living up until modern times. Gun powder was the only explosive in wide use until the middle of the 19th century, when it was superseded by nitroglycerine-based explosives."

At that point, we had all had enough of the history lesson, preferring to proceed to Freddie's backyard to try our luck as chemists.

We had long ago built a small fire pit behind the Ziglers' garage. This is where we went to smoke dried reeds broken from bushes in Freddie's backyard or, more recently, Lipton tea emptied from tea bags into corncob pipes, also available at Lowenthal's pharmacy. With this new discovery for the formulation for gun powder, we were soon making Roman candles (a Coke bottle filled with the dusty powder and a gauze wick). When lit, it would shoot a sparkly flume 4-5 feet into the air. Or, worse yet, we would fashion small pipe bombs out of small 1/2" pieces of copper pipe stolen from Northside Hardware by Freddie, filled with powder and both ends hammered shut, ends bent back. If you threw that baby into our little campfire you could get quite a bang. Yes, we were coming closer to blowing ourselves up than we could possibly imagine.

It was only natural that, as our flame-induced explosions became louder, someone would throw down the gauntlet. One sunny Tuesday afternoon in early August, Wally suggested that a contest was in order. We were to pick teams of two each to see who could devise the loudest bang or bomb, if you will. To assure he would win, he mandated the teams. His bomb-mate would be Carl, leaving the improbable alliance of Freddie and me. Fred glommed onto this proposal with his typical gusto. He knew what Wally was thinking. Fred and I would not stand a chance against the two honor students.

"Well, we will show them," Fred later advised me. "We may not be stars in the classroom, but we were fearless."

It had been deemed that the contest would be held at 8:30 PM on the following Saturday, giving the two teams four days to design their entries. Just one rule was agreed upon. No pipe-filled objects were permitted. We had learned our lesson a couple of weeks earlier when we threw an oversized gun powder-filled copper pipe into the fire. As always, we ran like banshees around Freddie's garage to the front side, assuming the one car contraption would act as a sufficient bomb barrier. This time, with fingers in ears, the three of us waited, knowing we were safe. When that baby exploded more loudly than anything we had devised, it took off several small limbs of a pin oak in the Zigler's backyard and landed a street over, some 200 feet from its origin in the fire.

The big bang also caused Mrs. Block, who live directly behind the Ziglers, to come running. That put an end to pipe bombs. But the scare that the big explosion had put into all four of us was tempered significantly by watching Mrs. Block try to run. Her gait was something between a turkey waddle and a hippo prance. Fred felt the turkey version was more accurate and from that point forward referred to Mrs. Block as "Tommy Trotter."

We agreed that we would conduct the respective explosions in the woods behind the garages in Swifton Village. The Swifton Apartments were a string of three-story red brick buildings built shortly after the war. They covered several blocks starting just down Grafton Avenue from my house. Adjacent to the southwest end of the complex, and within 50 yards of Fred's house and mine, there were two-plus acres of thick woods that provided cover for some of our most serious mischief. Holding the contest in the woods would reduce the chance of getting caught. It was also sufficiently removed from Mrs. Block's prying eyes and ears. Starting a forest fire never entered our minds.

On a very hot Thursday in August, seeking a breeze, Freddie and I took our planning session out to my front porch glider. With the contest just two days away, we had to come up with a plan immediately so that we could run a test the next day. The first step for Fred and me was to take inventory of our cache of bang-making materials. Freddie and I had each purchased a good supply of firecrackers and cherry bombs from Wally after his father, Bip, had driven him to Kentucky to stock up. Such things were illegal in Ohio. While Fred was certain that Wally had overcharged us, I had a less cynical view and appreciated the shipping service provided by Bip Bohl.

Between Fred and myself, we had ten 20-count packs of 2" firecrackers, the same number of 1½ inchers, plus 33 cherry bombs. The real challenge was to devise a way to get a single big bang versus a string of small bangs. In the past, we would light a whole string of firecrackers, and the result would be a sequence of twenty quick back-to-back explosions, sort of like machine gun fire.

As mentioned, the only barrier to our regular Zigler backyard monkey business was snoopy old Mrs. Block, or "Tommy Trotter" as she was now known. The divorced mother of a very weird Marty Block spent an inordinate amount of time spying from her kitchen window on the next street over. Our little fire pit at the rear of the Ziglers' wood shed garage was only slightly hidden from her view by the summer milk weed vines growing on the chain link fence that separated the Zigler home from the Block abode. Given the boom volume we were seeking, Fred and I decided it would be best to avoid old lady Block during our test run.

After considering several possibilities, we decided to use the basement garage at my house. We reasoned that the block walls of the garage and basement would sufficiently muffle the anticipated explosion. And, with my mother working at Maternity Modes in the Swifton Shopping Center every Friday, the coast would be clear for a test.

With our test site decided upon, we set out to design our contest entry. As stated, we struggled with the problem of getting a single "boom" rather than a long stream of "bangs" out of our strings of firecrackers. We reasoned that we must devise some sort of trigger that would accomplish this.

I first suggested that we build a fire and throw our contraption into it. Freddie responded, "For criminey sakes, Stert, don't be such a Schmoe, we always do that in my backyard, and we get a tommy-gun effect, not an atom bomb. Plus, you can't build a cockamamie fire in your garage. Do you want to burn the damned house down?"

He had a point.

"OK, already. You're right. But there must be a solution."

As we sat on the front porch glider gazing out onto Grafton Avenue, gently rocking forward and back, both in deep thought, nothing came to either of us. I suggested we go to our basement clubhouse. Down there, we moved the pants stretchers off of the pool table and began rolling pool balls across the table to each other.

Fred finally exclaimed, "Jeesel Pete, Stert, I've got it. If we can't use the fire pit in my backyard, let's create one we can use in your garage!"

He continued, "What if we built a fire in a box and then covered it with a shield of some kind that would put it out immediately after the doggone thing blew up?"

I contemplated what he was proposing. Finally, I digested his proposal, and now my mind was racing.

Now it was my creative juices in action as I spoke my thoughts out loud, "OK. What if we were to line a cigar box with cotton and then layer in our firecrackers and cherry bombs? We could soak the cotton with lighter fluid and use a string wick like we have in your backyard. Except this time, we could cover it with my dad's cement tray. You know, the one he uses to mix concrete in. We make a long wick. Then we light it, cover the cigar box with the tray and skedaddle up the steps and wait for it to go off. Whaddaya think?"

Fred was silent for more than half a minute before he responded, "What if the cigar box catches on fire?"

"With the tray over it, any fire would go right out. Right? And we could put a garbage can on it to hold it down. Heck, as an added precaution, we could connect the garden hose to the laundry tub over there," I said, pointing to the deep basin that my mother used to drain our round, free-standing washing machine with its rolling wringers.

More silence from Fred as he noodled my description of things. He finally responded, "OK, I get it. So, when can we run a test in the garage?"

I thought for a second then said, "Well, tomorrow is test day, because my mom works all day at Maternity Modes, and the coast will be clear."

My mom had recently taken a part-time job at a store in the new Swifton Shopping Center that catered to pregnant women, selling nothing but maternity wear. After my father was passed over for a hoped-for promotion at Fifth Third Bank, my mother decided she needed to get a job. Employment at Maternity Modes two days a week became the result after much contentious debate between my parents. But that's another story.

"OK," I continued. "Let's see how we can rig the cigar box."

With that, I headed up the basement steps with Freddie in tow. I checked on my mother who was visiting with Mrs. Gates next door... great timing. We went into my bedroom, and I emptied an Ibold cigar box that contained my bag of marbles. It also contained all of my firecrackers and cherry bombs.

Next, I went to the bathroom, where I reached for a large Johnson and Johnson box of cotton that sat unused in the bathroom closet. With the cigar box, cotton box and explosives in hand, Freddie and I headed back down the basement stairs.

I ran into my dad's little workshop and yanked a ball of string form the bottom drawer of his self-made wooden tool chest. We laid our cache of bomb goods out on the pool table. Only one important ingredient was missing.

I ran back upstairs to the small humidor that sat next to an easy chair in front of the living room window, where my father kept his small collection of pipes. Four stood up on the left side in their hollowed out sitting spots on the base of the pipe rack, stems neatly held in place by small holes above. Three more sat in similar fashion on the right side. It was easy to identify his favorites by the gnarly teeth marks in the stems. In the center of the humidor was a small cabinet door, behind which my father stored pipe tobacco, pipe cleaners, matches, a couple of zippo lighters and most importantly two small cans of lighter fluid. I grabbed the can that was new, and thus full of the needed liquid and sprinted back down the steps to the basement.

We now had everything in the prescribed recipe. Now we went to the storage room at the front end of the basement, under my parent's bedroom. Here we found a medium sized box holding Christmas lights, into which I stuffed our cache. This was a perfect hiding place. It was unlikely that anyone would show any interest in the box until December, which was four months off.

Now all Freddie and I had to do was wait for Thursday to turn into Friday and my mother's ten o'clock departure for work.

The balance of Thursday was routine. Freddie and I went upstairs and turned on the TV just in time to catch our pal String Bean and his gang on Channel 9. Like clockwork, as The Bean was going off the air, we heard the ding, ding, ding of Nick, the ice cream man, coming down the hill toward us. After once again determining that Nick had no tutti fruity popsicles, Fred and I both settled on grape. We then occupied the middle of Grafton Avenue in front of my house tossing a baseball until it was time to head a street over to Newfield Avenue where we were having dinner with my Aunts Win and Lois as well as Uncle Joe and cousins Paul and Rick. My Aunt Lois was making her famous chili and spaghetti.

I walked over to the Newfield house, the back of which was clearly visible from the front of our house. A quick dash through the side yard of Adams house and a small leap over the short wire fence that stood as an ineffective barrier, and I was in Aunt Win's backyard. My mother had taken our pale green '51 Chevy up to the bus stop at the corner of Reading Road and Portman Avenue to collect my father when he jumped off the #37 Elbron-Price Hill -Bond Hill-Roselawn bus.

No sooner had I cleared the fence than my seven-year-old cousin Paul appeared out of the back door with basketball in hand. At his age, he couldn't dribble and couldn't shoot. Other than that, he was showing great promise.

My Aunt Lois and Uncle Joe had just returned from three years in Germany the previous March. They had exited the train at the Norwood Train Station with Paul and two-year-old Rick in tow. It was the first time we had laid eyes on Rick, who was born in a Military Hospital between Garmish and Munich. They moved in with Aunt Win, displacing my mother's Uncle Hal Loewenstine, who had been renting a room from Aunt Win for over a year.

Both Rick and Paul had glommed on to me, like the badly needed older brother they had been told about while in Germany. And I enjoyed having a couple of "younger brothers" who lived elsewhere, thus not invading my space.

It was a full table on this Thursday as Uncle Hal showed up, as did Aunt Win's ex-husband Bill Sutton. Uncle Bill was always welcome at our dinner table as long as he showed up sober. And sober was not a natural state of being for him at 6:00 PM. On this day, he clearly had avoided the bottle and was welcome to throw back some chili.

It was a great Thursday evening with Uncle Joe telling about how he was almost killed while helping the Italians defend Trieste from the aggression of Marshall Tito of Yugoslavia in early 1953, and my father telling us all, once again, how he was almost killed at least ten times while at sea during World War II.

Uncle Bill had no war stories, as he had been a bit to old and was also missing parts of two fingers, both disqualifying him for service during the war. But despite his digit deficiency, he sat down at the Baldwin upright after dinner and played some old standards like "Roll Out the Barrel," "That Old Gang of Mine" and "Peg of My Heart" with great style and gusto. Had he and my father realized what really great people they were when sober, neither of them would have taken another drink. Unfortunately, such was not the case with either one of them.

We didn't know it at the time, but this was the last time we would hear Bill Sutton play that old upright in my aunt's living room. His liver lost its battle with the booze later in the year, and he passed away shortly after his 57th birthday.

I woke up Friday morning with the sun peeking through my bedroom window and to the sound of the garbage man hauling our trashcans from the backyard to the curb. After a quick bowl of Cheerios, I brushed my teeth, threw on some jeans and a blue tee shirt and headed out the back door and up the hill through the Graft's yard to Freddie's house on Laconia Avenue.

We killed some time with a couple of games of Horse in his backyard. As required by law, and in my life, my mother was the law, we headed back to my house to report in before she left for work. Fred and I endured the standard speech about behavior, eating a proper lunch and then some more about behavior. On this particular morning, our promise to behave was a bigger lie than normal.

With my mother headed in the direction of Swifton Shopping Center, Fred and I were now free to assemble our contest prototype. We retrieved our little kit from the basement storage room and went about our task with diligence, as if working on the next iteration of the hydrogen bomb. First, we carefully layered about a quarter inch of cotton into the bottom of the Ibold cigar box. I then lightly soaked the cotton with lighter fluid.

Once we were certain the fluid wasn't seeping out of the bottom of the box, Fred layered in two rows of 1-1/2 firecrackers, six per row. Another layer of cotton was added, again lightly soaked with lighter fluid followed by a second packet of 1-1/2 inchers.

Yet another coating of soaked cotton was put in place. Now, for the **pièce de résistance:**

to enhance the bang value, the top layer would consist of two rows of 2-inch firecrackers laid into the center of the cotton and a cherry bomb in each corner.

The only thing left was to assure an effective system to guarantee a successful ignition of our little treasure. Using an old pick from my father's workshop, I punched a small hole in the Ibold box near one of the cherry bombs. The wick of the selected cherry bomb was poked through the hole exposing about two-thirds of the wick. While I was doing this, Fred was cutting off a six-inch piece of string for our "time wick."

Our explosive device was now complete and ready to test. Next, we went half way up the basement steps and out the back door, taking a right on the pad of concrete next to the retaining wall that held our back yard three feet above the pad. With two quick right turns, we stood beside the water tap halfway down the side of our house. I carefully unscrewed the hose from the tap, taking care not to disturb my father's prized rose bushes.

Making sure none of the Gates family next door was spying on us, we dragged the hose back to the rear door and hauled it to the basement. We quickly attached the hose to the laundry tub waterspout and extended the 50-foot hose across the basement, dropping the nozzle next to the door that led to the garage.

Fred, using more caution than was necessary, carried the bomb to the garage. My father's metal cement mixing pan stood upright against the far side of the empty garage. I grabbed it while Fred retrieved the small ash can that sat next to it. With the bomb situated in the center of the garage, we looked at each other for confirmation that we were ready to run our test. My stomach was churning with concern. I think Freddie's was as well.

Fred carefully laid the piece of string across the exposed cherry bomb wick while I knelt next

to him, matches in hand. I struck a match and laid the flame to the end of the string Fred held out toward me. The string took the flame, and Freddie quickly blew it out. As always, the string continued to smolder.

We quickly put the pan over the bomb and situated the ash can on top of the pan. Our work was done. We sprinted from the garage through the basement and up the stairs into our kitchen. The two of us headed for the piano bench in the living room with a commitment as if that had been the plan. Without thinking about it, this placed our two young asses directly above the bomb.

And there we sat. With our backs to the piano, we waited and waited and waited, too afraid to move. Neither of us spoke, being too busy holding our breath. After at least five minutes, Freddie finally broke the silence.

"What the Sam hell is going on down there? The doggone thing should have gone off by now."

I know, I responded. "Do you think we should go look?"

He didn't want to answer. And I was in no hurry to journey to the garage only to be blown up. We sat in silence for another couple of minutes until Fred said, "Well, shit-fire, I can't stand this. I'm going down there." Without much commitment, yet knowing my manhood left me no choice, I said, "OK. Let's go."

Down the stairs we went. We walked slowly over to the garage door, each of us waiting for the other to open it. Finally, I reached out and cautiously turned the knob. I opened the door and peeked inside. Everything stood there just as we had left it.

I reached the ash can and lifted it off the pan. Fred, finally showing great courage, lifted the tray with his head turned away from the impending threat of losing it. The bomb sat there undisturbed. The string wick had burned out, displaying only a slightly black char where we had lit it. It finally hit me. We had snuffed the oxygen needed for the string to smolder by covering it with the pan. I ran this theory past Fred who looked relieved to still have his head and all of his fingers.

Without much enthusiasm, he said, "Yea, maybe that could be it. Now what?"

I quickly responded, "Simple. We just put a small stick under one end of the pan to allow a little air to keep the string smoldering."

"What the heck. It can't hurt to try. I just want to get this over with. Let's give it a shot."

I went back into my dad's workshop while Fred prepared a new piece of string, deftly using his two-blade Hammer Brand pocketknife to cut a six-inch length. I dug through various bins in the workshop until I found two identical pieces of wood. I had surmised I needed two pieces to be sure we didn't have to deal with a wobbling pan.

Equipped with what we needed, Fred and I hastened back to the garage. With less enthusiasm than with the first try, we went about repeating the process. As Fred lowered the pan, I slid the two thin pieces of wood strategically into place. Fred, in a great rush, placed the ash can on the tray.

This time we sprinted even faster to our spots on the piano bench, still failing to recognize that we sat directly above our experiment.

As before, we waited and waited. Fred softly breathed the words, "Holy cow, this isn't going to work, is it?

Before I could agree, I was lifted up from the piano bench. Later we both agreed that we felt the explosion before we heard it. But what we heard was much more forceful than what we felt. Even with wood and lath and plaster between us, Fred and I heard a bang well beyond anything we had ever devised in his backyard fire pit. No CO2 capsule and no pipe bomb in our past could match the

"KAAAAAABOOOOOOOM!!! we heard on that August Friday afternoon.

We sat back on the bench wondering what to do next. Finally Fred reacted, "Holy Shit, Stert. We need to get down there. What if the house is on fire?"

We rushed to the basement to be met with smoke coming at us up the steps. Next, the smell hit us. I instinctively opened the back door. Later I realized that might have proven to be a mistake, as it could have provided a draft for a fire. We forged ahead into the smoke-filled garage. No trace of flames was evident. I quickly raised the garage door expecting to find the whole neighborhood outside. There was not a soul in sight.

I turned back to Freddie, who stood in the middle of the garage assessing the damage. As the smoke lifted, we could see the cement pan on the side of the garage and the ash can on its side at the other end of the garage. There were charred pieces of cotton and Ibold cigar box everywhere. I peeked out the garage, amazed not to see a single neighbor.

Fred and I looked at each other, and we both broke into a nervous uncontrolled laughter. We checked the ash can and cement pan for damage. The only flaw we found was an almost invisible burn spot on the pan.

"You have to be kidding," Freddie screamed at me. "No fire, no damage to the can, no damage to the cockamamie pan, no broken garage door windows."

As he finished his rant about our good fortune, I heard from behind me, "Boytz. Vat vas dat noiseee I heered? Is you boytz all ret?"

It was our next-door neighbor, the Jewish widow, Mrs. Kaufmann. She and the late Mr. Kaufmann had immigrated to the United States from Germany before the first World War. They had settled in the very German Cincinnati and raised three children. Their eldest, Saul Kaufman, was stricken with polio as a child and walked with a serious limp. He still lived at home and worked as a pharmacist. Her younger children, Maureen and Max, had jobs and had long ago moved out.

Collectively, the Kaufmanns were about the best neighbors you could hope for. All three kids were friendly and welcoming when we moved next door in 1953. Mrs. Kaufmann was a sweet, engaging lady who had taken an immediate liking to me. Her only drawback was her thick German accident which made her difficult to understand.

Once in a while, she would revert back to Yiddish as she had standing outside my garage door. "Oy, dershrokn," she mumbled. Fred laughed and whispered to me, "She said she was frightened in Yiddish." Then he laughed again and said to me, "She was frightened and I was scared shitless!"

It looked like our only problem at the moment was containing my Jewish neighbor who continued to babble in Yiddish.

"Look Mrs. Kauffman," I began. "As you can see, everything is all right. Freddie here and I were working a little chemistry project. But we have learned our lesson. No more chemistry at home… I promise."

This sweet old lady got it. She had raised three children of her own. She reached out and squeezed my cheek and said, "Vell, vee vill zee abot dat chimest-ry oft yours, you lettle mieskeit. Boot, no mort oft diss chimest-ry. Okey-doke?"

Fred came right back, "You betcha Mrs. Kaufmann… No more Chemistry." Mrs. Kaufmann turned on her heels and headed home.

Then I heard Freddie say, "Oh, oh."

"What do you mean Oh, oh and what is a mieskeit?" I asked.

"Well, 'Meiskeit" means ugly little person. But she's a Yenta and meant it in a nice way. *Oh, oh* means you better take a look at this," he said pointing to the garage ceiling.

I walked to where he was standing and looked to where he was pointing. There was a chunk of plaster about 2 inches in diameter missing from the ceiling. Oh, oh was right.

Finally, a dose of reality must have hit Fred as he announced, "Well, not a damned thing you can do about that. Do you think old lady Kaufmann will keep her big trap shut? At any rate, we need to clean this garage up."

I looked out the garage door once again. The smoke had dissipated, and there was no sign that anyone other than Mrs. Kaufmann had a clue as to what had happened in my garage.

We got hard at work in cleaning up the garage. We were smart enough to collect all of the debris in a paper grocery bag and haul it to the woods behind Swifton Village. The spot where we had anticipated holding the bomb contest ultimately became the burial plot for our experiment gone wrong.

Around 3:30 that afternoon, Fred and I had thoroughly cleaned up our mess and returned the hose to its proper place. The only evidence of the ill-advise test was the small chunk missing from the garage ceiling. I was convinced my father would be asking me about that before the sun set.

We would have to tell Wally and Carl about our test and advise them that we were getting out of the bomb making business. We would concede victory to them, even though we were sure the explosion we had fired off in my garage would have been a clear winner.

We found Wally and Carl in Wally's unattached garage tinkering with the 1952 Chevy Bip Bohl had purchased for his 14-year-old son. Bip had reasoned that by the time Wally could drive, he would know that car inside out and have something safe to drive. Carl and Wally both loved working on that pile of junk. Fred and I had little use for such things.

We gave our two friends a blow-by-blow account of our bombastic adventure, including my Yiddish-filled exchange with Mrs. Kaufmann. If they had any doubt about our story, they could visit my Jewish neighbor and dig up the evidence in the Swifton Village Woods.

Wally and Carl still planned to set off their entry the next night. Fred and I wished them good luck and vowed to be in Chicago at the time.

As it turned out, they did go through with exploding their bomb, leaving a big crater in the floor of the woods, raising a great deal of commotion from residents of two buildings in Swifton, one of whom summoned the fire department.

Fred and I wisely spent almost two hours at Pasquale's Pizzeria nursing a medium pepperoni pizza and making sure we had an alibi disassociating us from Carl and Wally that night.

When the final dust had settled, all four of us, in spite of our outrageous stupidity, escaped the entire process unscathed.

I waited for weeks for my father to ask about the garage ceiling. When my parents finally moved from that glorious little Cape Cod in 1967, the missing chunk still hovered over the family car, forever undetected.

There is no such thing as a perfect crime. In early December of 1957, with a newly purchased Scotch Pine Christmas tree sitting in the living room, my mother dug into a box of bubble lights that she and I loved so much and pulled out a cherry bomb. Whoops!

Popular Science
February 1956

Ibold Cigar Box

1957

You gotta be a football hero
To get along
With the beautiful girls

From *You Gotta be a Football Hero*
By Al Sherman, Buddy Fields and Al Lewis

FIRST SNAP

The sound of my name snapped me out of my fixation on Bonnie Shaffer, cheerleader extraordinaire. The second time I heard it more clearly. "Stertmeyer, do you want to play football or sit there and watch?"

I bolted from the bench, still disbelieving my ears. Coach Castelli was putting me in. What was he thinking? He was putting me, a sophomore, into a football game. I sprinted toward the huddle before he had a chance to reconsider his folly. Clearly, he had lost his mind. Not only had he put me into the game, but there was Ziggy Fritz facing the ten of us, calling the play. The coach had just put in a second-string halfback and a third-string quarterback. Yea, Castelli had gone mad.

Fred looked me straight in the eye and called my number. "Forty-two counter right on two. That's forty-two-counter right on two. Ready, break!" Forty-two counter right - that was me (*four* for left halfback and *two* for the 2-hole, meaning run over the right guard).

Holy mackerel, I thought. This was happening too fast. Here we were, half way through the third quarter of the first game of my sophomore year, down 20-0, and they expected me to run the ball.

My knees wobbled as we broke from the huddle. We were in a "full-house backfield" alignment, meaning we were in a straight T-formation. Fred was under center, with Wally Bohl four yards directly behind him, at fullback. I was to Wally's left and Bob Stumpf was equal distance to his right. We went through the routine we had practiced maybe a million times since the start of summer practice on August 20th. Wally, Bob and I stretched our arms to both sides, fingers almost touching to establish the proper alignment. This gave me a perfect view of our left guard Bobby Nebolski's butt as he went to his three-point stance.

My heart was pounding so hard I could feel the impact on my shoulder pads as Fred began to bark signals.

"Ready - Blue - Fifty-three This means *ready* as in, I'm not ready. *Blue* for Woodward blue and white, rah, rah, rah. And *53*, meaning there were five Hughes players at the line of scrimmage and three more at the linebacker positions, all eight seemingly looking right at me.

Fred repeated the call, Blue - Fifty-three - Hut - Hut. On the second hut, Bob Kingsbury snapped the ball to Fred. Bohl and Stumpf sprinted left. Fred turned left from center. I, as choreographed, took one abbreviated step to the left and then countered back to the right at a 45-degree angle, keying on the back side of Steve Metzcar, our right guard, and away from the flow.

The scheme called for everyone on the line to the left of our right tackle to block their man back to the left. The right tackle and end were to block their men to the right. This enabled the defensive man opposite Metzcar to come through. But Nebolski was supposed to cut back to the right inside of Ziggy Fritz and clobber that guy as he came through. This is known as a trap play, where the pulling guard was to surprise the hopefully dim-witted opponent whom we have baited with the trap.

As I watched all of this develop in front of me, Fred laid the ball in my breadbasket as I gained speed. The huge hole that was to be cleared for me to sprint through never developed. Instead of a hole, what I saw was something akin to the Rock of Gibraltar. Nebolski hit the wall first, and then the wall crashed into me. I was smothered by what seemed to be the entire Hughes team, followed by the brass section of their band.

Now buried by a mass of humanity, fighting desperately to retain the pigskin, I was punched, kicked and scratched as I felt the pressure of even more weight being added to the mountain on top of me. I assumed that it must be their cheerleaders now piling on in retribution for me lusting after Bonnie Shaffer. And just in case the physical pain wasn't enough to get my attention, the guy closest to me had some unkind words about my parentage. So, this is high school football, I thought.

I'm proud to say that I held on to the ball. From above me, I heard one of the officials blow his whistle and then say, "OK, OK. That's it boys. Use the ground to get up."

I must have looked like the ground to each and every Hughes player. First a hand pressed my helmet to the dirt beneath me. Then a cleated shoe came down on the back of my right hand. I gritted my teeth but refused to let out the scream of pain welling up in my throat. Finally, with every one off of me, I used the ground to get up.

I looked up to see Tommy Johnson trot onto the field. "You're out, Stert," he said with a wry smile.

As I jogged off the field, I quickly noted a cheering Bonnie Shaffer, the large white *W* glaring at me from her protruding blue sweater. It was a painful and ominous start to my high school football career. I hate forty-two counter right, I thought to myself. How about calling *twenty-two counter left*. Let Stumpf get stomped.

1958

Now who's that babe with the fabulous shadow?
It's only one scene, but to me it don't matter
Her movies get down like you won't find in my hometown
They won't believe it when they see what they're seein'

From *Dirty Movies*
By Van Halen

My Projector

Mark Morris had been baiting our little gang for more than two weeks in the summer of 1958.

"My dad has this dirty movie in his closet tucked in the pocket of his tuxedo," he continued to insist.

"But we don't have a projector. Otherwise, I'd show it to you guys."

Freddie Zigler piped in, "Bullshit, Morris. If you don't have a projector, how do you know it's a dirty movie? And, who the hell owns a tux?"

"I don't need no cockamamie projector, Zigler. I held it up to the light and checked out part of it. Trust me, it's pure sex, man. And my dad owns a tuxedo because he's a Mason, and they wear them a lot."

"Well, that part is true," I offered. "My dad is a Mason and he owns a tux. They have a few events every year where he has to wear that monkey suit."

"Shut up Stert," Fred snapped at me. "I don't want to hear about your dad's stupid tuxedo. And tell me this, why do our dads all hide this kind of dreck in clothing? I'll guarantee if you are looking for rubbers, just check their sock drawer."

"Well, find me a projector, and I'll prove it to you," Morris insisted.

Morris had moved into Swifton Village during the previous school year. Swifton was a large apartment complex that sat just down the street from my house. It consisted of several blocks of three-story red brick buildings that had popped up after the war, in the northern end of Bond Hill, the suburb in Cincinnati where we all lived.

As it turned out, Mark was a really fantastic drummer. The previous year our gang's leader, Wally Bohl, had purchased a very cool and expensive used set of Leedy and Ludwig drums fully equipped with crash, ride, splash and hi-hat cymbals, all in pristine condition.

The problem for Wally was that he didn't play the drums. So, he enlisted Mark's assistance in learning how to play, and in so doing, brought Morris into our "Black Shirt Gang." The group, started the previous summer, consisted of Wally, Fred Zigler, Carl Schiele and me. We often wore black tee shirts, sleeves carefully rolled up, hood-style.

We were already quite efficient at teenage mischief before Mark showed up. With this new addition, our summer vacation behavior of 1958 started going off of the *Mischief Meter*. He was an only child, as were Carl, Wally and I, except he had no parental supervision. His parents never seemed to be a round. His dad was a traveling salesman. Nobody seemed to know where his mother was all day, but she was never home.

Wally threw down the gauntlet by saying, "OK, Mark, we have a projector. I'll get it and we'll take a look at your little movie."

An hour later, we had gathered in Mark's dining room in his second -loor apartment on Rhode Island Avenue. Mark disappeared into a bedroom and returned with a six-inch reel.

Unfortunately, the film was 16 mm, while Wally's projector was an 8 mm contraption.

"Son-of-a bitch," Mark exclaimed. "That won't work."

I hesitated for a minute or two while we all gawked at the reel and the projector trying to will them to match up.

Finally, I said with not much conviction, "We have a 16 mm projector. But I don't know if my mom will let me bring it here. And we sure can't use it at my house."

"Jiminy Christmas," Carl said. "Don't be such a pussy Ran. Just go get the damned projector, will ya?"

It was true that our gang had pulled off a bunch of shenanigans over the past two summers without ever getting caught, including going on a joy ride in Freddie's family car when he was only 14, and almost blowing up my house testing a bomb Fred and I had made for a bomb contest with Wally and Carl.

While the rest of our posse seemed unconcerned with breaking the rules, I was always afraid of getting caught. I was sure my mother had some special radar when it came to this kind of thing, but truthfully, she didn't.

Finally, I agreed and Freddie and I headed off to my house. When we got there, Fred took over.

"Hey Mrs. S., we need to borrow your projector. Mark Morris has some baseball movies we want to watch. We'll bring it back in a couple of hours, OK?"

Totally clueless, she bought right into his BS.

"Sure. It's in the storeroom in the basement. You boys be careful with it. Your dad will have a fit if you break it."

"Oh, don't worry Mrs. S. We'll guard it with our lives. Promise," Fred stated.

I had yet to say a word, as we rushed down the steps that led from our kitchen to the basement. I grabbed the projector, and we reversed our course.

As we headed out the front door, my mother yelled for the millionth time, "don't slam the screen door, young man."

I gingerly closed the screen and off we went down Grafton Avenue. Before we got two doors away, we saw Wally headed at us with his projector in hand.

"Where you going Bohldini?" Fred asked.

"Screw Morris and his stupid movie," Wally said. "He's a prick."

"What's going on?" I inquired.

Without answering, Wally brushed by us and kept going up Grafton toward his house three blocks away on Dale Road.

"What's with him?" Fred asked.

I shrugged as we continued onward to the Morris Art Theater, projector in hand.

When we arrived, we found Mark and Carl both with mischievous smiles.

"Give me that thing," Mark demanded.

"Hold on," I said. "What's up with Wally?"

"Well, to tell you the truth, he just can't stand it when he's not in charge," Mark said.

Carl agreed, saying, "That's true. He got pissed off when Mark wouldn't let him look at the film. He even tried to grab the darn thing. Then he and Mark said a few things to each other about projectors and drums. The next thing you know, he's headed for the hills."

"His loss," said Mark.

Then, "OK, Randy. Here's the movie. Plug in and let's get started. Boys, your education is about to start, and this isn't health class. Roll 'em, baby!"

While Mark pulled the shades in the living room and dining room, I threaded the film through our little Bell and Howell, plugged it into a nearby outlet and hit the switch.

After a few flashes of numbers and letters, a man who looked more like a hobo than a playboy appeared, walking down some railroad tracks. His path led him to a little shack, which he entered, to be greeted by a fairly attractive woman. With that my carnal knowledge quickly expanded.

While Carl and I watched in total silence, Fred and Mark provided running play-by-play of the action.

"Oh, my God," screamed Fred. "He's taking her clothes off."

"Look at that body!" Mark yelled with a laugh.

"Holy shit," said Fred.

"Look at that thing," screamed Mark as the hobo dropped his drawers.

"What's she doing to him?" Fred giggled.

"I'll tell you what she's doing," Mark offered.

Please don't, I thought, as I watched with total fascination.

"I thought there was only one way to do that," Fred admitted.

"Are, you kidding," Mark came back. "They're just warming up."

Speaking of warming up, I realized how hot the apartment had gotten with the windows closed and the shades drawn on this hot summer afternoon.

Freddie continued, "Are you kidding? Look at that. I had no idea."

Then, "Is he hurting her?"

"No, stupid, that's how she shows pleasure," Mark explained.

"Bullshit, he's hurting her."

The escapades went on for about ten minutes, while Mark and Fred maintained their constant banter and Carl and I remained totally silent, trying to comprehend the action on the field, if you will.

The film reached its climax, you might say, with cheers from Fred and Mark and relief for me. They were in pig heaven, and I sort of felt like I needed a shower.

"Let's watch it again," Fred insisted.

"Nope, that's it, boys. That little baby is headed back to the tux," said Mark.

"I assume you know how to rewind it, Stertmeyer?" Morris asked, looking at me.

I did, indeed. And I couldn't do it fast enough. I was sure my parents would find some forensic evidence on the projector that would lead to my grounding for the rest of my life.

Fred just kept repeating, "Holy shit. That was unbelievable. Holy shit. Holy shit. I mean holy shit!"

After Mark returned from his parent's bedroom and opened the shades and the windows he exclaimed, "Well boys, that's how it's done. You are welcome. Too bad Wally still remains a sexual imbecile. It's his own fault."

"Thanks Mark," I said with absolutely no conviction.

"I'm buggin' out of here," I then reported with total conviction.

"Me too," said Carl.

"Let's go to my house and shoot some baskets," Fred suggested.

Carl and I agreed, as I guess we needed to burn some energy. Mark, on the other hand advised us that he was going to put some Benny Goodman on his record player and try to keep up with Gene Krupa on his drums.

The three of us bid him farewell. I dropped off the Bell and Howell right where I had found it, hoping it wasn't giving off signals of what had just run through it. We all headed up the hill in my back yard to Freddie's and his driveway basket.

Our game of horse seemed to be extra competitive that afternoon.

None of us saw Wally for the next three days. Finally, we connected at baseball practice, but not a word was spoken about the little *dirty movie.*

Finally, two days after that, Freddie, Carl, Wally and I were hanging out at Swifton Shopping Center, as we often did. As we were all making a small candy purchase at Murphy's Five and Dime, Fred finally brought the film up to Wally.

"Shut up, Zigler. I don't want to hear about it or Mark Morris," Wally exclaimed loudly.

"OK, cool it, man," Fred, said.

To break the tension, Carl suggested, "Let's head down to Pasquale's and get a pizza."

And with that the original four-man Black Shirt Gang was reunited. Food cures a lot of ills.

Wally reclaimed his unofficial title of King of the Gang, and Mark Morris was no longer a member. The two of them finally made up to a degree, mostly related to Wally's desire to become a decent drummer. But that 16 mm film had created a deep chasm in their friendship. Never having been a big fan of Mark Morris, that was fine with me.

More than sixty years later, Fred Zigler and I still joke about that day often. But not once have we ever discussed it with Wally.

Swifton Villages Apartments

Bell and Howell 16 mm Projector

1959

It's coming down
Snow pains on the motor veins
Keeps your business on the ground
It's coming down
Slow day for the teacher
And her wheels are spinning now

From *Snow Days*
By Trip Shakespeare

Snow Day

Wednesday, March 11, 1959, started like any other typical school day. In 1959, weather forecasting didn't have Doppler available to give folks a proper heads-up for storms that may be baring down on them. So, when my Big Ben alarm rang its wake-up call, my first thought was a hopeful mental plea that old Doc Tyson would not be throwing one of his pop-up quizzes at us in first period physics class.

Then I peeked out of one of my two bedroom windows to discover golf ball size snowflakes coming down so hard I could barely see the Gates' house less than twenty feet from where my nose was pressed to very cold glass.

To me, this was exciting news. I do not believe that Cincinnati Public schools ever can canceled school due to snow during my first eleven years of taking advantage of their free and mandatory schooling. But what I saw out my window did provide hope that Doc Tyson would be late getting to his first-floor lab-type classroom at Woodward High, allaying my concern of a quiz for which I was woefully ill-prepared.

I heard my father exit our one bathroom, and I scrambled quickly to the shower. After breakfast and the requisite teeth brushing, I checked out the Channel 5 News where good old weatherman, Tony Sands, was reporting what was quite apparent... we were in the midst of a late winter blizzard. Thanks, Tony... you're the best.

Promptly at 7:45, Freddie Zigler rapped aggressively on our front door as he had been doing since we entered the seventh grade at Woodward in

September, 1954. My mother was ready.

She opened the door and demanded, "You just stay right there on the porch, Freddie. I won't have you dragging that snow all over my living room, you hear?"

"Yes ma'am, Mrs. S. But ask Randy to hurry. It's damned cold out here."

"Watch your language, young man," my Mother commanded.

"Sorry Mrs. S."

I saved Freddie from more of my Mother's rage by grabbing my books, fully bundled for the snow in my heaviest waist-length winter coat, snap-on rubber boots, wool-lined brown leather gloves and the mother-mandated hook knit beanie, loyally colored in Woodward Bulldog blue and white. Other than wearing different colored jackets, Fred and I could have been an all-male version of the Bobbsey Twins.

"You pull that hat over your ears," my mother insisted.

"OK," I responded, completely ignoring her as Fred and I negotiated the front steps that lead to the Grafton Avenue sidewalk.

Fred and I took our normal route through the Swifton Apartments that sat four houses north of my home, then through Swifton Shopping Center, something of a colossus in 1959 Cincinnati. As we crossed Reading Road from Swifton to the half-moon entrance driveway to Woodward, it was apparent that this was no normal storm. Where there usually would have been a dozen or so buses in front of the yellow buff brick three-story high school, there was only one lone bus parked with a few classmates hurrying through the deep snow anxious to escape the cold.

Fred and I entered the front hall to find a smiling Stuart Hodesh anxious to inform us that we were not to go to our homeroom. Most of the teachers had not yet arrived, so we were being herded into the large auditorium, just off of the front hall.

If a class of 502 students were to have a contest to crown an official class clown, Stuart would have been a finalist. He was one happy son-of-a-gun, always sporting a smile and quick with a joke or a quip. A few of these won him a one-way ticket to the principal's office.

For example (and there were many), our sophomore year, in biology class, our teacher, Bob Connelly, was showing off a box that showcased a butterfly collection from a pretty little number named Tillie McGuire.

Connelly tilted the box toward the class and started to make a point, "Now, if you will look here in Tillie's box..."

Before he could finish, Stuart yelled out, "I'd like to look in Tillie's box!"

That resulted in a red-faced Tillie McGuire, an angry Bob Connelly and an escorted trip to visit the assistant-principal for Hodesh. Stuart's reward was a half hour detention after school.

Freddie would have been strong competition for Stuart in the clown department.

Just two weeks before our snow storm, we were in heath class. Stretching the limits for 1959, our teacher, Mr. Mayberry, was showing a sex education film on venereal disease. Up on the pull-down screen at the front of the room was a grainy image of a doctor explaining the issues with the spread of gonorrhea and syphilis. The Doc was emphasizing the 1959 version of what we would today we call *contact tracing*.

As the film progressed, the doctor was interviewing an alleged victim of syphilis, explaining why he must identify all of the girls with whom he may have had sex.

Doctor *Sex Police* asked the clean-cut boy several questions as Fred whispered to a small group of us in the back of the room, "That prude couldn't get laid if he was the last man on earth."

Then the doc queried, "Now son, who else have you had sex with?"

Before the Eagle Scott could answer, Fred yelled out, "Your daughter, Doc!"

That lit up the room with thunderous laughter, as well as igniting a healthy dose of rage from Mr. Mayberry. To add to the theater of the absurd, our teacher, John Mayberry, had a bit speech impediment. To be blunt, he had the same trouble with his *Rs* as did Elmer Fudd (You cwazy *wabbit*).

"All wight, Fweddie Zigwa, I've had enough of youuu wediculous behaviow. You can just head down to the pwincipal's office."

Of course, with that, both Fred and Stuart Hodesh broke out with uncontrollable laughter. Mayberry explained the buddy system to Stuart.

"You think this cwazy behaviow is funny Stewwhat? Well, then you can join Zigwa to the pwincipal's office.

Yea, Stuart and Fred were kings of the clowns at Woodward.

Fred, Stuart and I entered the auditorium, seeking to strategically place ourselves in the back row closest to the exits. Barry Ross, Micky Hoffman and A.J. Friedman were of similar mind. The six of us blocked of the back-row entrance from the right-side aisle. The auditorium was abuzz with excitement over the delay to our school day.

The dependable science teacher, Max Coyle, was directing traffic with his now famous, "Hello, friend. How are you this morning, friend? OK, find a seat, friend."

The former Northwestern football star, and renowned lunchroom monitor, knew nobody's name. Everyone was "friend."

But none of us were surprised that he had plowed through the snow in order to be on the job at Woodward on time. If Max Coyle was anything, he was dependable (and a *friend*).

Slowly a few classmates trickled into the auditorium, most, like Fred and me, coming from homes in Bond Hill and Roselawn and within walking distance of the oldest public-school west of the Alleghanies (*We are the Bulldogs... the mighty, mighty Bulldogs*).

I waved to friends Spike Spiegel and Bob Noodles Neuman who were grabbing seats a few rows in front of us. They both lived in the Swifton apartments, an easy skate into Woodward in the snow. Spike was a world class ping pong (or as he called it, *table tennis*) player, having done an exhibition with a Chinese World Champion in the Woodward Gym a couple of years earlier. Noodles was the star of our basketball team, and had just lost a close race for the city scoring title to a friend of mine, Joby Haynes from Withrow High School. Joby's dad worked with my father at Fifth Third Bank, and we had been pals for a very long time.

At around 8:30, Mr. McSpadden, our choir director walked on stage with a mic in his hand. Mr. Mc was a big deal at Woodward, having written both a new fight song and Alma Mater when the most recent iteration of the school opened its doors in September of 1953. He also led Woodward's biggest event of each year, The Showcase, a major talent review featuring at least 20% of the schools 3,000 students.

Our junior year's version entitled *Down to Earth,* had just drawn the curtain in this very same auditorium the previous Saturday night.

McSpadden tapped a couple of times on the mic. Convinced he would be heard, he advised the small group of students that we should expect to spend at least the first two periods imprisoned where we sat. Then, to assure that the federal government would continue to subsidize our milk money, he led us in the pledge to flag. On Flag Day five years earlier, the phrase "under God" had been added to the pledge... So much for the separation of church and state.

Doing the pledge was fine. We did it every morning in our homerooms before heading off to our first period class (no Physics class on this day, thank you Mother Nature). But then, McSpadden got a bit hoaky. He insisted we all sing the Alma Mater, which in my opinion was *hoaky*.

Here's the deal. In this new McSpadden version, near the end, there is a little stanza that goes, "I pledge my heart, my head, my hand and bid thee, God speed, Woodward." Now the stanza is OK, I guess. But here's the rub. When singing it you are required to take your right hand and touch your heart, your head and raise your hand (like in the pledge to the flag) to correspond with singing those words. Wait, it gets worse. On the *God spe*ed part, you have to move your right hand in an exaggerated waving motion, left to right. It was just too close to a Nazi salute for my taste. But I was in the fifth grade when Mr. Mc wrote the damned thing, and he never asked for my opinion.

At this point, I was processing the sustained boredom that lie ahead. As if he were reading my mind, Fred jabbed me in the ribs and said in a whisper, "Let's get the hell out of here."

"Do you mean sneak out and skip school?" I asked

"You ain't whistling Dixie, there, Stert. Come on, we can head to the team room and go out the back way."

"Where do you want to go?" I questioned him being more of a *plan* kind of guy than Fred.

"Shit fire, Stert. What the hell. Let's hitch hike downtown," he proposed.

"Downtown! Are you kidding me?" I exclaimed to loudly.

Still whispering, Fred said, "Pipe down, will ya? Sure, why not. How much cash do you have on you?"

I thought for a second then answered, "Well, enough for lunch for the next three days and, maybe, a little extra."

"Great. I'm actually sitting on a five spot, believe it or not. That's enough for a movie and a bus ride home, if we hitch our way into town. C'mon, whaddaya say?"

"Wait, I have my emergency bus tokens. I have two in my change purse I think," I said pulling out the little egg-shaped piece of rubber that opened like a crying baby's mouth when you pressed the ends. Sure-enough I had four quarters, two dimes and three pennies, plus two dime-sized Cincinnati bus tokens.

I thought for a second longer. This wouldn't be my first rodeo. Sandy Schwartz and I had skipped school the previous fall and drove up to Dayton in his little Metropolitan. The only glitch had been running out of gas five miles from home with no cash left for gas. Some nice sales guy bailed us out with a buck for gas that day.

"OK. What the hell. Let's do it. We're juniors, for Pete's sake. We've earned some fun. Of course, my mother will kill me if she finds out. But she's killed me before. I believe in resurrection."

I looked over to A.J. Friedman who was sitting next to me and said, "Hey, A.J., we're out of here. Enjoy sing the fight song and the rest of the torture."

"Where the hell are you two going?" he asked.

"Downtown to rob a bank," I joked.

With that, Fred and I headed for the door to the front hall. There we hit the first obstacle, Max Coyle, who asked, "OK, friends, where you two think you're going?"

Fred, always thinking faster than me, said, "Mr. Coyle, we have an English test coming up and just want to go to our locker to get our books. OK?"

Coyle hesitated, then smiled and unlocked the prison door, OK, friends. But you get back here lickity split, ya hear?"

"Yes sir," we chorused.

Out the door we went, taking a quick right through another door that led to a long hall next to the auditorium. At the end of the hall, we took the stairs one flight down that deposited us at the entrance to the team room. I had just been assigned a new locker a week earlier with the start of baseball practice. I quickly worked the combination on my lock, and Fred and I deposited our books inside for safe keeping. Then we stepped outside into the blizzard, doing a half jog up the south side of the building to Reading Road.

Feeling a bit giddy at first, we found the fairly wet snow made great snowballs, which we threw at signs and each other. We quickly realized that wet gloves were not going to be a good idea, so we employed the one on our right hand to seek a ride. In the deep snow, none of the few cars that crept by us had an interest in picking up a couple of snowmen. We sloshed our way south. Finally, at the entrance to the Maketewah Country Club, a sleek brand new two-tone 1957 DeSoto with its double headlights and fancy big rear fins slid to a stop next to us.

Fred grabbed the passenger door and opened it as we discovered a well-dressed business-like driver who asked where we were headed.

"Downtown," Fred answered.

"Well, I can take you as far as Clinton Springs. Dust off that snow and jump in."

Fred slid in next to the driver and I scampered into the back seat after banging the snow off of my boots, closing the heavy door behind me.

The drive went pretty smoothly, the big DeSoto negotiating through the snow until we hit the intersection of Reading Road and Victory Parkway. Reading turned into a substantial hill at that point as it skirted the east side of Avon Field where my Uncle Joe had taught me how to play golf. Not how to play well... just how to play. On this day, the course looked more like a ski resort.

There were cars and trucks scattered all over the half-mile hill leading up to Paddock Road. Suddenly we were dead in the water. After sitting for about five minutes Fred said, Hey Stert, we better walk up the hill."

I couldn't argue. So, we thanked the man in the gray flannel suit, exited the nice DeSoto and began our trudge up the little mountain. Walking was tough, but we were a couple of young jocks, and we soldiered on.

At the top, we paused to catch our breath, crossed over Paddock Road, noting that Lorretta's Food Shop across the street was closed. We passed the Chinese restaurant owned by the family of our classmate, Ken Quan, and then by Weil Funeral Home. The whole time we were ready to stick out our thumbs, but the options were zero. Ironically, as we came to Clinton Springs Road, our DeSoto chauffeur turned in front of us, tooting his baritone horn, proving that our walk had been a colossal waste of energy. Oh, well.

In front of Glueck's Pharmacy, we finally hit pay-dirt. A very nice older gentleman stopped and motioned for us to get into his two-door Ford Crestliner that I guessed was a 1950 or 1951 model. Glueck's Pharmacy was significant for a few reasons. First, our good friend, Eddie Wikas, worked there. Second, I had dated the owner's daughter, Bonnie Glueck, the previous year. Third, her uncle was the world-renowned archaeologist and President of Hebrew Union College, Nelson Glueck. And now, there was a fourth reason. At the pharmacy's front door, an old Ford had saved us from pending frost-bite.

This time, we had hit the jackpot. The driver was headed to work downtown. We slowly advanced into town where the driver eventually pulled into the Walnut Street Garage at 11:15. It had taken us over two and a half hours to get from Woodward into the city with yet another irony for it was Stuart Hodesh's father who owned the garage where we were summarily dumped from the Ford.

The snow had yet to stop. The city was eerily quiet and almost deserted.

Fred said, "Man, I'm freezing and hungry. Let's get something to eat."

"We need to watch our dough," I reminded him.

"That's true," he agreed. "How about, Izzy's? We can get a corned beef sandwich. It comes with a potato pancake."

"Sounds good, but do you want to walk that far? Plus, I don't have enough money for that. Maybe a cheap snack and a hot chocolate would be good, though."

He thought for a moment and then agreed. "Yea, that is too far in this snow. And we do need to conserve our coins. How about Mills Cafeteria? We can check out the movies at the Palace, the Keith's and the Albee on the way."

"I approve that plan Ziggy-Fritz. I always knew you were a genius."

"Yea, right,' he grunted.

We both drew our coat collars up over our necks and headed south on Walnut Street as the wind blew the snow right into our face. Along the way we checked out the bill at the Keith's Theater. They were playing *The Tunnel of Love,* a Doris Day film.

"No way," Fred said with determination. "I'm not spending good money to listen to Doris Day sing sickening crap to Gig Young."

"OK," I agreed, knowing there was no point in arguing. I just wanted to get somewhere warm.

At Fountain Square we darted over to the Albee Theater, to discover that a new film entitled Bell, Book and Candle, staring Jimmy Stewart and Kim Novak was playing with the next showing schedule to start at 12:45. Perfect. Who doesn't love Jimmy Stewart? And speaking of love; we had both fallen in love with Kim Novak after seeing her in *The Eddie Duchan Story* and *Picnic.*

So, we hurried the block and a half to Mills, on Fourth Street.

"Let's go say hi to your dad," Fred joked, as we scampered past the Fifth Third Union Trust Bank at Forth and Walnut where my father worked.

"Yea, great idea. Then we can see if we can find a torture chamber to visit, so I can get ready to face my mother," I replied.

We walked into Mills under the big blue and white windmill sign, shaking off the snow, and grabbed a couple of trays. There was no one in line. I started to do the math. Movies at downtown Theaters were expensive. The movie was going to set me back a whole seventy-five cents. Fred had pointed out that a movie without popcorn was a crime that could get you jail time. And a bus ride home would be a token. Ok, I had plenty of scratch for a little something. I just had to be sure that I ended the day with two quarters in the bank for lunch on Thursday and Friday.

We hovered over the Mills Cafeteria choices embracing the warmth more than the food. Fred, after a short contemplation, decided on a piece of apple pie and a hot cocoa, while I chose the glazed donut and the same drink. We were both now twenty-cents poorer.

The place had only a few patrons, and we were able to find a window seat where we could watch a few pedestrians along Fourth Street, heads down fighting off the snow.

The food was a welcome comfort after the past three hours, as I wondered what might be going on back at Woodward. Water was free at Mills. We were on a budget and washed down our meals with H2O.

Fred checked his watch and said, "OK, Kim baby, here we come."

We threw our coats, caps and gloves back on and headed back out toward the Albee. The huge theater had opened on Christmas Eve, 1927 just in time for the introduction of *Talkies*, as they then were called. At a cost of just over four million dollars, The Albee was Cincinnati's grandest movie palace. The day it opened it featured a Clara Bow film, *Get Your Man* as well as five different vaudeville acts on stage. The 3,500-seat theater had a huge Wurlitzer pipe organ that sat to the left of the stage.

As we walked down the long luxurious entry, Fred said, "Nothing goes better with Kim than a box of popcorn."

We walked up to the empty concession stand, where we both plopped down two dimes; fifteen cents for a box of corn and a nickel for some Jujubes, or, in Fred's case, Milk Duds. A nice older lady, dressed in a smart red uniform fetched the goods. Then, in front of two large brass doors, we handed our tickets to a gentleman dressed like he could have been standing guard at Buckingham Palace.

With the day's heavy snow, there were so few patrons that we felt like a couple of small balls in very tall weeds. We chose seats in the center about half way down leaving a seat between us in order to stretch out.

Previews were playing. We learned that if we wished to skip school again in a week, we could see a John Wayne film entitled *Rio Bravo*. After the previews the Albee entertained us with a Tom and Jerry cartoon.

Then the lights in the almost dark theater went down some more, the curtains opened wider and the feature film came on. Suddenly, I realized something I should have thought of before we ever headed out in the snow.

I said to Fred, "Jiminy Crickets, I'm going to miss baseball practice. Coach Von Holle will really be ticked off."

Fred looked at me like I had two heads and laughed his reply, "Are you shitting me Stert? He'll be lucky if he even got to school. Have you noticed the weather? There's not going to be any damned baseball practice today."

I mulled that over as I watched the opening credits and noticed that Jack Lemmon and Ernie Kovacs were both in the movie.

"I sure as heck hope you're right," I whispered to him.

"Of course, I'm right. Probably half of the team didn't even show up today."

With that we turned our attention to Kim Novak. Novak and Kovacs. How could we go wrong? Fred was already half way through his popcorn and I had yet to pop the top on mine.

Much of the nuisances of the movie were over our eleventh-grade education and would only resonate with me long after I earned my Master's Degree. But Fred and I, unable to think deep, still found great entertainment in the film, even from our narrow perspective.

Kim Novak played the role of Gillian Holroyd, a witch living in Greenwich Village. A publisher named Shep Henderson, played by Stewart, moves into the apartment above hers.

As it evolved, Henderson was engaged to Holroyd's old college adversary, Merle Kittridge, played by Janice Rule. Thus, Gillian uses her Persian cat, Pyewacket to cast a love spell on Shep. Low and behold, Shep immediately falls for Gillian and dumps all over Merle the morning of their wedding.

Then Gillian works her magic so that author Sidney Redlitch (Ernie Kovacs) visits Shep in the hope that Shep will publish his next book, about witches in New York. When Gillian learns that her warlock brother, Nicky (Jack Lemmon), is collaborating with Sidney, she begins to worry that

Shep will learn about her true nature, including the spell she has placed upon him. Predictably, Gillian finds herself actually falling in love with Shep, something that will make her lose her powers. In the end, she must make a choice as to what she really wants.

As the closing credits rolled, I felt fairly certain that even with Doris Day playing the role of Gillian, Fred might have enjoyed Bell, Book and Candle. But she had not and Kim Novak had and that was all Fred wanted to discuss.

"I bet if you look up *sexy* in Webster's there's a picture of Kim Novak,' he gushed.

"Yea, she's pretty hot," I agreed.

"Well, Stert, we made a good call on this one. Those schmucks are probably rubbing their sore asses from sitting in the auditorium all day" Fred asserted.

Then, "That Kim Novak sure has some mysterious eyes, don't you think?" he asked not really expecting an answer.

"But she has plenty of other assets, I can tell ya," he continued.

Fred was right. Kim Novak was captivating, and we had both been captured yet once again by her looks and her soft throaty voice, just as we had been watching her in *The Eddie Duchan Story, Pal Joey, and Picnic.*

But what was mostly on my mind as we exited the Albee into a brighter afternoon with just a light snow falling now, was how to complete the crime without getting caught.

Fred suggested we should head across the street to Rollman's and do a little shopping with no buying allowed.

"No siree Bob," I exclaimed. "First, if my dad decides to head home early, we might wind up on the same bus. And, for me, that would be the bus to hell. Second, how do I explain to my mother if I get home at five rather than four?"

Freddie came around to my way of thinking. The time was of no issue for him as both of his parents worked at their hardwood store in Northside. But he knew my Mother, and he understood.

So, instead of heading left toward Rollman's, we headed right toward

Government Square and its block-long bus stop. The snow on the sidewalks had turned to a fairly deep and wet slush. It only took less than a block of sloshing to get to the center of Fifth Street in front of the Government Building which housed the Post Office. This was the main bus stop for downtown. All buses made a stop here.

Fred I and I had two choices for the trip home.

The number 32 Bus, with its header that said *Bond Hill/Elbron* was the best choice for Fred, as it would drop us off at Rhode Island and Rockingham, just a short walk up a steep hill to Fred's house. The other choice was the number 43 Bus, known as the *Bond Hill/Roselawn*. This is the bus my father took every day. It ran straight out Reading Road and would drop us at Portman Avenue across from the Maketewah Country Club. This would require a longer walk, but with no steep hills.

Taking over as the senior manager, I insisted, "Let's stand here at Walnut Street and see whether the 43 or the 32 comes first. I hope it's the 43 because it will get us home faster."

Fred came back with, "I don't give a rat's tit which one it is. It's still colder than a witch's tit out here, and we are getting the first thing that shows up."

We had a plan. After less than three minutes of waiting, we saw the number 32 make the slight S-shape negotiation on Fifth Street required by the placement of the island in its center which accommodated the magnificent Tyler Davidson Fountain. We rushed the required eight spaces east, to discover that we were the only two in the queue for the good old 43.

I dug out one of my two bus tokens from by rubber crying baby and dropped it into the slot machine type cash taker and watched it ping pong to the bottom. Fred did the same with a real American dime, and we hustled to the back of the bus. The last seat was our spot because of the extra leg room it offered. No sign of my father. I was mentally urging the driver to get the big orange and cream-colored bus and move, knowing we would sit for a few minutes. The Government Square stop is where the buses got back on schedule. But we started moving right away. Of course, with all of that snow, everything was behind schedule.

There was a lot more snow for the bus to contend with than there were paying customers on this Wednesday in March. One rider got on at Seventh Street. Not another soul seemed to need the number 43 until we got to Rockdale Avenue in South Avondale. That same person got off in front of Lorretta's Food Shop in North Avondale, leaving the rest of the ride solely for Fred and me.

As we finally rolled into Bond Hill where Fred and I lived, it began to seem that, while not the perfect crime, we were about to get away with our little high school attendance misdemeanor. The bus continued past Dale Road. As it approached Bella Vista (a bit of a misnomer), Fred reached up and pulled the cord strung overhead, alerting the driver that we wished to exit his limousine at Portman Avenue. We hopped up from our seats and, when the side bi-fold doors opened, jumped down into the snow piles at the bus stop.

We had just one more leaf to turn. We would both need excuses from one of our parents to hand into our homeroom teacher Mr. Thurin, the next morning. I would write Fred's and he would write mine. I took some comfort in the fact that both my father and Fred were left-handed. Of course, Mr. Thurin didn't know this. But it still made me feel better.

Suddenly, I felt like a character from *The Blackboard Jungle.* Another crime (Fred and Randy) would go wrong like theirs (Sam Jaffe and Sterling Hayden). Well, the crime was done. All that was left was the cover-up.

I continued to fret, while Fred continued his infatuation with Kim.

Fred decided to walk with me to my house on Grafton Avenue, and then cut up to his Casa la Laconia through my backyard.

"What if my mother sees us coming from the wrong direction?" I worried out loud.

"Jesus, Stert. Relax. We pulled it off. God bless Jimmie Stewart and the guy in the DeSoto. Hell, in two weeks we have Easter Vacation, then the baseball season and before you know what hit us, we will be seniors and run Woodward for a year.

Per usual, Fred was right. Dad was late for dinner due to a slow bus ride home on the Number 43. He bitched about work and the snow throughout the entire meal. But we got dinner featuring my mother's famous beef tongue in a sweet and sour sauce over noodles and homemade apple sauce. And being in the mist of lent, my mother had also made her once-a-year beignets to the delight of both my father and me. Mom had put her snow day to good use.

That evening we all settled in front of the TV to watch Wagon Train and then The Millionaire, where the dependable John Beresford Tipton, gave away another million bucks to some down-on-their-luck character.

The next morning, when Fred knocked his arrival at my front door, I was feeling like Tipton had paid me a visit. It seemed that Fred was also feeling like a million bucks as we trekked through the melting snow on our way to school.

We faced a lot of questions from those in the know, like A. J. Friedman, Stuart Hodesh and my other good pals, Sandy Schwartz and Eddie Wikas. We knew we would not be betrayed and willfully shared our story from start to finish, with just a few embellishments. The emphasis was clearly on Kim Novak.

At 8:20, Fred and I walked into our homeroom and unobtrusively laid two carefully crafted excuse notes on Mr. Thurin's desk.

I did pay one small price for the whole snowy sojourn. Doc Theisen started my first period Physics class by handing out one of his pop quizzes. There were no questions about witches or cats with funny names. When I got it back the next morning, I was happy enough to see a large red C on my paper.

Several years later Fred and I learned the Biblical significance the title *Bell Book and Candle* as well as why the name *Pyewacket* had a special relationship to witchdom.

But as we have looked back on that day, what we remember most is that, on a very cold snowy Wednesday, Kim Novak provided just the warmth we needed.

Bell, Book and Candle

1959 DeSoto

The grand entry – Albee Theater

1959

Let me entertain you,
Let me make you smile,
I'll do a few tricks,
Some old and then some new tricks,
I'm very versatile.

From *Let Me Entertain You* (Gypsy)
By Julie Styne and Stephen Sondheim

HOT CHILI

The clanging of the telephone awakened me from my fantasy of walking along the beach with Margie Freeman, still the undeclared love of my life. In my fantasy, I was the love of hers. The incessant ringing snapped me back to the reality that Margie Freeman probably hadn't given me a second thought in over a year.

I walked from my room through the hallway and into the dining room where I lifted the receiver to my ear. Freddie was at the other end. He responded to my *hello* with a flurry of indiscernible patter. All I could make out was something about fake driver's licenses.

"Ziggy Fritz, slow down will ya? I can't understand a word you're saying."

I heard him take a deep breath and then he said, "I got us two fake ID's. Well not fake. What I got is my cousin's Milton's driver's license. And, not only that, Stert, I also have his roommate's license. You know, you met him. Jerry Goldman. And Goldman is 5 foot eleven and has brown eyes and blue hair – I mean blue eyes and brown hair, just like you. And, you know Milton has the same color eyes and hair as me. And, well this is perfect, don't ya see. Can you believe it? This is...?"

I interrupted his babbling. "Freddie, what the heck are you talking about?"

"Don't ya get it, Cat? We're going to the Gayety!"

I let that sink in for a minute. I pondered what Fred had just said. The Gayety, with its unusual spelling, was the notorious burlesque house downtown on Vine Street, ironically just three doors north of the new Public Library. Those two buildings were closely separated by a small magazine-newspaper shop and the Empress Chili Parlor. Empress Chili, the pre-cursor to what would later be referred to as *Cincinnati Chili*, had taken its name from the Empress Theater next door, before it changed its name to the Gayety.

Freddie was offering every 17-year-old boy's real fantasy. All thoughts of my true love, Margie Freeman, had disappeared with the mention of the Gayety. Now my teenage brain was dealing with visions of live naked women. We had all talked about this often. We had heard the stories from some of the seniors who, already having turned 18, had witnessed the glory of burlesque.

"Hey, Stert. You still there?" Freddie asked.

"Uh, yea. I'm here."

"Well whaddaya think? I checked the *Post*. They run all day long from noon until 2:00 AM. I asked my dad if I could have the car tonight. I can pick ya up right after dinner. There's some dame called Chili Pepper there tonight. Jeepers Creepers, can you believe this? This is going to be great."

I continued to think through Fred's proposal. Finally, I asked, "What if we get caught? They could call the cops on us. And they'll take the licenses from us. My mother would kill me, and when she's finished, she'd have my father kill me again."

"Oh, bull. C'mon Stert. This is the chance of a lifetime. Milton told me they don't even give a flying leap if you fit the description on the driver's license. Just as long as it says you're 18, you can stroll right in. C'mon, don't ya want to feast your eyes on Chili Pepper? Hey, we walked right into the Guild last month to see *And God Created Woman*. Remember? They didn't even ask for identification. First Bardot and now Pepper."

I thought about that for a second. The Guild was what was referred to in the jargon of the day as an *Art Theater*, meaning it showed foreign films. What made *And God Created Women* special is that it opened with a very naked French actress named Brigitte Bardot stretched across a bed. Nudity had come to the movies, as impossible as that seemed in the winter of 1959. And Fred was right. We had waltzed right into the Guild three weeks earlier with our pals Wally Bohl and Carl Shiele.

We had decided to just show up at the Guild and see if they would sell us tickets without proving we were 18 years old, which none of us were. As always, breaking the rules had been nerve-racking for me. Even though the ad in the *Cincinnati Post* clearly stated in bold print, "YOU MUST BE 18 TO ENTER," we were not challenged at the ticket booth, and, within minutes of taking our seats we were happily gazing at a very naked and very beautiful Brigitte Bardot.

I returned my attention to Freddie, "How much does it cost?" I asked.

"Two bucks," was his quick reply.

"Two dollars? Geezooie, that's more than I'll make all day tomorrow working at the drugstore, including tips," I complained.

"You gotta look at the return on the investment, Cat," Freddie persisted. "For two bits you get a lousy movie; for two bucks you get a live, breathing, naked Chili Pepper. C'mon, you won't regret it, I promise."

I thought a moment longer and then said without much conviction, "OK. I'm in. I'll tell my mom we're going to a movie. Let's check on what's playing at the 20th Century."

Freddie came back with another quick response, indicating he had thought this well through, "I already thought of that. There's a great double feature playing. *One Eyed Jacks* is on at 7:15, followed by some Doris Day movie at 9:00. We've already seen *One Eyed Jacks,* and who cares about Doris Day anyway?"

Fred then did his imitation of Marlon Brando calling Carl Malden a slime eating pig from *One Eyed Jacks,* followed by his hideous but entertaining giggle.

"I like Doris Day," I said.

"You like Doris Day? Are you kidding me? I'm offering Chili Pepper!! Do want to see Goodie-two-shoes or Chili's-two-tits? You are never going to see Doris Day's tits, that's for sure"

He had a point.

"OK," I said. "Pick me up at 6:45."

"Great. We're going to see some genuine schmooie tonight, Stert."

With that Fred dismissed me with a click at his end.

At 6:40, I heard the horn from the Ziglers' 1956 red and white Buick blasting out front. I grabbed my pea jacket and headed for the door. My mother yelled from the kitchen, "You be sure you're home by midnight, young man."

"I will," I promised, thankful that she had not noticed how nervous I was at dinner.

My father was playing with the rabbit ears on top of the TV in his constant quest for a better picture. "You guys got a couple of hot dates tonight?" he joked.

Hot is right, I thought, as I bolted out the front door.

Freddie was sporting the grin of the cat that got the bird, and he was totally wired. On the drive into town, he talked a mile a minute, and I had to constantly tell him to slow down. He was a man on a mission, and I was a nervous wreck.

"I'll take Victory Parkway rather than Reading Road into town," he advised. "I think it is much faster."

The chosen route took us past Xavier University, The Cincinnati Lawn Bowling Club, Walnut Hills High School, and the red brick castle known as Hoffman School where I had attended kindergarten through the fifth grade, then past the Alms Hotel and through picturesque Eden Park. Even in the dark of a winter's night, Eden Park was beautiful with the clearly visible silhouettes of such landmarks as the huge glass conservatory, the waterworks and its two large collection ponds, the stately Cincinnati Art Museum and, of all things, the bronze statue of Romulus and Remus suckling a wolf, a gift to the city from Italian fascist Benito Mussolini.

Once in town, we found a parking place on Court Street. Fred locked the doors on the Buick and pulled two stiff paper licenses out of his wallet.

"Here, this one is yours."

I looked at it under the dim light of the street lamp. I couldn't believe my eyes. I held in my hands the driver's license of one Marsha Goldman, a 19-year old female with brown eyes and black hair.

"What the heck is this?" I demanded.

"Whaddaya mean?" Fred asked.

"You expect me to try to get into the Gayety Theater with the license of a girl?"

"Let me see that," Fred said tearing the license from my hand. I pointed to the *F* in the box marked *Sex*.

He studied it for a moment then exclaimed, "My goddamn cousin. This is Jerry's sister's license. Is this his idea of a joke?"

He sprinted to the corner pulling a nickel from his pocket. He proceeded to attack the payphone that stood at the southeast corner of Court and Vine Streets.

Finally, I heard him scream into the phone, "Milton, what's the deal? You gave me Marsha Goldman's license. Are you nuts?"

He listened for ten seconds or so, and then without saying a word slammed the phone back on the hook.

"Damn him," Fred muttered. Then, "Well, screw him. We're going to the Gayety."

"What?" I asked.

"We're going to the Gayety" he repeated. "Tonight, we are incognito. They won't even look at these damned licenses"

With that, he marched at full stride in the direction of the Gayety Burlesque Theater.

"Wait a minute," I protested. "You've got to be kidding."

"I'm not kidding. We're going to plop down our two dollars and these cockamamie licenses, and we're going to feast our eyes on every inch of Chili Pepper."

Before I could gather my thoughts, I was standing in front of the ticket window of the Gayety Theater watching Fred hand some emaciated old man a fin and a piece of paper identifying him as a 22-year-old college student.

"Thank you, sir," said the old codger. "Don't forget to check out our concessions".

With that, he hit a button that produced Fred's ticket. Fred grabbed it and his three dollars in change, looked back at me and disappeared into the theater. Shaking like a willow in a tornado, I slid my two bucks through the slot along with Marsha Goldberg's driver's license. The old man picked up the license, examining it closely through thick bi-focal black-framed glasses. He then looked up at me and said, "Thank you, Miss Goldberg".

Up popped my ticket. After three attempts, I finally retrieved it from the slot and dashed through the door only half hearing his plea for me to visit the concession stand.

Inside the door stood a smiling Freddie Zigler, his expression saying, *see how easy that was.* Behind Fred stood the highly touted concessions counter, upon which sat an enormous light blue-gray Persian cat fast asleep. And behind the counter, perched on a wooden stool was a middle-aged, huge breasted, not too skinny bleached blond woman in a tight-fitting red dress, whose appearance immediately brought to mind the word *floozy*. She smiled back at us as a one-inch ash fell to the floor from a half-smoked Pall Mall dangling from her thin ruby red lips.

Freddie whispered in my ear, "What a skag."

Unaware of Fred's review, she asked with a thick southern accent, "Kin I git youuu boy-ez enyting?"

Her emphasis on *boy-ez* indicated there was no doubt in her mind we were too young to be there gawking at her titanic breasts, three fourths of which hung abundantly out of her low cut red dress.

"No thanks," we replied in unison as we quickly turned left to walk up the badly frayed carpet leading to double doors that undoubtedly lead into the Gayety Theatre.

I suddenly became aware of a strong vibration beneath my feet, well timed with a muffled and repeating thud. When Freddie opened the door, I realized this phenomenon was caused by the banging of an aggressive drummer in a live eight- piece band playing from an orchestra pit at the front of the theater.

As my eyes began to focus on my new environment, I noted that the band sat in a pit snuggled between the stage and a semi-circle walkway. On the walkway marching to the drummer's harsh, determined beat, I saw what could have been the younger sister of the concession floozy.

She was totally nude except for three strategically placed items that a more knowledgeable Freddie advised me were called a *G-String* and *Pasties. How did he know all of this,* I wondered?

Frankly, it was not a pretty sight. She had enough bust and butt for at least three women. Her backside resembled a couple of partially deflated basketballs, including the dimples. Worse yet, her pendulous bosoms swung apart and back together like a couple of bell clangors. The fire-engine-red painted lips, inch-long thick black eyelashes, pastel blue-green eyelids, and silky long mane dyed a hideous shade of yellow, showing weeks of dark root growth, completed this monstrosity of womanhood.

She did a rhythmical march, stopping every so often to smile, wink and gyrate her massive hips in a fashion that I had never before seen. It was clear that she thought this was seductive, as did most of the old drunks in the place, not to mention Freddie. I, on the other hand, felt uncomfortable, unmoved and a little ill.

The band played on, a bit long on trumpets, trombones and drums. Meanwhile, the Goodyear Blimp strutting around the runway, found her way back to center stage, did what Fred advised was a *bump and grind* three times and reached up with great flourish removing the sequined pasties to reveal dark brown nipples the size of baseballs. This was followed by one more proud stroll around the walkway as several of the inebriated patrons up front screamed for her to "Take it off! Take it all off!!"

She and the drummer were working now in a convoluted concert. She would *bump and grind* to the exact, yet harsh *ba-dum* beat of the drum. In between the *ba* and the *dum* her breast swung away from each other. As with all pendulums, what swings out, must swing back. And the drummer timed his strike of his high-hat cymbal at the exact time her bovine breasts banged back together.

I assumed that the cries to "take it off" (Freddie had joined the chorus) referred to the G-String, unless she was wearing a wig. I prayed she would leave both the G-String and the hair on and that somebody would get out the hook and take her off the stage. Mercifully, the music ended without any additional stripping, and the poor thing exited stage right.

Immediately from the left entered Abbott and Costello, or so it seemed.

The tall one even talked like Bud Abbott and the little one walked like, but acted even dumber than, Lou Costello. And though I suspected that, while the real Abbott and Costello were not exactly fashion plates, they would not have been caught dead in the clothing that adorned their pretenders now prancing across the Gayety stage. Everything these two yahoos wore existed of stripes, plaids or polka dots and was three sizes too large. The only exception was Costello's hat, which was way too small.

I mentioned to Freddie that they reminded me of the comedians Bud Abbott and Lou Costello.

"Well, hell yes, Hep Cat, how do you think Abbott and Costello got started?" he exclaimed.

I processed that for a moment while the tall one pointed to the other side of the stage and said, "OK, ladies and germs, let's hear it for the very beautiful Miss Powder Puff."

If he was referring to the departed stripper, he was clearly blind. Sure enough, Powder Puff quickly appeared took at dipping sort of a bow then disappeared again behind the curtain and the two goofballs on stage went into their shtick.

They started with a bit about bullfighting, which included references to "the Queen's box."

Abbott *(explaining to Costello): "When the matador comes into the bull ring, he looks at the Queen's box."*

Costello*: "(Looks at the audience, raises his eyebrows and smiles) "He looks at the Queen's box?"*

Abbott*: "Yes, of course, he looks at the Queen's box. And, you know, he carries his weapon in his pants?"*

Costello*: "He has his weapon in his pants?" (Big smile). "Yea, dats where I keeps my weapon too."*

Abbott*: "Yes. He calls his weapon a Veduga. He hides his Veduga and his Banderillas under his Muleta. When he gets to the Queen's box, he pulls out his Veduga and shows it to her."*

Costello*: "You're shitting me!"*

Abbott: *"No ,I am not shitting you. In fact, the Matador will usually also offer his Banderillas to the Queen. If she likes the Matador, she will let him into her box and will kiss his Veduga and his Banderillas for good luck."*

Costello: *"This guy is in the Queen's box and she is kissing his Veduga and his Banderillas. Sounds to me like he already has pretty good luck."*

And so the banter went on from there, bringing the house down with laughter. They eventually went from the Queen's Box to another bit that included poor Powder Puff, who had, thank God, put some clothes back on. The drummer contributed to that bit with a quick tapping of his snare drum with each punch line.

From there, they brought up the house lights and started selling an array of dirty magazines and sexual novelties which were being distributed by two scantily dressed women, one working each of the two main aisles in the theater. Allegedly the most risqué of their goods came directly to their stage from Paris, France (although the peep-hole gadget Fred bought for a buck said *Made in Japan* on the side).

When I pointed this out, Freddie's retort was, "Who cares? There's a naked blonde inside, isn't there?"

Eventually, Bud and Lou exited the stage. The house lights came down, replaced by a single spotlight on the center of the rich crimson red curtain as a drum roll started. Then a deep baritone voice announced, "And now, ladies and gentlemen, straight from her engagement at the famous Roxy Theater in Miami Beach, Florida, the Gayety Theater is proud to welcome to our Cincinnati stage, the beautiful and incomparable Miss Chili Pepper!"

With that, the most beautiful woman I had ever seen in my 17 short years burst through the curtain. Her smile alone could have lit the theater. She wore a long royal blue sequined gown, blue velvet gloves that went well above her elbows and matching four-inch high heels. I estimated she was about 5' 4" tall. Her features were simply perfect. She was spectacular…a Goddess.

She had long flowing dark brown hair that framed her perfectly sculpted features. Her large brown eyes were mesmerizing, almost frightening, as she looked right into mine. She was Aphrodite. No, she was Athena. She was Venus. But she was no myth... she was real... a walking, breathing vision. Wait, she was Elizabeth Taylor, or Grace Kelly, or Debra Paget. I gave up. She was better than any of the others.

Unlike the harsh music the band had played for Powder Puff, Chili Pepper slowly strolled to a much softer beat. When she got to the center of the circular runway she stopped, put her right hand to her full red lips, looked directly into my eyes and blew me a kiss.

Freddie exclaimed, "Can you believe it? She looked right at me and blew me a kiss."

Wait a minute, I thought. She clearly blew that kiss to me. Then I realized the whole theater was silent except for the soft tune to which she was gliding across the stage. The entire crowd was mesmerized.

Finally, she came back to the walkway, stopped, and slowly removed her left glove tugging on one finger at a time. Watching that glove come off was the most sensuous thing I had ever seen.

That quickly changed. The removal of glove number two was sexier yet. When she returned to the main stage, she turned her back to the audience, delicately put her right arm behind her, reached up to the top of the blue gown and took the zipper between her thumb and index finger. Ever so slowly, the zipper came down, as she stopped several times for the big tease.

The zipper ended below the small of her back. Now her hands went to her shoulders, as she deftly took the gown from her right shoulder. With her back still to us, she lowered the gown from her other shoulder, looking over it to tease us further with a smile and a wink. With great deliberation, she then stepped out of the gown, letting it drop to the floor, revealing a feminine posterior unlike anything I had seen before.

She had a delicate girlish form, one that might have seemed vulnerable, yet she was all woman, fully in charge. There was such a grace in her look and movements which I would soon realize was extremely rare in the world of striptease.

She turned to face us now, revealing a tight stomach accentuated by a flawless navel. Her shape was pure, unspoiled and immaculate in every sense.

I sat there, a teenage voyeur, totally spellbound and more than a little aroused. She continued, as she was required to do—moving, swaying, dipping, smiling, captivating.

I took a quick glance at Fred noting that he too was transfixed, his mouth wide open in awed disbelief. I then realized that I held the same pose as my good friend.

When she reached behind her to unhook the blue lace bra, I feared I might stop breathing. Could she get any more perfect? My first glimpse at her natural, full breasts answered that question with a resounding *yes!*

The music had taken on a stronger beat, and Chili Pepper proved that she could bump and grind, but with a level of sophistication unlike the raw crudeness of Powder Puff. Her gyrations were sexy but soft.

Finally, she was down to the famous G-String. Chili Pepper glided to the center of the walkway and again gazed directly into my eyes. I was certain of it. I guess I had expected to feel the emotion of lust, as I had for Brigitte Bardot, earlier in the year. Instead, I felt engaged with Miss Pepper in a way that seemed more like love than lust. Of course, it was a major itch that I could not scratch.

Then she was gone. She had spent about ten minutes in my life. And in that short period, the fantasy was in place. Could I possibly ever find a woman as beautiful as Chili Pepper?

Freddie was shaking my arm, awaking me from the trance. He was screaming in my ear.

"She'll be back out again!! We have to stay for the midnight show. I have to see her again."

Midnight show?

"You be sure you're home by midnight young man," my mother's words came back to me.

Just as I was about to allow the reverie of seeing Chili Pepper once more take over, I heard Fred say, "Oh, shit."

He quickly slid down in his seat.

"What?" I asked.

"Don't turn around," he commanded. "The Levinsons and the Cohens just came in," he reported.

"What?" I again asked.

"Get down, dammit! Mr. & Mrs. Levinson and Mr. and Mrs. Cohen just came in here and are sitting about 4 rows behind us."

"Who?"

"Jesus H. Christ, Stert. Steve Levinson's mom and dad and Mike Cohen's mom and dad. If they see us, we're goners."

Now it registered. What were nice Jewish couples doing in a place like the Gayety? My education continued. Fred whispered an explanation of why the Levinsons and Cohens were taking in a burlesque show. What he described could clearly not apply to my parents. I was certain. My mother never got horny. I was sure. *Sorry, Dad.*

Fred's total focus had shifted from Chili Pepper to planning our escape. I was thinking more quickly than he was at this point.

I said to Freddie, "Hey, just before Chili Pepper came out, the lights went dark and they put a small spotlight on the middle of the curtain. Maybe they will do that before the next stripper comes out."

No sooner had I said this than the lights went dark. Freddie scrambled over me like a scared cat, whispering, "Let's get out of here."

He did not have to ask twice as I was hot on his heels. As we burst through the door leading to the lobby, Fred ran head on into a large handsome man, knocking a box of popcorn out of the man's hands.

As Fred stepped back the man said, "Well, Freddie Zigler, where are you rushing off too?"

I heard Fred say, "Oh, hi, Mr. Ritter. I'm sorry." It was Dave Ritter's father. Dave was in our class at Woodward.

The man laughed an understanding chuckle. "So, Fred, I am guessing your mom and dad probably don't know what you're up to tonight. Right?"

"Well, Mr. Ritter, I didn't tell them I was coming here." Fred answered.

"Then we should probably keep this between you, me and Stertmeyer here, don't you think?" he said looking over at me.

"Gee, that would be good if we could do that Mr. Ritter."

"There is a second part to this deal, though," Mr. Ritter said.

"Sure, anything you want Mr. Ritter," Fred responded.

"Here's the deal. I overheard Dave talking on the phone this morning. He was here last night and saw this Chili Pepper gal and was telling someone how great she was. He doesn't know that I know he was here. And he doesn't need to know that I am here with the Levinsons and the Cohens. Do I make myself clear as a bell, boys?"

"Yessir," we chimed in unison.

"Good, then go ahead and get out of here and think fondly of me years from now."

He didn't have to ask twice. We sprinted out the door onto Vine Street. We took a few steps north, looked at each other and burst into hysterical laughter.

"Wholly kripes, Stert," Fred exclaimed. "Can you believe that girl? Have you ever laid eyes on anything like that? She has to be the most gorgeous creature on the earth. And then we run smack into Ritter's old man. Was he keen or was he keen? What a night."

Freddie did a little celebration dance. I watched and laughed at my friend. We finished the walk to the car in silence, both of us processing the last 2 ½ hours, including the glorious Chili Pepper.

As we drove north from downtown, Fred did what he often did. He would pose the most oddly inspired questions.

This time he said to me, "Ya know, Stert, Roy Rogers has Dale Evans and Bob Steele, and Hopalong , and Wild Bill Hickok always get the girls. Do you think that fat Andy Devine or that old codger, Gabby Hayes ever get laid?"

Now there was a question inspired by who knows what, but odd, no doubt.

We had time to stop at Frisch's Big Boy on the way home and opted for the Mount Vernon location on Reading Road (AKA: *Jew Frisch's*) rather than the Pleasant Ridge shop (AKA: *Hood Frisch's*). We saw several class mates who had their cars pulled up next to drive-up speakers, most of them already chowing down on Big Boys, fries, or the new Brawny Lad sandwich (prime ground beef, a thick slice of Bermuda onion, Frisch's tartar sauce on a toasted rye bun). Fred made the rounds to tell all who would listen about the Queen's Box, Powder Puff, Abbott and Costello, and especially Chili Pepper. But not a word was spoken about Mr. Ritter and his friends.

I had already blown my cash at the Gayety and only had enough scratch for a small Coke. I delighted in Fred's rendition of our evening at the Gayety. No longer angry with his cousin, he relished in telling about the two licenses we had used to get in.

As midnight approached, we headed home laughing all the way. I walked in the door at one minute after twelve and was, as always, greeted my mother sitting in the living room pretending to read a recent edition of *Readers Digest*.

"Did you have fun at the movies?" she asked.

Why was she asking this, I wondered? Had Mr. Ritter reported us after all?

"Sure," I answered, trying not to show my panic.

To my immediate relief, she commanded, "Well, we should both get to bed."

With that she was off to her bedroom.

I brushed my teeth, quickly undressed and then slid between the sheets. The vision of Chili Pepper was already beginning to blur, but it was with a feeling of affection for my new dream girl rather than lusty desire that I drifted off to sleep.

Of course, I did not begin to understand the concept of looking at a woman as a sexual object that night as I gazed upon the wonders of Chili Pepper. Objectification is defined as an attitude that regards a person as a commodity or as an object for use, with little or no regard for a person's personality or character.

So, sue us. Fred and I were guilty as charged. We were seventeen and this was the fifties, the age of Marilyn Monroe, Jane Russell, and the birth of Playboy Magazine. Fortunately, I would soon learn that a meaningful, respectful love comes from digging much deeper.

Yet, as the vision of a really hot Chili Pepper dims and blurs, she still stands in my mind as the standard of physical beauty. The Gayety Theater eventually went the way of all Burlesque venues. On April 10 and 11, 1970, Cincinnati said goodbye to the Gayety Burlesque Theater with a black-tie sendoff. It was replaced by an expansion of the Cincinnati Library… so, just as it was on that Saturday night in 1959, it still stands as a place for learning.

The Gayety Burlesk Theater
(They were not much at spelling)

Chili Pepper Publicity Photo Circa 1959

Photo by Gene Laverne

1959

What you say just can't be true
When the story's stretched
And so far-fetched
That you're lacking an excuse
You Lied Your mother allowed you just one white lie

From *You Lied*
By Green Day

THE STICKSAS

This is a tale of three young lads seeking some self-realization through the affections of pretty young girls. It is a story that began with an accidental run-in at Cincinnati Gardens.

I had an ongoing connection with Cincinnati Gardens from the day I first gazed into the bowels of the half-finished building in 1948. My father had driven my mother and me past it one Sunday on our way back from Rest Haven Cemetery, where we had visited the haloed ground in which my Grandmother Cosey Theobald was buried.

Dad insisted that he and I sneak in through an open construction door to take a peek. He explained that this would become Cincinnati's version of Madison Square Gardens; a place where sports history would be made. As I gazed up at the girders supporting a naked ceiling and then down to the stair-cased concrete that would eventually hold more than 11,000 seats, I established a six-year-old's fondness for this building, sensing that it would be a part of my future.

And, indeed it would be. The week it opened in 1949, the University of Cincinnati played Butler and Xavier University played a highly touted Kentucky team in basketball. And a scrappy Cincinnati bred prizefighter named Ezzard Charles beat Joey Maxim in 15 rounds, making him the number one contender to challenge Joe Louis for the heavy weight title. My father read to me accounts of these events from the sports section of the *Cincinnati Post*, reminding me that he had predicted great things for the Gardens.

Then we moved to Bond Hill in 1953, just three blocks from this red brick palace with the huge carved limestone athletes adorning the front façade, and my father and I took immediate advantage of our new locale. In the first year alone, I saw my first college basketball game with the great Clarence "Bevo" Francis from little Rio Grande College, my first prize fight, my first professional hockey game, and, with my Aunt Win, a circus and the Ice Capades.

Seeing Bevo Francis was especially memorable. He was a mammoth human being who had twice scored over 100 points in a basketball game. Thanks to him, his tiny little school from south central Ohio was taking on and beating a lot of the big dogs in college basketball.

But what I really loved was hockey. Every chance I had; I would go to the Gardens to see the Cincinnati Mohawks. It seemed that they beat everyone they played, winning several International Hockey League championships in the 1950's.

It was only natural that I would learn to skate and to play amateur hockey. And then a big dream came true. I got a job on the Ice Patrol. With that came a level of prestige to which I was unaccustomed.

From the moment I donned the sweater of the Ice Patrol at Cincinnati Gardens, I had felt certain that it would pay big dividends in terms of attracting beautiful girls. But after almost two years as a member of the ice police, I was batting a great big fat zero - zilch.

Frankly, I had begun to doubt the value of the sweater, and worse yet, I was also seriously doubted myself.

Then, bam, I crashed into Judy Hall. I had been gazing at the unattainable Susan Franklin spinning at mid-ice, her skirt lifted by the momentum of her spin into the form of an umbrella. As my dad would have put it, I was *taking a serious gander at her unbelievable pins*. Completely distracted, skating on autopilot, I failed to see this little brunette headed right at me.

Though she saw me coming, she was new to the game and couldn't stop. I heard her scream just as I smacked head on into her. We went down in a heap. Embarrassed, I quickly jumped up to find myself looking into the most beautiful blue eyes you could hope to see. The embarrassed anger I was feeling quickly melted away when I gazed into those eyes.

As she failed in her attempt to get up, it became apparent that this was her first day on skates. I finally came to my senses and reached down to assist her to her feet. It seemed that she was as shy as I. While searching for words, I gave her the quick once over.

In addition to those marvelous eyes, she had dark brown hair parted in the center, flipping up at the shoulder. Her features were that of an Irish girl, but with the dark complexion of an Italian (God bless America, you old melting pot). I found nothing to complain about in regard to her appearance from below the neck either.

Finally, I said to her, "Do you know you were skating in the wrong direction?"

Wrong thing to say – her eyes began to well with tears. "Is this your first time on skates?" I asked.

It seemed she had no voice, but she did shake her head in the affirmative. Per usual, my shyness was not contributing much to the moment.

Then, as if someone had flipped a switch, with the verve and tone of an operatic soprano, she went into a tirade, "I didn't want to come here. My mother made me. This is crazy - just because it's a school trip. It's summer vacation. My friends didn't have to come. But, oh no, my mother makes Jenny and me go on all of these summer outings. Next week we have to go to the Zoo Opera. I hate the opera. I hate ice-skating. Jesus, Mary and Joseph, why can't I just enjoy my summer like Jerri and Patty?" (An Irish-Italian ***Catholic***, I was guessing).

She looked at me as if I were to provide an answer. In my typical simpleton fashion, I said, "I kinda like the opera. I go with my aunt. Madame Butterfly is great"

She looked at me as if to say, *are you kidding me... are you totally nuts?*

"Who are Jenny, Jerry and Patty?" I asked. She looked away blankly and then looked back at me and muttered, "What?" I was now feeling like a total dolt.

Then, "Oh, Jenny's my younger sister. And Jerri and Patty are my two best friends."

Continuing my dimwitted approach to this golden opportunity, I asked,

"One of your best friends is a guy?"

"What?"

"Jerry? A guy is your best friend?"

With utter disgust she replied, "Jerri is not a guy. J-E-R-R-I…Jerri Kellerman…has been my best *girl* friend since 3rd grade!"

"Oh."

"Help me get off this ice, will ya?" she pleaded. I held out my left hand and took her left elbow with my right hand guiding her to the exit near the red line.

With uncharacteristic courage, I asked her, "Can I buy you a Coke?"

She finally displayed the slightest grin, revealing the full impact of her perfect white teeth. "Yes, I guess so."

I helped her to a table near the concession stand, dug into my pocket, discovering that I had three nickels, one more than needed for two small cokes. When I returned with the drinks, she was more relaxed, having removed her skates. She now displayed a full, very lovely smile.

"Thanks for your help," she said.

"Would you like to go out some time?" I blurted out; clearly more surprised that I had asked the question than was she at hearing it.

"Sure," she responded without pause, her smile expanding and her eyes displaying just a hint of embarrassment.

Being off the ice socializing with a paying customer was a violation of the *Ice Police Code of Ethics.* I was just about to take my first sip of Coke when Marty Peck, the official boss of the Ice Patrol and a former goalie for the Cincinnati Mohawks, came up from behind me and said, "Hey, Slick, am I paying you twenty-five cents an hour to patrol the ice or to chase skirts?"

I stood up almost knocking my Coke onto the blue-eyed girl seated across from me. "Sorry, Marty. I was just helping her off the ice."

"Yea, right. Well, get back on the ice and see who else you can help."

Marty spun away from us. When I turned back to her, she slid a small piece of napkin toward me. On it she had written *Judy MU8232.* Finally, it registered with me that it was her name and phone number – Mulberry

8232.

"Call me," she said.

"OK. I will," I promised as I turned to walk back to the rink.

"Hey." I heard her call after me. "What's your name?"

Looking back at her it seemed the hardest question in the world to answer. Finally it came to me. "Randy. My name is Randy"

"Hi, Randy. I'm Judy. Judy Hall. Thanks for the Coke."

Not having the sense to say *you're welcome,* or anything else, for that matter, I scurried back to the ice, stuffing the napkin into my sweater pocket.

I made a quick decision as I glided back onto the rink. This needed to be a team sport. There was safety in numbers, and I had to pick my team carefully. I had failed the first time I had chosen help to gain a beautiful girl's heart. I had lost Susan Anderson's attention to Wally Bohl the previous summer. He had the better car, the better looks, and the greater confidence.

No, this time my team would not be Wally, Carl and Fred. This was a job for the tag team of Randy, Sandy and Ed. Something told me that Judy and her two friends would match up perfectly with the Schvantz, Wike and me. And, depending on just how Catholic she was, it might matter that I had a Catholic grandfather.

As it turned out, I could not have been more correct in my choice. My friendship with Sandy Schwartz and Eddie Wikas had evolved into something special in recent months aided by the new found mobility provided by being able to drive. We were quickly becoming a close-knit mini-fraternity, referring to ourselves as the Three-O-Trio.

To solidify the singularity of our special little group, we made sure to use only our recently assigned nicknames. While many of my close friends already called me "Stert", Sandy and Eddie were in need of new monikers. In Ed's case we showed little creativity. Just as my last name had been shortened from Stertmeyer to "Stert", we decided to reduce Wikas to "Wike".

Sandy, on the other hand was looking for something unique. I had suggested we call him *Soapy*, based on a character in the *Chip Hilton* books I had been reading. Soapy Smith, as created by the author and former, Long Island University basketball coach, Claire Bee, was Sandy reincarnate.

The *Chip Hilton* stories centered around a little tight-knit group that included Biggie Cohen a mammoth lineman on the football team, Speed Morris, a fleet-footed running back, Chip Hilton, the hero quarterback and, of course, Soapy Smith, the mischievous happy-go-lucky group clown.

As I read my way through the Hilton Series from *Touchdown Pass* to *30 Seconds to Play* to *Homerun Hero* and beyond, the similarity between Soapy and Sandy became more and more apparent to me. So, I tried to sell Sandy on "*Soapy*" as his new nickname.

But Sandy simply did not like the name, and didn't like to read. So, while the connection made sense to me, Sandy chose to nix that option.

Next I suggested we call him "Bermuda". This thought evolved from a joke I had heard on the Red Buttons Show. It was one of those groaners whose silly punch line was *Bermuda Schwartz*. Bermuda shorts were quite the rage at the time, and I loved the thought of replacing "shorts" with "Schwartz". But that didn't strike a chord either; maybe because Sandy was, well, short.

So, we had to dig deeper. In the end we chose irony.

Sandy, since we first were required to swim in the nude in 7th grade gym class, had confronted head-on and with abundant humor the fact that he was not the most well-endowed young man in the Class of '60. Thus, we made a rather wide segue from Schwartz to Schvantz, a Yiddish term for that particular portion of the male anatomy where Sandy found himself somewhat lacking. As I had learned from my many Jewish friends, the word *Schvantz* was a vernacular term for the more popular Yiddish words *schmeckel, schmuck, schlong* or *putz* used to describe the penis. At any rate, in Sandy's defense, it turned out he was just a late bloomer.

Thus, when I burst through the front screen door when I got home that afternoon, I made a beeline for the phone, not failing to note the sweet smell of a peach pie baking in the oven. That probably meant fried chicken for dinner. But it was Thursday, which usually meant roast beef with roasted potatoes and carrots. Then again, Mom always made fried chicken when she baked a fresh peach pie in the summer. For a second I got distracted savoring the prospect of chicken, mashed potatoes and gravy, and peach pie a la mode followed by the *Untouchables* with Robert Stack as Elliot Ness on television. Who cared if it was chicken or roast beef? I loved them both. This was shaping up into quite a Thursday.

Getting back to business, I quickly dialed Jefferson 5644. The phone rang twice and then I heard the annoying voice of Sandy's sister Lynn at the other end.

"Hellllooo!!!" She screamed in my ear.

"Lynn, is Sandy there?" I asked.

"Maybe he is and maybe he ain't. Who wants to know?"

Knowing she knew doggone well that it was me, and wanting to strangle her, I collected myself and calmly said, "This is Randy. May I speak with your brother please?"

I heard her place the phone down and then shriek, "Sanford, it's one of your moron friends on the phone."

In the distance Sandy yelled back, "Who is it?"

"That creep, Randy, and hurry up. I have to call Susan."

Finally, Sandy picked up the phone and said, "Hey, Stert, what's crackin'?"

"I'll tell you what's crackin'. Schvantz, I just met the most beautiful girl in the world at the Gardens. Her name is Judy Hall and she has two friends who are dying to meet you and Wike!" I lied.

"Yea?"

"Yea. No kidding. And, they're Shicksas," I said using the new word I had learned recently from Eddie to describe non-Jewish girls. For some reason, all of my Jewish friends were dying to go out with Shicksas.

"Shicksas? Wow, that's cool. Where do they go to school?" Sandy asked.

"St. Mary's in Hyde Park."

"Really? Three rich Catholishas, huh," Sandy said, processing all of this information.

"Well, I don't know if they're rich, but I know one of them is gorgeous."

"Of course, they're rich," he replied. "Everybody in Hyde Park is rich."

"I didn't say they were from Hyde Park. I said they went to school in Hyde Park."

He thought about that for second and then said, "Yea, they could be from Oakley, which is even better. More likely to put out if they're from Oakley," he surmised.

"We'll take them to the Twin Drive-In and do some major schnoofing," he continued, referring to the drive-in theater with its back-to-back screens across the street from Frisch's Restaurant on Reading Road.

"Ya think they'd go to the drive-in on the first date?" I asked.

"Shit fire Stert, I don't know. All we can do is ask."

Sandy paused and then said, "But what if they're a couple of skags? We need to get a gander at this Judy's friends before we go wasting good money on them."

I processed his point for a moment and then replied, "Well, if they live in or near Hyde Park, maybe we could suggest they go to the dance up in Ault Park Saturday night."

The Schvantz jumped on that thought like it had been his idea.

"We'll get them up to Ault Park. That's what we'll do. If they're decent, I'll take the best looking one and Wike can have the fat one. There's always a fat one. If the two Catholisha friends are both fat, we'll say hi and go on our merry way. All right, this is pretty neat. All ya have to do is get them up to Ault Park. If we're lucky, they'll be a couple of hot schmooies from Oakley that love to schnoof."

He continued, "Have you told Wike yet?"

"No," I answered.

"Good. When you call him, ya gotta tell him I have dibs on the good lookin' one. He won't care. He'll be happy to get some "bare-hand" from any female that's breathing."

I laughed at this, knowing how true it was.

At that point, the Schvantz' dim-witted sister Lynn picked up the extension, rudely demanding that we get off the phone. This both ticked me off and made me, once again, jealous that the Schwartz family had two phones while we had only one with a party line. Oh, well.

So, I said to Lynn, "Great manners, gorgeous" (which she was not) and to Sandy a quick, "Good-bye."

I then immediately picked the phone back up and dialed Wikas at Elmhurst 3521. Eddie's older brother Jack answered and politely asked me how the baseball team was doing. I gave him a quick report, and he handed the phone to Ed.

I went through the same discussion with Eddie that I had with Sandy. He listened without interruption until I explained the action plan to which Sandy and I had agreed. At that point, he interrupted and said, "I'm going to wind up with the ugly one, right?"

I came back with, "Hey Wike, I haven't even met her friends. But obviously you can't have Judy. She's my discovery."

"The Schvantz is going to take the hot one. I'll get the one that's fat and wears thick glasses," he mused.

"Gee wilikers, Wike, Judy is a great looking girl. She won't have any fat, ugly friends. C'mon', Cat, let's do this," I pleaded.

After a few seconds of silence, he reluctantly responded, "Well, OK, I'll do it if we can meet them first at Ault Park. You set it up, but I want to get a gander at this chick before I spend any money on her."

"You got a deal", I said.

I hung up the phone just as my mother and Aunt Win were putting dinner on our large round dining room table. As was the case with most Thursday family dinners, Mom had made roast beef with mashed potatoes and carrots cooked to the point of surrender in the juices of the roast. Around the dark walnut table sat Mom, Dad, Aunt Win as well as my Aunt Lois and my cousins, Paul and Rick.

My Uncle Joe had gone off to Germany to do spy work for the United States Army, leaving Aunt Lois and the two boys behind. They shared a house with Aunt Win, a street over from us. We had a clear view of the back of their house at 5422 Newfield Avenue from our living room window at 5426 Grafton Avenue. The three sisters were about as close as siblings could be, often at the expense of their marriages.

Rick was only five years old and still a picky eater. On the other hand,

Paul and I cleaned our plates and then scarfed down seconds.

Per usual, the dinner patter included my dad's usual bitching about the bank and Aunt Win's typical complaining about things at Woliver's Drugstore while the kids at the table were encouraged to review their summer day.

With unusual enthusiasm, I reported on the gorgeous girl I had met on the Cincinnati Gardens ice. My father gave me an understanding poke in the ribs. However, my mother and aunts seemed rather displeased when I mentioned that Judy Hall went to St. Mary's High School which, of course, meant she was Catholic. Prejudice is a funny emotion and who knows where the three sisters' negative feeling regarding Catholics was born. But it existed, starting with my grandfather, Henry Stertmeyer. According to my mother, my grandfather had two serious shortcomings; he was Catholic, and he was a Democrat. So, I changed the subject from my little Catholic girl to my upcoming baseball game against a very good Oak Hills team scheduled for Sunday afternoon at Roselawn Park.

Still feeling the euphoria of my discovery of the little ice-skating beauty, in uncharacteristic fashion I willingly helped with the dishes, after which the adults took their coffee to our front porch, hoping for the relief of an evening breeze.

My dad and I took Rick and Paul to the backyard to work on the daunting task of turning them into baseball players. Paul was improving significantly. He was playing second base for the Bond Hill Merchants Knothole team that I coached with my friend Freddie Zigler. Rick, while full of enthusiasm, was hopeless. He was only 5 years old, I told myself.

At 7:00 o'clock, I snuck into the house, pulled the crumbled piece of paper from my pocket and dialed the phone number placed there by Judy Hall. After three rings, the merry voice of a lady played through the wires into my right ear. "Hellll-o," the voice sang.

My voice had finished its adolescent change more than two years earlier. Yet, sounding like a thirteen-year-old, I squeaked into the phone, "May I speak with Judy please?"

The happy singsong voice at the other end quickly changed to something more akin to Cinderella's wicked stepmother, "Who's calling?"

"This is Randy," I squeaked back.

"Oh, you're the nice boy she met today at the Gardens," she replied like a mother anxious to get her daughters married off and out of the house. This was encouraging.

"Yes ma'am, thank you," I said.

"Hold on, I'll get Judy."

After almost a full minute of muffled mumbling, Judye came on the line with that same sweet innocent voice from earlier that day, "Hi, Randy."

"Hi," was all I could think of as a reply, followed by a long painful pause.

"Are you there?" she asked.

Realizing I must say something soon, I rambled right into my pre-planned spiel.

"So, listen, I was wondering if you ever go up to the Ault Park dance on Saturdays. You know, it's close to where you live. And you have two friends, and I have two friends. And it would be really neat if your two friends met my two friends. And, of course, you would come with your two friends, and I would come with my two friends and - well, you know - it could be pretty neat" ... quick pause for a deep breath, then, "Well, what do you think? Do you think that's a good idea? If you do, maybe we could meet this Saturday. You know the Cliff Lash Orchestra from the Ruth Lyons Show will be playing. What do you think?"

I finally found the good sense to shut up.

She giggled the sweetest little giggle you could hope to hear. "Well, Jerri, Patty and I go to Ault Park sometimes. First let me ask my mom."

After more inaudible background sounds, she came back on the line. "Mom says I can go if either Jerri or Patty go too. Mom said she could drop us off and pick us back up. She takes us everywhere. I will call Patty and Jerri to see if they can go. What are your friends' names?"

"Sandy and Eddie," I replied.

"So, you can have a guy friend named Sandy, but I can't have a girl friend named Jerri," she joked.

"I guess you have a point. His real name is Sanford, but don't ever call him that," I advised.

"Well, it sounds to me like Sandy and Jerri might be made for each other. She refuses to answer to Geraldine. She's a real pistol. What is Eddie like? Does he like shy quiet girls?"

Uh oh, I thought... *Here it comes.*

"It depends on what the shy quiet girl looks like," I answered, digging for some information on Judy's other friend.

"Well she wears glasses, but she is as cute as a button. She's just a little shy. So what about Eddie? Is he some big jock?"

I measured my response.

"Not exactly a jock. He's kinda thin and has a rather large nose (sorry Wike). But he is involved in sports. He's the team manager for football and basketball."

"Oh, so he's the guy that runs on the field with the water bucket. Right?"

"Yea, he's that guy,"

Our conversation was now into a rhythm, and it felt good.

"Cute, shy girl with glasses meets skinny water boy with big nose," she laughed. "Sounds perfect."

She had a sweet personality, and I was falling in love.

At that point, I heard a muted male voice in the background.

"I have to go. I'll call Jerri and Patty to see if they can go to Ault Park on Saturday. I'll call you back. What's your phone number?"

"Melrose 0080," I reported.

"OK. Bye." Then there was a click and she was gone.

Just before *The Untouchables* was about to come on channel 12 at 9:00 O'clock, our phone rang. I bolted from the couch and dashed to the dining room, certain my new love Judy Hall was calling. As my English teacher Miss Magrish would have me say, *it was she*. Within 15 seconds *she* confirmed our meeting at Ault Park in two days, agreeing that Jerri and Sandy would hook up, leaving Eddie and Patty with little choice but to embrace the opportunity to settle for each other.

I, in turn, quickly reported this to the Schvantz and Wike. Sandy was beside himself with excitement, while Eddie was resigned to cast his fate to the dance. When Sandy learned Jerri Kellerman was from Oakley rather than Hyde Park, his excitement level went up a couple of octaves.

"This is perfect, Stert. There's no doubt in my mind that I'll get some bare tit if we can get them to the drive-in," he asserted.

I reminded him, "We aren't going to the drive-in. We are meeting them at Ault Park. You'll be lucky to get bare hand. And you will have to dance with her to get that."

He responded with his classic misplaced logic, paraphrasing that great German humanitarian, Adolph Hitler, "Today the hand, tomorrow the tit!"

I rolled my eyes at the phone as he demanded that I drive so he could get Jerri Kellerman into the back seat. I reminded Sandy that they already had a ride with Judy's mother in order to protect them from predators like him. And, besides, the back seat of my car was reserved for Wike. The Schvantz would be riding "Shotgun."

"Jeezuee, Stert, you have to set your sites higher, Cat," he screamed into the phone. "Our next date will be to the drive-in and Wikas can drive by himself. I get your back seat."

"We'll see," I said.

After calling Eddie, our plan was to get to Ault Park at 8:00 PM sharp so that we could view the wonder of the Catholic girls in all of their glory before the sun set.

The next two days flew by quickly. Before you could say "nookie," it was 7:15 on Saturday night, and I was honking the horn of my 1949 Dodge in front of Sandy's house on Stover Avenue in Golf Manor. Within another ten minutes, Eddie was safely tucked into the lush, yet fake, velour of my back seat. With all windows rolled down, the Three-O Trio was ready to Carpe Noctem!!

Seizing the night included proving, as we had many times before, that some 17year olds should probably not be given the keys to a car. Our little trio had developed a couple of car games in recent months. One we called the *Old Combination* and the other *Under 20 Night*.

The *Old Combination* involved doing (you guessed it) a *combination* of things, and in rapid sequence. This required the front passenger window to be rolled down, as it always was in the hot summer months. As the car approached some innocent victim, the driver would slam on the brakes creating a screeching sound from the tires. The person sitting in the front passenger seat or rear right passenger seat, or better yet, both, would slam the side of the car with a wide-open palm and then scream at the top of their lungs. The *Old Combination* never failed to scare the bejeebies out of the poor unknowing pedestrian.

Generally, after picking up their eyeballs and reinserting them and then self-resuscitating their heart, the victim would typically conjure up words they might otherwise not use, rapidly spewing them uncontrollably forth as they pumped an angry fist in our direction.

My 1949 Dodge was a magnificent old classic car that we had named "The Nose" because of the long-pointed style of its hood. Later, when Sandy bought a tiny Metropolitan, we dubbed it, "The Nostril."

When I drove the Nose, we did have a backup for the *Combination.* In the case when there was a car traveling too closely behind, making slamming on the brakes a bad idea, *the Nose* had the distinct ability to provide the loudest backfire you could imagine. This was accomplished by simply turning off the ignition key for a few seconds. When you turned it back on, the exhaust that had accumulated in the muffler would release, providing a controlled explosion worthy of a Sherman Tank. This usually had an *Old Combination*-type effect on the victim.

The Schvantz did try this once, and only once, in his mother's brand-new fire engine red 1958 Buick. Sadly, different cars give different results. In this instance, he did get quite a big boom. But in doing so, he also blew a fist-size hole in the Buick's muffler. I guess they were not making cars like they used to. That was not a good night for the Schvantz.

On the other hand, any car we got a hold of was plenty good for *Under 20 Night.* The rules here were simple. Whoever drove that night had to keep the car at a speed of 20 miles per hour, or less – a perpetual school zone, if you will. The real challenge was to pick routes to our ultimate destination that would result in the longest possible convoy. Heavily traveled two lane roads with great distances between traffic lights and a speed limit of

35 MPH were best. Eventually the driver would pull off the road and we would count the effect of our effort.

Teenage boys are, by nature, competitive. Thus, *Under 20 Night* became an ongoing contest. Sandy was the very best, because he had the least fear or concern about what people thought. He looked upon pissing-off people as an art.

One night, he accumulated an unwilling convoy of 28 very unhappy motorists, exceeding his previous record by nine cars. This, plus a few successful Combinations, produced a gleeful evening for us all.

At any rate, on this Saturday evening we were all too excited about what lay ahead to get into our regular tomfoolery. We rolled down the final hill on Observatory Avenue as the Ault Park Pavilion came into sight. We parked on the backside of the Pavilion, which afforded us a beautiful view of Lunken Airport and the Ohio River flowing peacefully from left to right in the background. I turned off my portable radio that hung from the rearview mirror, removed it and locked it in the glove compartment. That little baby was always locked into WSAI – 1360 Radio, which featured an ongoing medley of the current Rock and Roll hits.

We then quickly exited the "Nose" and headed up the steps where music provided by the Cliff Lash Orchestra beckoned.

Ault Park was a splendid treasure that sat between the upscale Cincinnati neighborhoods of Hyde Park and Mount Lookout. The park provided lush gardens, magnificent vistas, abundant picnic areas and bike and hiking trails. Every summer, the Cincinnati version of the Soap Box Derby was held on a steep slope of Observatory Avenue, the winners qualifying for the big race in Akron. My friend Wally Bohl twice competed in the Derby, driving an orange crate-based vehicle that Freddie Zigler, Carl Schiele and I had helped him construct. Wally never finished in the money, but it was fun nonetheless.

The crown jewel of Ault Park was its Grand Pavilion which sat on the highest point in the park. With imposing stairways on both sides, it was framed by magnificent gardens and offered majestic overlooks, isolated coves and a cascading waterfall between the west side steps. And, of course, there was the open-to-the-stars dance floor.

It was to this welcoming environment that the Three-O Trio came on a beautiful Cincinnati summer night. We mingled through the abundant young crowd, looking for a trio of Catholic girls. Suddenly, I felt a tap on my shoulder. I turned around to find a smiling Judy Hall. With her stood a gorgeous blonde and a studious looking brunette. I had no trouble identifying which one was Jerri Kellerman. Neither did the Schvantz and Wike.

Judy was in charge as I again fell into an embarrassing silence.

"Randy, these are my friends Jerri and Patty," she said.

As I stood there like a complete dolt, Sandy stepped forward and said, "Hi, I'm Sandy," as he extended his hand to Jerri. He then reached back and pulled Wike toward Patty, saying, "and this is Eddie, but we call him Wike."

The Cliff Lash Band was now playing the song "Autumn Leaves."

Sandy said, "This is a great number. Come on, Jerri, let's dance."

They disappeared onto the dance floor faster than you could say *Fred Astaire*.

Judy looked at me in an inviting manner.

"I should warn you, I am not a great dancer," I informed her.

She said, "I've seen you ice skate. Anyone who skates as well as you can is certainly able to dance."

She took me by the hand and led me out to the floor which was open to the clear, starry night. *Just do your best,* I told myself while mentally thanking my Aunt Win for the dance lessons she had provided the year before at the Arthur Murray Dance Studio. Judy tucked herself close to me as we responded to the music.

The rest of the night was a dream. We danced for over an hour, my specialties being the foxtrot and the jitterbug. Even Eddie found the courage to give it a run with Patty, although she held him at a distance sufficient through which to drive a Mack truck. Judy and I fell into a comfortable mix of conversation and dance. When I pulled her closer to me, she squeezed my hand invitingly. We learned about each other as we moved to the music, including the fact that we both had fathers who liked their beer more than was healthy.

Completely lost in one another, we finally realized that Sandy and Jerri had gone missing. Sandy's words came back to me, "Today the hand, tomorrow the tit."

Was he running ahead of schedule, I wondered? Judy and I took a break and walked to the rail where we leaned against the limestone balustrade, holding hands. We turned to look down into the valley, where the runway lights of Lunken Airport twinkled below. Then I spotted Sandy and Jerri inside the "Nose." He was busy at his task, which was ***not*** teaching her how to drive a stick shift.

Judy saw the same thing. She quickly removed her hand from mine and demanded strongly, "We have to go put a stop to that. Sometimes Jerri doesn't have the sense she was born with. That is not the way a nice Catholic girl should be behaving! She'll spend an hour at confession next week."

My first thought was how I might get Judy to spend at least ten minutes at confession.

Off she went, down the steps toward my Dodge, as I trailed behind. Jerri saw us coming and broke the hold Sandy had on her. Sadly, Judy's mood had changed from *romance* to *Sister Mary Alice*. She ran around to the passenger door, opened it, reached into the car and extracted Jerri with the force of a Suma Wrestler.

"Come on, Jerri, my mom will be here in a few minutes, and we have to meet her over by the garden," Judy demanded.

Sandy just sat there, dumbfounded with this new development.

Judy turned to me and said, "Thanks, Randy. I had a wonderful evening. I like you a lot. I'm not so sure about your friend there," flipping her pretty head in Sandy's direction.

With that, up the hill she went, pushing Jerri ahead of her. And that ended our *practice date* with the Catholic girls, or as Sandy called them in Pig Yiddish, "the Catholishas."

Wike soon came down the steps in our direction.

"What happened?" he asked. "Those three ran out of here like Jerry the mouse being chased by Tom the cat."

"Long story," Sandy said. "The short version is that Judy didn't like that I had gotten to first base with Jerri and was headed to second."

There was nothing left for us to do but head home and polish off our adventure with a couple of *Combinations* and a few backfires. We may have given one man waiting at a bus stop on Edwards Road a minor coronary. In between our auto shenanigans, I had to listen to the Schvantz and Wike wax romantic about their new loves from St. Mary's High School… two really hot *Catholishas*.

It took me a couple of days to get up the courage to call Judy. When I reached her on the phone, she was sweet and encouraging, telling me again what a good time she had with me at Ault Park.

I kind of stammered an apology about Sandy's behavior. She was cool about the whole thing, even contrite about how she had reacted.

"That's OK. It was as much Jerri's fault as it was Sandy's," she admitted. "Jerri is not like Patty and me. She thinks making out with every good-looking guy she meets is perfectly normal. It is going to get her in trouble one of these days."

I processed this, realizing the message was that I had best keep my hands to myself and encourage Sandy and Eddie to do the same. But her tone was reassuring. So, I forged ahead.

"How would the three of you like to go to the Oakley Drive-In on Saturday?" I asked.

The silence at the other end of the line was a bit disconcerting. I filled the pregnant pause with, "*Gidget*" is playing. It is supposed to be great. You know, Sandra Dee, Cliff Robertson and James Darren. It would be fun."

More silence.

"I'll be sure Sandy behaves," I told her.

Continued silence.

Finally, she said, "Patty and I are not allowed to go to the drive-in. Of course, Jerri is."

This time I was silent.

She filled the void, "I guess we could tell our parents that we were going to a movie at the Twentieth Century Theater. I don't like lying to my parents, but they are just way too strict. I love the drive-in. Let me talk to Patty."

"What about Jerri?" I quizzed.

"Oh, that won't be a problem. All she talked about at church yesterday was what a great kisser Sandy is. She'll go in a heartbeat. I'll call Patty. If she agrees, Eddie will have to call to ask her. She has a little pride you know."

"No sweat," I promised. "Eddie will call her."

"OK. Give me a half an hour and call me back. Just remember, we have to be sure our parents think we are going to the Twentieth Century, not the drive-in."

"We can all keep a secret. Mums the word," I assured her.

She hung up, and I started to stare at the clock. Not wanting to seem overly anxious, I waited forty-five minutes before I picked the phone back up.

Judy answered after a single ring.

"Hi, there" I said.

"Hi," she happily responded.

"How did it go?" I asked.

"Great. Patty seems to like the Water Boy," she giggled. "She's in. Just make sure Eddie calls her to ask her personally. And be sure those two friends of yours remember not to mention the drive-in."

"No problem," I assured her again.

"Now here's the rest of the deal," she stated firmly. "You will drive, right? 'Cause I want Jerri in the same car with me so I can be sure she behaves. Does Eddie have a car? I know I don't have to worry about Patty."

God, she sounds like the Mother Superior, I thought to myself.

"Yea, Eddie can use his father's or his brother's car. That won't be a problem."

She continued, "Great. Then you all pick me up first. You will have to meet my parents and my sister. Then we will pick up Jerri. From there, we can go get Patty. You will have to meet her parents too. OK?"

"Sure," I said, knowing this was all non-negotiable.

"You guys will all spring for popcorn and Cokes, right?

"You bet. Popcorn and Cokes it is. You can even have some Milk Duds if you like."

"You're so nice, Randy," she cooed.

"You too," I offered. "So, we will pick you up around 7:00 on Saturday. How do I find your house?" She gave me the directions and Patty's phone number so Wike could call, and we said good-bye.

I immediately picked the phone back up and dialed Elmhurst 3521. Wike answered the phone. I reviewed the rules of the game as set forth by Judy Hall. He was OK with all of the requirements. He seemed to like Patty.

"Stert, if she could lose those glasses she'd be really pretty," he said. "You know they have these new things called contact lenses. She could get a set of those and become a real looker; don't you think?"

"Sure," I halfheartedly agreed.

As soon as Wike and I finished discussing how to beautify Patty Jansen, we hung up and I phoned Sandy to tell him the plans were in place. Sandy was chomping at the bit.

"This is great," he shouted with exuberance. "Saturday night at the Passion Pit! Get ready Jerri Kellerman. Here comes the Schvantz. Your bra is mine!!"

"Schvantz, please don't screw this up. Just wait until you take her out by yourself before you start the body exploration phase, please," I pleaded.

"OK, OK. But if she slips my hand under her blouse, don't expect me to pull it away."

As it turned out, our bigger problem was with Eddie, not Sandy. As fate would have it, Eddie had shared our plan with his younger brother Sandy Wikas, who let the cat out of the bag with Mrs. Wikas.

Manya Wikas and her husband Morris were first generation American immigrants. Both spoke with thick Russian accents and were devout Jews. They had fled Russia with their families during the Bolshevik Revolution.

After landing in Cincinnati, they met and married, having three sons. Eddie was the middle child. Morris Wikas had become a house painter, developing a successful business despite his sixth-grade education. The Wikas' were wonderful people. But they were very strict with their boys.

Manya had prohibited Eddie and his two brothers from dating non-Jewish girls, or *Shiksas*, as they were called in Yiddish. On Thursday before our Saturday date, Mrs. Wikas ambushed the Schvantz and me while we were all sitting in the Wikas' kitchen.

She looked me straight in the eye and said, "Rondy, vat ist dis abut you feekzing Ettie oop vit da Schicksas?"

Thinking uncharacteristically fast I said to her, "No, no Mrs. Wikas, they are nice rich Jewish girls from good Jewish families. My date is Judy Hallischevski. And Sandy here is going out with Jerri Kellermanchevitz. And Eddie's date is a good Orthodox Jew named Patty Jansenovitz. They all go to Lady Daugherty's Private School in Walnut Hills. Half the girls there are Jewish. Patty's dad is a doctor and they live in North Avondale. You would really like the Jansenovitz'," I lied to her. (Forgive me, Father, for I have sinned).

"But my lettel Sondy tolt me dey vas Schicksas," she insisted. "My boytz dunnt goes oot vit da Schicksas."

Eddie, picked up my lead. "Mom, Sandy got confused. You know I wouldn't take out any Shicksas. I swear." (Forgive him, Father, for he has sinned).

She eyed all three of us and finally said, "Vell, OK den. Dey sount like neece gulrtz. Buut, I bitter nut cotch youze going oot vit da Schicksas," she reminded her middle son.

With that, a disaster was avoided. As far as Manya Wikas was concerned, there would be no Schicksas for the Three-O Trio!!

When we exited the Wikas house, Sandy and Eddie both grabbed me, laughing out their congratulations.

"How the hell did you come up with those cockamamie names?" Sandy asked.

"That was beyond brilliant", Eddie said, slapping me on the back.

"Judy Hallischevski? Jerri Kellermanschevitz? Are you kidding me?" Sandy enthused.

"I don't know," I explained. "Those names just popped into my head, and I was off to the races."

Our date with the *Catholishas* lay just two days ahead.

On Saturday morning, the Bond Hill Merchants won their very first game ever, upsetting the Roselawn Blues. That spring, Freddie Zigler and I had taken on the impossible task of trying to patch together 14 ragtag kids into something resembling a baseball team. When my cousin Paul and Fred's brother Ron failed to make a team, we had talked Jerry Lewin, the head of the district knothole baseball league, into letting us coach all of the rejects. It took us the entire summer to finally get them a single win.

My cousin Paul had two hits, while Fred's brother Ron had gone four for four including a game winning single. Needless to say, my Saturday was off to a good start. All was great in my world as I looked ahead to my date with Judy Hall.

Saturday evening came and after a shower, scrubbing well with a fresh bar of Lifebuoy (my father claimed it gave you a manly smell), I dressed in khakis, a navy blue Izod shirt properly regaled with a green alligator, brown penny loafers, tan socks and finished with a splash of Old Spice. I brushed my teeth three times just in case.

With that, I jumped into the Nose and headed to Stover Avenue to pick up the Schvantz. He rushed to the car with great enthusiasm, and we took off for Garden Lane to collect Wike.

Eddie dashed out the door looking back at his mother who wore a definite look of angst. But she remained silent as Eddie slid into his brother's 1951 Ford. He started the engine and our two-car convoy took off to Oakley and a night at the Passion Pit with the *Catholishas*.

Following Judy's directions, we pulled up to her modest, yet freshly painted, Cape Cod house. I exited the "Nose" and walked cautiously to the front door, to be greeted by a fairly attractive woman who seemed old enough to be Judy's grandmother.

"Hello," she welcomed me with a friendly smile. "You must be Randy.

I'm Judy's mother. Please come in."

After I stepped into the house, she stuck her head out the door and motioned for Eddie and Sandy to come in as well. They complied.

Sitting in a large hideous yellow, brown and green plaid chair with feet up on a matching ottoman sat a weathered older man firmly grasping a long neck Hudapohl beer. From the blank stare he gave me, I conclude that it was not his first Hudy of the day. Judy came rushing down the steps followed by her younger look-alike sister Jenny, who I remembered from our first meeting at Cincinnati Gardens.

Judy looked the image of Annette Funicello, regaled in full pleated tartan plaid skirt, which clashed badly with her father's chair, and a simple white blouse. The outfit was perfectly complimented by her black and white saddle shoes and lace fringed pure white socks. Her hair was coiffed exactly as it had been on the day we met.

As Eddie and Sandy entered the house, Judy nodded to the old man in the plaid chair and said, "This is my dad."

I respectfully extended my hand and said, "Hello, Mr. Hall."

He looked up at me, ignoring my outstretched hand and acknowledged me with a muffled grunt, quickly returning his attention to the television in the corner of the small living room where the Lawrence Welk show was in full bloom.

Oh, boy, I thought.

"Dad, this is Randy and his friends Sandy and Eddie."

He now looked my friends up and down and grunted again.

Judy reacted knowingly, suggesting it was time to get going.

"We don't want to be late for the movie at the Twentieth Century," she announced with purpose.

Mrs. Hall, totally ignoring her husband, wished us a nice evening at the movies and guided us all toward the door.

"Good night, Mom," Judy said.

"Good night, dear. Remember to be home by midnight," said Mrs. Hall.

Judy then addressed her father, "Good night, Dad."

He ignored Judy and looked me square in the eye as if to say, *I know damn well you are taking my daughter to the drive-in, and if you lay a hand on her I will shove this bottle down your throat and pull it out of your ass.*

Judy's potential, as my future wife, had been seriously compromised. I certainly did not see myself sitting around the table at Thanksgiving while this illiterate drunk carved the turkey. I didn't want to be anywhere near him when he was wielding a knife.

I rushed out the door and didn't look back.

Judy jumped into the front seat of the Nose after Sandy had scrambled into the back seat. With Judy navigating, we drove the three short blocks to Jerri Kellerman's house where *parent meeting* did not seem to be a requirement. Once Jerri was in the back seat of the Nose with Sandy, we drove about two miles to Grace Avenue in the more stylish neighborhood of Hyde Park. As it turned out, Patty Jansen lived just a block from my Aunt Dorothy and Uncle George.

If the visit to Judy's home was tense, our call at the Jansen's large stylish brick home was bizarre.

Judy insisted we all go in to meet the Jansens. You could have fit Judy's entire house into the Jansen's living room. And a good thing too, because when we walked in, we were greeted by Patty, her parents and her eleven siblings (Pope Pius XII would be proud of Mr. and Mrs. Jansen… no birth control being practiced under this roof). It was wall-to-wall kids gathered around the biggest television I had ever seen. It was housed in a grand piece of furniture that also included a hi-fi record player. After the introductions everybody turned their attention to the TV.

The Cincinnati Reds game was just coming on the air. As the announcer, George Bryson, proclaimed, "And now ladies and gentlemen, our National Anthem," the entire Jansen family rose to their feet.

Sandy gave me an inquisitive look as the Star Spangled Banner began to play on the TV. With that, the Jansen Tabernacle Choir all began to sing. As the Three-O-Trio stood there totally dumbfounded, Mr. Jansen turned a gaze on me that said, *What's with you, bub? Are you a Commie or something? You had best start singing if you know what's good for you.*

Sandy and Eddie picked up on the message, and we all did our best to fight the urge to bust out laughing as we began to sing along.

Upon completion, we realized that Mr. and Mrs. Jansen were pretty well lit. Their drink of choice seemed to be an amber colored liquor called Jameson. I surmised this by the presence of a half empty green bottle with a cream-colored label that said, "John Jameson and Sons Fine Irish Whiskey," that sat prominently in front of Mr. Jansen on a coffee table. As my father had taught me, they were slurping their whiskey "neat" ... no ice to ruin the power of the beast.

Unlike Mr. Hall, Mr. Jansen seemed happy to have one less kid between him and the ballgame. Maybe he had plans for working on kid number 13 later in the evening. He and his wife, along with the rest of the choir, harmonized a happy goodbye, and we were off.

On the short drive, Sandy was in a serious search for cars with one headlight burned out, or a p*adiddle* as it was known. The sun was setting and most cars now had their headlights on. There was a simple set of rules for this little game. If a guy saw such a car and yelled *padiddle* before one of the girls, they were awarded with a kiss. The kadiddle also applied. That simply meant a taillight had burned out... a kiss still the reward. And, oh yes, if a girl called the padiddle, she got to punch her date. I was into more mature car games like the *Old Combination* and *Under 20 Night.*

The Schvantz was rewarded midway down Madison Road when he spotted an old black Studebaker coming at us with only the right headlight aglow. Jerri happily complied while I watched through the rear view mirror as she grabbed his face with both hands and lathered a big, long, wet one on my pal. Judy moved closer to the door, indicating to me that she did not play that game.

Jerri, showing her true colors, reached over the seat and planted a kiss half on my mouth and half on my cheek, saying, "Poor Randy, if Judy won't play by the rules, I'll just have to take care of things."

Want to trade, Sandy? I thought to myself.

Within a short time, we made a right turn off of Madison Road into the entrance of the Oakley Drive-In. There was a pretty good line of cars in the queue as Wike in his brother's Ford fell in behind us. After almost five minutes of slowly inching forward, I handed a single green George Washington out my window to a very bored lady. She peered into my car to be sure there weren't more than two people tucked in the backseat. The ticket fee was a quarter per head. She calculated four times twenty-five cents equaled one dollar and waived us in.

I guided the Nose to a perfect spot to the right of, and just behind, the concession stand. Seconds later, Wike and the Ford, with its precious cargo, Patty Jansen, settled into the spot to our right. The stage was set.

I took a look at the pink and powder blue sky back to the west and estimated we had about ten minutes before the big screen would shift from the solicitation to visit the concession stand, featuring the dancing popcorn box and various candy characters, to *Gidget* starring Sandra Dee, America's new sweetheart.

Remembering my promise to Judy of corn and Cokes, I asked Sandy if he wanted to go with me to collect the goods. Instead, he dug deep into is right pocket and extracted a dollar bill, handed it to me and suggested Wike would be happy to make the popcorn-run. Jerri, taking Sandy's lead, strongly recommended Judy go with me... four hands are better than two, etc.

Judy clearly read what was up. Yet, she agreed to join me. I guess she figured Sandy and Jerri would not get into too much trouble with dusk still hovering over the drive-in.

"Get us some Milk Duds too, will ya Stert?" Sandy asked.

"Duds it is," I responded.

I went around to help her out of the Nose. She immediately took my hand, gave it a squeeze and off we went, just like the dancing popcorn box. This was encouraging. Eddie and Patty followed several steps behind, leaving the Schvantz alone with his willing prey.

Once the corn, Cokes and Duds were collected, we headed back to our little piece of Oakley Drive-In real estate. As I had expected, Sandy and Jerri were doing their warm up exercises (small gentle kisses, sans groping... Sandy knew how to pace himself).

Judy punched a box of popcorn through the open back window into

Jerri's unsuspecting face and said knowingly, "Well, that was predictable. Your promise to Father Joe and to Patty and me didn't last long."

Jerri's only response was to grab the popcorn and Coke that followed and to slide back suggestively against the Schvantz. Sandy just looked at me with a "what the hell" gaze.

Once back into the Nose, it became apparent that Judy's entire focus was going to be on keeping her friend Jerri pure, while totally ignoring me. She did a half turn so as to have a view of both the Oakley Drive-In screen and the back seat of the Nose. She hugged the passenger door like it was her best friend, and engaged Sandy in small talk so as to distract him from his mission.

As I sat there dealing with my conundrum, the big screen in front of us lit up to reveal the Loony Tunes logo through which burst the famous Bugs Bunny. The speaker that hung from my window and was tethered to a pole next to the Nose wasn't loud enough for Sandy, who loved Bugs Bunny. So I reached to my left and gave its single knob a quarter of a turn, bringing up the volume to Sandy's satisfaction.

The cartoon was titled "Baton Bunny" and was filled with the typical Bugs mischief as he outsmarted his antagonist at every turn (*What's up Doc?*). The laughs from the backseat, with help from the rear view mirror, told me that the Schvantz and Jerri Kellerman were in snuggle-mode. On the other hand, Judy Hall was snuggling with the passenger door. A glance over at the Wike's Ford revealed that Patty Jansen was also a card holding member of the hug-the-door-club.

This made no sense to me. Judy had been so welcoming the week before when we danced at Ault Park. Her whole persona had been warm, even affectionate.

After Bugs finished his on-screen adventures (*That's all folks!!!*), the previews revealed that Sandra Dee would be back at the Oakley Drive-In again the following week in a movie entitled *Imitation of Life*, co-starring Lana Turner. The way the night was going for Eddie and me, I didn't see us rushing back for another go with the ice cubes we had brought to see *Gidget*.

Nevertheless, I was here, and I reasoned I should continue to at least attract some attention from my date. I slid my hand across the seat and took Judy's hand in mine. She responded with an encouraging squeeze. Just as quickly she took her hand away, while again trying to distract Sandy with idle chatter about what was going on up on the screen.

Gidget finally started in full Technicolor and Cinemascope on the new wider Oakley screen, with little Sandra Dee looking for love on Malibu Beach, pursued by seven beach hunks including Kahoona, a cigar chomping surfer played by Cliff Robertson, and the obvious winner, the continually singing Moondoggie played by James Darren.

In the back seat, Sandy was doing better than Moondoggie, while up front, I was failing miserably, just like Kahoona. The only thing I was missing was the cigar.

Sandy took a high school break from his back seat shenanigans. When you were going at it like he was, you needed to pace yourself. He decided his next challenge would be to get Gidget (Judy) into the unlikely arms of Kahoona (me).

He whispered in Jerri's ear, and they scooted over to the other side of the back seat, directly behind Judy.

"Judy, can you slide a little to the left? We can't see," the Schvantz requested.

Judy took a look behind her, noting she wasn't even close to impairing their view and shot Sandy a disgusted look and me an innocent smile.

Sandy planted a couple of quick kisses on his date, just to be sure she didn't lose interest, then said to my date, "Judy, is your dress stuck in the door?"

With an unbelievable dose of naiveté, Judy opened the passenger door, looked down at her pleated tartan skirt and said with complete innocence, "No, I don't think it is. Why would you think that?"

As she closed the door, thanks to the uncontrolled laughter coming from Jerri, the real point of Sandy's question became clear. She shot Sandy another evil eye, then gave me a look that wasn't exactly inviting.

At that point, I concluded that for me, this night was a bust, so I turned my attention to Gidget, Kahoona, Moondoggie and the other five beach dolts. Moondoggie kept singing. When his voice needed a rest, the semi-famous Four Preps stepped into the void.

Gidget went from a good girl Judy Hall type to an affectionate Moondoggie girlfriend, just a little to the right of Jerri Kellerman. This hour and half beach transformation had no impact on Judy Hall whatsoever. She remained in love with the Nose's passenger door.

Every once in a while, the sound of a quick hand slap could be heard from the back seat as Jerri would giggle, "Stop that, Sandy," without any real conviction.

Five minutes later, more giggling and, "Now Sandy, you just stop that. I'm not that kind of girl."

Frequent glances over into the Ford indicated that both Wike and Patty were enjoying the movie at a great distance from each other. I knew before the night had even started that Eddie had resolved that Patty was a nice yet non-passionate girl, and this was simply a night at the movies.

I, on the other hand was confused and a bit hurt, as I had done nothing to precipitate Judy's rejection. She had been warm, almost affectionate the week before dancing close to me at Ault Park.

As the night progressed, up on the big Oakley Drive-In screen, Gidget continued to warm to Moondoggie's advances. My date was another matter. Like the Dog man, all I was seeking was the warmth of a soft mellow kiss or two. All Judy Hall was offering was the hard-cold-shoulder.

The show available in my rear view mirror proved more interesting, though more depressing, than the one I had paid good money to watch. By midway in the film, the back seat gymnastics had made it clear that the Schvantz had reached his goal of successful physiological exploration... *today the hand and the tit.* Oh well. Good for him, bad for me.

Judy was as aware of the backseat calisthenics as was I. Rather than any thoughts of embracing me, she continued to hug the passenger door like it was the love of her life. I could tell from the view beyond Judy that Patty Jansen was going steady with the Ford's passenger door as well. What did those doors have that Wike and I didn't?

As I continued to peek at the view in the mirror, I noted the Schvantz' hand continue its exploration from the inside of Jerri's sweater. With her full cooperation, I watched as he slipped his hand from her front to her back, clearly in search of the clasp of her bra.

Before he could complete his task, Judy Hall came to life. She released her grasp on the door, turning toward the back seat of the Nose and screamed in a voice that completely unnerved me, "All right you two! That is enough! Jerri, I will not sit here any longer while you let Sandy grope you. It is time to go home. Randy, would you please start the car?"

Jerri pulled away from the Schvantz and snapped to attention like a private responding to the orders of a general, while Sandy was checking his left hand to be sure all his fingers were still attached.

"Randy, please start the car," Judy repeated like a woman possessed.

I was still trying to get my mind to catch up to my eyes and ears. I looked past Judy to Ed in the Ford, who seemed to be struggling with it all as well. Poor Patty sat next to Ed, clearly unaware of what was going on in the Nose.

Jerri, who seemed to have collected herself, began to plead with her obsessed friend, "Oh, come on, Judy. We are all enjoying the movie. Don't be such a prude. Watch the movie and eat your popcorn."

Judy ignored her and insisted yet again that I start the car and take her home.

I made eye contact with Sandy, and immediately we knew we were having the same thought.

The Nose had another special feature. You started the Dodge by turning the key clockwise and then pushing a separate starter button on the dashboard. However, if you turned the key counterclockwise, before you pushed the starter button, the engine would turn over, rumble, but not engage the required spark needed to start her up.

Like a bridge player holding the final trump card, I calmly pulled the car key from my pocket, inserted it into the key slot, gave it a deft turn to the left and innocently pushed the starter button.

Gerum, gerum, gerum, responded the engine. Then nothing. Again, gerum, gerum, gerum. Nothing. A third feigned attempt… same result.

Judy looked inquisitively at me and demanded, "What's wrong?"

"I don't know," I lied. "It doesn't seem to want to start."

"Well, try again," she demanded.

Now fighting back laughter while avoiding Sandy's glance in the mirror, I hit the button.

Gerum, gerum, gerum, putt, putt, gerum.

"Well," I said, "she's an old car and can be a little temperamental. We need to give her a few minutes."

"No! That's crazy. Try again! Get this rattletrap to start," Judy screamed at me.

With that, my tolerance threshold had been hit.

I looked my little raven-haired Catholic square in the eye and said, "Judy, I am sorry that my friend and your friend have offended your moral standards. But you know what? I had nothing to do with that. And you have treated me like I have leprosy all night. And furthermore, don't you dare refer to the Nose as a *rattletrap*. You sure seem to be in love with her door over there. Maybe you and the door can go out next time. You sure don't seem to need me."

The same little tear that I had seen as she lay on the Cincinnati Gardens ice, reappeared in her eye. She looked back a Jerri, then return her eyes to me. In a perfect Jekyll and Hyde moment, she leaned over and kissed me firmly on the lips and then said, "I am so sorry. You are such a sweet guy."

She took my right hand into both of hers, leaned in and tenderly kissed me again. This time I was ready and responded with my own share of warmth.

Judy then wiped the lingering tear from her eye and said, "Who cares about the two of them?" nodding her head toward the back seat.

"Let's enjoy the movie," she purred, as she snuggled against me.

I went into my best Moondoggie persona and put my arm around her, breathing in the wonder of her perfume. For the rest of the movie, we held each other without a word and only an occasional kiss. Yet I wondered about her Jekyll and Hyde behavior.

After the credits, she slid from my grasp and smiled in a way that said it was time to go. I turned the key to the Nose to the right, hit the starter button, and the old girl roared to a confident start.

Judy showed relief and gave my hand a squeeze. I looked over at Wike and the Ford came to life. I glanced at the round white clock at the center of the Nose's dash, noting it was only 10:15. Too soon for the night to end, I thought.

I usually guarded my limited funds dearly. But what the hell, I wasn't ready to return the new Judy to her drunken father yet.

"Hey, it's only 10:15. Whaddaya say we stop at Frisch's for a Big Boy?" I suggested.

The Schvantz and Jerri harmonized their immediate agreement. Judy hesitated and then said, "OK, that sounds nice."

I yelled through the open window to Wike, "Hey, we're headed to Frisch's." Ed nodded, and Patty smiled her agreement.

Our two-car caravan exited the Oakley Drive-In taking a left on Madison Road. In less than a mile, we took another left onto the uphill entrance to what we called "Drive-In Frisch's."

The various Frisch's around town had been given an array of aliases to match our perception of their clientele. The original Frisch's on Reading Road in Bond Hill known as the Mount Vernon Frisch's had been dubbed "Jew Frisch's," simply because it laid at the epicenter of the predominately Jewish neighborhoods of North Avondale, Bond Hill and Amberley Village. The brand-new location in Roselawn was conversely referred to as "Gentile Frisch's," even though Jews and Gentiles frequented both locations in similar numbers.

Because of the frequent use of Montgomery Road for drag racing, the engine-revving boys of the streets that hung out there had christened the Silverton eatery just north of Pleasant Ridge as "Hood Frisch's." The city's largest Frisch's just down the road from the upscale neighborhoods of Mariemont and Indian Hill known to the rest of the world as Frisch's Mainliner, was appropriately referred to as "Snob Frisch's."

Perhaps the least popular location for us was the one we had chosen on this particular night. The moniker of "Drive-In Frisch's" had been assigned simply because the only time we ever frequented it was on the rare occasion we sojourned our way to the Oakley Drive-In.

There were several other locations of Cincinnati's favorite burger joint. They collectively were referred to as either "Too far to drive Frisch's" or "You're dating the wrong girl Frisch's."

In any case, the Big Boys, French fries, coleslaw and strawberry pie were all dependably the same at whichever location we visited.

On this night, we pulled the Nose up to an outdoor order station with its microphone and highly visual backlit menu. Eddie and Patty Jansen piled into the Nose. We kept the ordering simple agreeing on the two-fisted Big Boy, French fries and Cokes for all. Within five minutes, a platter piled high with food arrived via an attractive carhop who attached the tray to the driver side window which I had rolled one third up to accommodate the contraption. Since I was the driver, I distributed the feast to the sardines crammed into the Nose.

Generally, when you add food to a party you wind up with a better party. This proved to be the case within the Nose on this August Saturday night. The laugh meter hit its max, as did the decibel meter.

Patty had taken over the job of practical practitioner from Judy. As she slurped her last sip of Coke, she reminded us all that it was 11:40 and we had to rush to make curfew. So we piled our trash onto the tray, pushed the order button, and within seconds the carhop waltzed up to collect the remains of our meal along with payment plus tip. The total bill came to $4.10. Sandy and Eddie both pushed a buck fifty in my direction. I, in turn added a dollar bill and two quarters to the pile of money and handed the gal $4.50 advising that she could keep the change.

It was agreed that while Sandy and I would return our dates in the order we had collected them, as Jerri did not have a curfew. Eddie would run Patty home, and then we would meet back up at Eddie's house. So off we went.

As I delivered Judy to the door, I leaned in to kiss her good night. But the old Judy reappeared, and she turned her head away with a shy smile.

"Not here," she whispered. "My father would go berserk."

Seeing that emaciated old drunk go berserk was not something I was anxious to witness. I instinctively put an extra foot of distance between Judy Hall and myself. She once again gave my hand a now familiar squeeze and softly whispered, "Call me."

I assured her that I would do just that.

When I got back to the Nose, Jerri giggled her thoughts on what just had happened at the front door of the Hall mansion.

"No kisses for you, handsome. Not that close to old man Hall. Good thing for you too. He'd kill you and then ask questions," she said with a big laugh.

In contrast to my goodnight experience, the Schvantz took his good time at Jerri's front door, sufficiently slathering her with several long lip-locks. He finally returned to my good old Dodge and we were off to Wike's place.

"That girl will put out like a mink," he advised me.

"So, it would seem," I grudgingly agreed.

"What's up with that little Shiksa of yours?" he asked.

"Heck if I know. She is a bit odd. And, Jerri was right about her dad. She told me he would go berserk if he caught me kissing her."

"Well, we need to ask them out again, that's for sure," Sandy insisted. "But I doubt if Wike will be too excited about an encore with four eyes, don't you agree?"

"You're probably right. I don't see that leading to the alter. We can ask him when we get to his house."

When we knocked on the Wikas front door, we were greeted by Manya Wikas.

"Cumpt in boytz," she said.

We followed her to the kitchen where we found Eddie and his older brother, Jack, pounding back a couple of Bartz red Cream Sodas straight from the bottle.

Mrs. Wikas looked at me and reported, "Vell, Rondy, I spokt vit your mutter abut deez girltz you ver vit tonight. She saet dat she dozent tink they ist da Shiksas. So, dis ist gut."

I responded, “Yes, Mrs. Wikas. That Patty Jansanovitz is a nice Jewish girl.” I could tell that Jack was now in on the joke as he almost sprayed the room with cream soda.

“Vell, I’m oft to da bet now,” Mrs. Wikas advised us all.

As the final sounds of her footsteps up the stairs faded, there was a choir of soft, controlled laughter. Jack Wikas shook his head with a wide grin and said, “I need better friends. You three guys are having way more fun than me. So how did things go at the Drive-In?”

“There’s three answers to that question,” Ed reported. The Schvantz has himself one hot schmooie, that’s for sure. And Stert at least got to do some making out eventually. On the other hand, I got the shy, studious ice cube. What’s new?”

Jack looked at his younger brother, and then at Sandy and me and asked, “So will there be a round two with the Catholic girls?”

Predictably, Sandy said, “Is the Pope Catholic?”

Jack looked at me for a response. I thought for a second and then stated, “Yea, I suppose so. The first half of the night I felt like I had terminal leprosy. But Judy is as cute as a button. And she kisses good, when she gets around to it. But I can sure do without ever seeing her father again. He is one scary cat.”

The focus now shifted to Wike who surprised us by saying. “As long as she’s breathing there’s hope. Sure, I’m up for another round of rejection.” He then told Jack about the National Anthem episode at the Jansen house. That provided the final laugh of the night. The Schvantz and I agreed it was time to head to the ranch.

On the drive back to drop Sandy off, he made it clear that his feelings for Jerri were lust, not love. There’s a news flash, I thought to myself. He insisted we immediately call and asked them out again before Jerri had a chance to find someone else. My instincts told me I was headed down a dead-end street that leads to a cemetery. But I agreed that I would take another go with Judy Hall.

When I reached my house on Grafton Avenue, I parked the Nose at the curb, locked her up and took the concrete steps in front of the house two at a time. I was feeling grumpy and ready for bed.

As was often the case, I found my mother sitting in the living room with a book in her hands. She jumped up from the chair and then jumped all over me with a cold blast of questions.

"So, young man, why were you out with Sticksas?" she demanded, badly pronouncing the Yiddish word 'Schicksas.'

Before I could respond, she continued, "Don't deny it! I know you were out with Sticksas. Mrs. Wikas called and wanted to know if you had fixed Eddie up with a Sticksa. I had to lie to her. She was so upset. I told her you wouldn't do such a thing. And, young man, I want to know just what is a Sticksa? Is that a Russian term for a bad girl? I want to know right this minute. What is a Sticksa and why are you involved with Sticksas?"

Now, I never talked back to my mother because I was familiar with the back of my father's hand (who fortunately was in bed sleeping off a couple of quarts of Bavarian Beer). But on this occasion, I went into an uncharacteristic rant.

"Mom, listen up for a second. You don't even know what you're talking about. The word is 'Schicksas' not Sticksas. You call yourself Jewish and you don't even know what a Shicksas is. It doesn't mean 'bad girl.' It means a girl who is not Jewish. Yes, I fixed Eddie up with someone who is not Jewish, like my father and Uncle Bill and Uncle Joe for example. And, oh yes, Uncle George married Aunt Dorothy, who according to you is a 'Sticksa' but in reality, is a 'Schicksa.' Whether you call these very nice girls 'Sticksas' or 'Schicksas', I haven't done anything wrong. Good night. You can let me know in the morning if I am being punished for talking back to you. I'm going to bed and dream about my pretty little Sticksa."

I spun around and headed to my room as my mother silently processed my tirade.

As it turned out, Paula Stertmeyer never uttered another word about Randy, Sandy, Eddie and the Sticksas.

Ultimately my relationship with Judy Hall went where most teenage relationships go… south…nowhere. We went out a few more times, usually with Sandy and Jerri. On a Labor Day double date to Winton Woods Park,

Jerri and I showed up in matching shirts making it look like I was dating her, not Judy Hall. Jerri and the Schvantz thought it was hilarious. It did provide a laugh and perhaps a subtle message.

My last date with the very pretty Judy Hall came when she asked me to her Homecoming dance at St. Mary's High School in the autumn of 1959. We had not spoken for over a month when she called to ask me to the dance. I told her I had a football game and would have to check and get back to her.

Interestingly, it was my mother, having overheard the conversation, who insisted I call Judy back and accept the date. It was good that I went. The combination of facing death once again in the presence of Mr. Hall and realizing how little Judy and I had in common as I tried to engage all of her Catholic friends, made me realize that it was the end of the trail for me and my little Sticksa.

One final footnote: My two Jewish pals Sandy Schwartz and Eddie Wikas both married nice Catholic girls. Sorry, Mrs. Wikas.

Cincinnati Gardens

The Garden's Ice Rink

Oakley Drive-In

The Nose – My'49 Dodge

Ault Park Pavilion Dance Floor

Ault Park Fountain

1960

Well, beat the drum and hold the phone...
So, say hey Willie, tell Ty Cobb and Joe DiMaggio
Don't say, "it ain't so", you know the time is now...
Got a beat-up glove, a home-made bat and a brand-new pair of shoes
You know I think it's time to give this game a ride.
Just a hit the ball and touch 'em all - a moment in the sun;
(Crack) it's gone and you can tell that one goodbye!
Oh, put me in coach
I'm ready to play – today
Oh, put me in coach
I'm ready to play – today
Look at me
Gotta be center field.

From *Centerfield*
By John Fogerty

THE CATCH

The late May afternoon blazed bright with the pastel colors of spring. A big day... a huge day... a last chance. Our senior year was winding down fast and with it the end of high school athletics. Win it today, or forever dream of what might have been. Yes, it was a perfect day to suit up in the Woodward white and blue; to don the cap with the big *W*; to lace up the freshly polished spikes.

The Roger Bacon nine, a powerful band of genuflecting Catholic boys, perhaps known more for their football prowess than for contributing to the national Pastime, stood as the final and toughest hurdle between our Bulldogs and a district championship. The winner of this game would face the winner of the West Hi – Elder game to be played this same day at a venue in Price Hill.

Promptly at 2:10 P.M., Bob Stump, Wally Bohl and I rose from our desks and dropped our excuse slips under the nose of Miss Jenny Fine, the spinster extraordinaire and Civics teacher pretty ordinary. Freddie Zigler yelled to us as we headed for the door to exit room 302, "Beat their Catholic butts." This brought a hearty round of laughter from our classmates and a look of serious angst from Miss Fine.

Freddie and I had long ago conferred upon Miss Fine the dubious title *Biddy Emeritus*. This day she looked most deserving of that assigned moniker. She was plainly adorned in a black skirt that hung down to her thick ankles, a white blouse two sizes too large and buttoned to the neck, Granny glasses sitting half way down the bridge of her Ichabod Crane nose, and black wide- heeled shoes that laced up the front. She had made it clear years ago that she had no use for athletics. I was certain she had no idea what was on the line for the Bulldog Nine this afternoon.

The locker room was abuzz with nervous patter. For the six seniors, this was almost too big. Over the last three years we had fallen in this game to the eventual state champions. In 1957, it was the improbable Reading Blue Devils and their one-man show, Claude Osteen (a Reds *Bonus Baby* who would later pitch in a World Series for the Dodgers) by a score of 3-0. In 1958, it was the Elder Panthers who stole one from us 3-2 on a bad pick-off throw by catcher Bob Schilling, in the bottom of the seventh. Then in 1959, it was Elder again, as we let another close game slip away 5-4. The pain of that loss still lingered.

Yet, for some reason, a feeling of peace had settled inside of me all day. The tension I had expected never materialized. It had been a fun day at school, especially in first period Chemistry class where we had a substitute for Nick *the Slick* Weiler. A frumpy, disheveled little old man with a thick German accent named Mr. Fish awaited us at 8:30 when we filed into the laboratory style classroom on the first floor of the south wing of Woodward High School.

Mr. Fish looking back at us through his Coke-bottle thick glasses advised us we were to see a movie on proper lab procedures and how to write a lab report. It was a bit late to be sharing this information as it was now the end of May, and we had learned all of this from Mr. Weiler the previous September.

Nonetheless, Mr. Fish walked to the projector in the rear of the room and asked, "Vill somptbotty in da frant please shut da lights?"

With that, Stuart Hodesh yelled out "Ant vill somptbotty in da bock turn off da door?"

The rest of the hour was filled with laughs supplied by Stuart and at the expense of Mr. Fish, who didn't seem to care. This seemed to set the relaxed tone for the rest of the school day.

So, even as I suited up - no knots in the stomach, no beads of sweat, and no feeling of panic - just a sense of calm and confidence. I went through my normal routine. Jock strap followed by sliding pads and gym shorts, then sanitary hose and high stirrup blue and white striped socks. Then, most importantly, the roll of the socks; down over my inverted pants at mid-calf to provide the style and protection of perfect blousing; the absolute sign of a real ball player. Finally, I pulled on my blue-sleeved jersey and proudly covered it with my uniform top displaying the number *10* on the back. Nothing else in my life filled me with more satisfaction than wearing the uniform of the Woodward Bulldog Baseball Team.

Each of my teammates went through their own version of this ritual. As I reached up to the top shelf of my locker to retrieve my hat and two sticks of Dentine gum, Coach Von Holle entered the locker room. He looked in my direction and threw me a wink. Bob Von Holle knew how much I loved the game, and I knew he loved me for it.

He called us to the center of the room. I knew - we all knew - what he was about to say. He was about to tell us as he had the previous three years, how he had come so close himself as a pitcher on the 1939 Withrow High School baseball team. He would explain how that loss had stayed with him to this day – how he had not, nor would he ever, get over it. He wanted more than that for us. Yes, he wanted us to experience the glory of the District Championship that had eluded him in 1939, not to mention our six seniors the past seasons. That is what we expected him to say, and that is exactly what he did say. No rah-rah stuff, just food for thought – just cause for reflection. That was how he lived and that was how he coached. Most of us respected that about him.

And so, we reflected as we walked to the parking lot to form our regular five-car convoy that would transport us to Solway Park and our date with Roger Bacon. As always, I rode with my friend and starting pitcher, Wally Bohl, and the other senior starters, shortstop Al Weisboro and catcher Bob Stumpf.

The next hour and a half were a blur. The ride from Woodward to the field at Solway was fast and quiet. This game was too important for the usual razzing and good-natured put downs.

Our warm-up was crisp and spirited. Coach chose Wally and me as Field Captains for the game. We took the ground rules from the umpires, and then, as the home team, we took the field. As I trotted out to center field, the calm in me remained. I looked in to see Wally taking his warm-up pitches and Coach von Holle pacing in front of our bench.

Wally was just wild enough to shake up the Roger Bacon hitters. In the first three innings, he walked five and struck out six. The ball never left the infield. I was getting bored out in centerfield.

We were not faring much better. Our first two batters struck out, looking at big breaking curve balls. I batted third and lifted a lazy fly ball right at their center fielder. We went down one-two-three again in the second. Al Weisboro looped a Texas Leaguer into right field to start the bottom of third, but nothing came of it.

Things unraveled for Wally in the fourth. He walked the lead-off hitter and hit the next guy square in the back. I yelled from my spot in center field, "Mon, Wally, Mon Babe, throw strikes, herp berp sha berp, mon babe."

I heard Coach von Holle echo the same sentiment in plain English, "Come on Wally, throw a damn strike will ya?"

Obedient to a fault, Wally grooved a fastball that their number three hitter slashed between Mitch Goldberg and the third base line for a bases-clearing double. *Here we go again,* I thought. Roger Bacon two, Bulldogs nothing.

But Wally settled into a rhythm and began to throw strikes in places where the Spartans didn't seem to be able to put their bats. He struck out the next three batters, and we trotted off the field down by two.

I knelt in the on-deck circle as Jerry Collins stepped in. Jerry took a ball and a strike and then slapped a hard grounder up the middle for a single.

As I walked to the plate, I noted that the unusual calm remained within me. I dug in with my right spike and looked to Coach for a signal. Two claps of his hands, and I was hitting away. Bacon's lefty, Timmy O'Donnell took his stretch, looked over at Jerry, leading off first, and let fly with his best fast ball. Never in my life had a pitched ball looked more in focus. When the ball left O'Donnell's hand, it looked like a volleyball. Half way to the plate, it looked like a basketball. By the time I began my swing, it had taken on the proportion of a beach ball.

The crack of the well-milled piece of ash I held in my hands making contact with the tightly wound, rawhide covered baseball was the purest, sweetest sound you could hope to hear. Before I dropped the bat to the ground, I knew that the game was tied. I watched the ball sail like a guided missile over the left fielder's head as I set sail around the bases. I was rounding third before he had caught up with the ball somewhere in the next county. Twenty-four Bulldogs greeted me at the plate. Right behind them was Coach von Holle.

We kept hitting the ball hard, but it was always right at a Spartan. As we came to bat in the bottom of the sixth, the score remained tied, and I was leading off. I looked at four straight balls and trotted down to first. Their coach cursed, O'Donnell crossed himself and Von Holle gave me the steal signal.

I took my lead off first, and O'Donnell threw over. I scrambled back to the bag. The three of us – O'Donnell, the Roger Bacon first baseman and I repeated this, three more times. Finally, O'Donnell looked over at me and then delivered a pitch to Bob Stumpf. I was off like the winged victory, sliding into second under the tag.

Two pitches later, Bob grounded to second. I moved easily over to third on the throw. Eddie Southard, perhaps our best hitter, stepped in. Sometimes the other guy's stupidity can really pay off. With one out and me representing the go-ahead run at third, you would expect an intentional walk. But, no, their coach decided to go mano a mano. He would pitch to Eddie.

Big mistake! Eddie took the second pitch high and long to right field. There was enough air under the ball to allow their right fielder to run it down. But I tagged up at third and trotted easily home to put us up by a run.

O'Donnell set our next two guys down in quick fashion. Coach called us together before we took the field for the last inning. He asked Wally, "Are you OK, son? You don't have to be a hero. Let me know if you're getting tired."

Wally looked at him like he had two heads. If Von Holle expected to get the ball from Wally, he would have to cut off his arm. He smiled at Wally and smacked the brim of his cap.

"OK, fellas, three outs and you are District Champs. You know what you have to do, Wally. Throw strikes. You have a great team behind you."

We took the field to the cheers of the one hundred plus Woodward fans that had made the trip down to Solway Field. As I crossed the pitcher's mound on my way to center field, I slapped Wally's butt with the back of my glove. "C'mon, Bohldini," I said. "Let's win us a trophy."

We looked at each other with determination and an air of confidence in one another that is only born after years of friendship. I knew, without question, that Wally was the guy we needed on the mound at this moment.

As I trotted to center field, I saw my father get off a bus on Spring Grove Avenue, just outside the ballpark. He was dressed in one of his summer weight banker's suits. I should have been thrilled to see him out there, striking a pose that screamed success. But there had been a few times lately when he had stumbled off the bus, or staggered slighting into the stands, the late afternoon bourbons taking over. However, today, I hardly gave him consideration. We needed three outs, and that was all that mattered. My eerie calm remained.

I watched as Wally stepped on the mound and began his wind up. In quick succession, he delivered a fast ball for a called strike, another high, hard fast ball that was swung on and missed, followed by a sweeping curve ball that left the batter flat footed, embarrassed, and most importantly, called out on strikes.

Wally was in a groove now, setting down the next batter on four pitches. The fans on the Blue and White side of the field in the third base stands were going wild, while on the maroon and maze side they were collectively clutching their rosary beads. I, too, had become a spectator, full of confidence that I would no longer be needed in our quest for a championship. It was all Wally, and I loved it.

As I expected, Wally quickly went up on the count, 0 and 2. Just as quickly, things turned. He threw a curve ball that was just too good. The batter missed it by a mile. So did our catcher, Bob Stumpf. What should have been *strike three, game over, let the celebration begin*, turned into *man on first and can this be happening again?*

Just like someone pulling on a loose thread, the inning began to unravel. Suddenly Wally could not find the plate, and in eight pitches Roger Bacon had the bases loaded. I saw my mother get up and walk behind the stands. Either she couldn't bear to watch, or she was trying to borrow some rosary beads.

Coach walked out to the mound. I hoped he could settle Wally down. I saw Wally slap his glove against his thigh and then pound it with his fist, both good signs. The bad news was that stepping up to the plate for Roger Bacon was John Durovcik, their All-State catcher. *Please Wally, don't groove one to this guy.*

I bent over, stretching my legs, touching the brim of my cap, smacking the pocket of my glove and shouting out my normal gibberish, "Mon, Wally, mon babe. You got 'em now, Herp berp sha berp, mon babe."

Abruptly, it occurred to me that through the entire game, I had yet to touch the ball in the field. The unexpected calm I had been feeling all day now sucked me into an eerie vacuum. The moment took on a mystical quality in which it seemed as if I were suspended above it all, watching the game unfold, including my own actions.

I crouched over, slightly up on my toes, readying myself for the next pitch. With the bases full, Wally took a full wind up. He delivered a fastball low and away. I saw Durovcik begin his swing. As he uncoiled, his right foot stepped toward third base and his bat angled downward at forty-five degrees taking dead aim at the pitch.

Instinctively, sensing my time was now, I moved to my right with a large crossover step, even before he made contact. In an instant, it was just me and the ball. The crack of the bat was solid, sending the ball on a hard, low trajectory toward left center field. My instincts told me that I would never get to it before it landed. I should run a route to cut it off before it skipped by me. Yet something forced me to override instinct as my personal radar locked in on a spot that seemed impossible to get to in time.

Now I was in a desperate dash to catch up with the sinking liner as it continued to slice away from me. I sprinted on, arms pumping, legs churning, never once taking my eye off of the ball. It was diving to earth as I launched myself at a spot I could not possibly reach. Something akin to the way a thermal holds a glider in the air, I felt elevated toward my chosen spot.

But I was not going to make it. My eyes finally lost sight of the ball as I stretched every fiber in me. Then I saw it again as it made contact with the webbing of my glove. I turned my left wrist clockwise in an attempt to keep my well-oiled McGregor-Goldsmith between the ground and the ball as I slammed hard onto the outfield grass.

I was filled with a sickening feeling. I could not feel the ball. I quickly rose to one knee, desperately searching for it off to my right - nothing. Then, there it was, like the proverbial snow cone, half in, half out of my glove's webbing. At the same time, the rest of the world came back into focus. I turned back toward the infield, raising my left hand to show the evidence. I saw the third base umpire, his right fist raised in similar fashion, indicating the final out of the game. Behind him a sea of blue and white rushed toward me. I was hit by a wave of teammates, coaches and friends, led by shortstop Al Weisboro.

There is nothing to compare to the collective celebration of team championship, especially when you are at the center of it. I found myself being hoisted up onto the shoulders of Bob Stumpf and Ron Young. I gazed to my left to see the look of relief on the face of my friend Wally Bohl as he rode upon the shoulders of Stuart Hodesh and Fred Zigler. From my perch, I looked down to see the expression of redemption on the face of my coach Bob von Holle. We were District Champs!

Like a swarm of bees, we eventually worked our way from center field back to our bench. Waiting there were my good friend Freddie Zigler, my tearful mother and my totally sober father. He was clearly filled with uncharacteristic pride.

"Nice catch Kiddo," he said. For me, that was like winning a second championship.

The following Thursday, there was a small piece in the *Bulldog Barks*, written by Sports Editor, Ed Grosswiler with the simple headline *The Catch*. That same day, we lost to the Elder Panthers yet once again, in the Regional game to determine what team from southern Ohio would play for the State Championship. Even though it was a lopsided loss to a clearly better team, the pain was unbearable.

The next day, my dad received a call from Buzz Boyle, a scout for the Cincinnati Reds, suggesting they might be interested in offering me an opportunity to play for their Geneva New York minor league team in the New York – Pennsylvania League. Much to my father's chagrin, I ultimately chose to play college baseball instead, an experience that would include many great games and thrills. But never again would I experience a moment as pure and as memorable as those few seconds at Solway Park in May of 1960.

Wally makes pitch against Roger Bacon – May 1960
(I am the speck over his right shoulder in Center Field)
(Bob Stumpf Catching)
Bulldogs Win!!

1962

They got one eye watching you
One eye on what you do
So be careful who it is you're talking to
They got one eye watching you

From *Major Minus*
By Coldplay

Doc's Eye

When I first enrolled at Miami University in Oxford Ohio in the fall of 1961, it was already a year late. Miami had always been my first choice after participating in a science fair on the campus during my junior year of high school. The campus was just spectacular.

Then in the Spring of 1960, as I was about to graduate from Woodward High School, a fellow named Ed Jucker dangled the possibility of a baseball scholarship at the University of Cincinnati in front of me, and, more importantly, in front of my parents. And that was that. Goodbye Miami. My mother never had wanted me to leave town for college and my father was good at math. Baseball scholarship equaled no tuition costs and college in my home town equated to no room and board expenses.

It seemed that I was destined to become a UC Bearcat rather than a Miami Redskin. Go Cats!

However, it was through a peculiar series of circumstances that I wound up at Miami a year later. Believe it or not, it started with Cincinnati's greatest basketball star ever, the remarkable Oscar Robertson. For, you see, Oscar graduated from Cincinnati at the same time that I graduated from Woodward.

Why would that matter? Fair question. With Oscar gone, the head basketball coach, George Smith, incorrectly reading the tea leaves, concluded that his career would be better served as the Athletic Director rather than continuing as the head coach. This left a vacancy that was filled by the UC varsity baseball coach, Ed Jucker. Yes, the very same Jucker who had invited me to play baseball at UC.

And, I might add, he was the very same Ed Jucker that lead the Bearcats to National Championships in 1961 and 1962 and within a whisker of a three-pete in 1963 (bad decision, George Smith).

With Jucker moving from baseball to basketball, a very nice chap named Glenn Sample became the new Bearcat head baseball coach. Unlike Jucker, he knew little of me. But in the fall of 1960, he was welcoming and encouraging. He would see how I did on the freshman team the next spring.

Whoops! That didn't work out so well. Just as practice was ready to begin in February, I came down with a serious case of the dreaded "kissing disease," mononucleosis. Now, that was OK with me on a couple of fronts.

First, the lab that did my initial blood test to see why I was so sick reported the wrong type of blood cells to my doctor. For about four hours on Friday, February 4th, I was misdiagnosed with leukemia. When you think you have leukemia (an absolute death sentence in 1961), you couldn't be happier to learn you will be sicker than a mongrel dog for a month or so, but alive.

The second reason "mono" turned out to be fine with me is that the very nice Coach Sample advised me that, since I was unable to play or even practice with the freshman team that spring, there would be no scholarship my sophomore year.

My mother fainted, my father checked his bank account, and I let out a scream of joy, that my friend Freddie Zigler heard a street away. For me, this meant Miami was back in play.

Those are the basic circumstances that delivered me from UC to Miami.

There were a new group of circumstances that led me to Mrs. McIntosh's farm in September of 1961.

After more than two weeks in bed for excessive kissing (that's another story), I reapplied to Miami, but my first semester grades at UC were left wanting. That put me on a wait list as I worked to improve my grades at UC.

A meager 2.0 grade point average in my first semester was improved to a 2.8 in the spring, and Miami came a knocking. Finally, my dream of matriculating in Oxford Ohio had come true. Just one problem... by the time I was accepted there were no upper-class dorm rooms available. The youth of America was growing faster in the early sixties than was the infrastructure on most college campuses.

But there were choices. Upper-class male students were permitted to live off campus. Que up Mrs. Ruth McIntosh. One of many options I explored was her farm at 317 W. Spring Street on the edge of Oxford, just across the railroad tracks from the old train station. Fortunately, to me, her farm did not seem to be on the wrong side of the tracks. Maybe a little too close to the tracks when trains roared by, though.

Mrs. Mac, as I would come to call her, was the widow of Oxford's first real veterinarian. Together, Doc McIntosh and his wife had produced and raised eleven children. The good doctor had passed away a few years earlier, and all of their eleven off-spring were grown and scattered across America.

Her eldest son, Bob, who had his own dairy farm on the northern side of Oxford, also worked the old McIntosh Spring Street homestead, where they grew corn and hay. 1961 would be Ruth McIntosh's first venture into the student room rental business. Her plan was to let one room on the first floor of the two-story clapboard seven-room house. This one room was to house two "well behaved" male students with a full semester's rent paid in advance. Doc's widow was no dummy.

While the walk from the farm to campus was a few extra blocks, it was by far the best place I had inspected with my mother. In addition, Mom hit it right off with Mrs. Mac, as they were both prolific piano players. There was a pristine Steinway upright in the living room. That sealed the deal for Mom.

The only wild card remaining was determining with whom I might be sharing sleeping and studying quarters. That question was resolved two days after we wrote our check for $120 to Mrs. Mac. Our home phone rang right after dinner. At the other end of the call was a high-pitched voice that introduced itself as Sidney Bernstein. He explained that he was to be my new roommate and advised me that he was from Chicago and was transferring to Miami from Northwestern University.

At first, he seemed like a good enough guy on the phone, but when I say "wild card," I hit the nail on the head with an emphasis on "wild."

After a few pleasantries, he turned up the heat, insisting he had to have the bed away from the window as he hated being cold when he slept. And he must have the wooden desk, if that was OK, telling me the metal desk was actually better (it was smaller with fewer drawers, and definitely not better). But I figured what the hell, I was just happy to be at Miami. I'll work things out with Sid when we finally meet.

Before we hung up, Bernstein advised me that his father had attended Miami before the War and had been in the Zeta Beta Tau Fraternity, making good old Sid a legacy (or fraternal gibberish for *if the ZBT boys didn't like him they were pretty much screwed*).

As a parting piece of advice, he said to me, "By the way, Randall, please do not call me Sid. I go by Sidney."

"OK, Sidney. I go by Randy," I replied.

He closed our conversation by saying, "I'll see you in two weeks down on the farm," with more than a hint of arrogant superiority. How bad could he be? I reasoned that I would go the extra mile with *Sidney.* I'd make it work.

As it turned out, I hardly saw him from the day we moved in, but at the start he put me straight about his stature in life.

He was a very polished and handsome Jewish kid standing about 6" 2" tall and trim, yet nonathletic, with bright brown eyes and dark curly hair slicked back with what proved to be an extra scoop of Brylcreem. I learned that he was from Highland Park, a highly upscale area in the northern suburbs of Chicago. His father was a prominent attorney with an office in "The Loop," who took the "train in" every day. The Bernsteins were members of the Lake Shore Country Club (good... finally a little something in common... I used to caddy at a country club).

"Dad is on the Board of Trustees for the Chicago Art Institute," he informed both me and Mrs. Mac the first day we were together. At the time, I had no idea what the Chicago Art Institute was. Maybe an art school in Chicago, I wondered. In my early adulthood, I would learn that it is one of the great art museums in America. I have visited and enjoyed it many times. But in 1961, as my pals would have said, "Well, la dee da!"

"And we have regular box seats right behind the Cubs dugout at Wrigley Field. Have you ever been there?" he asked, continuing before I could answer. "I've met Ernie Banks. And we spend a lot of time at our lake house on Deer Lake up by Boyne Mountain in Michigan in the summer. And of course, we ski at Boyne a couple of times each winter."

La dee triple da, I thought. *Wait until my friends get a load of this guy.*

As it turned out, while Sidney's parents thought he was majoring in Economics, he was actually majoring in beer and girls and doing pretty well with the girls and even better with the beer.

Fortunately, I rarely saw him from early morning until late at night. If he showed up before I was asleep, he usually staggered and weaved his way into our room anxious to describe in detail his latest coed conquest. This served me well as a sleep aid.

I quickly learned from a couple of his ZBT brothers who were in my Geology 101 class that Sidney may or may not go to one of his morning classes, but he was easy to find from lunch on, usually at Al and Larry's, one of Oxford's most popular watering holes. He never attended his afternoon classes.

Long story short, Sidney was so deep into flailing and failing by Thanksgiving, his pursuit of a degree in Economics miscarried and he didn't return to Miami and the farmhouse after our Christmas break, never to be heard of again. Good riddance, *Sid*.

This left me happily alone as I chased a good Miami education and a place on the freshman baseball team. Freshmen were not permitted by the NCAA to play varsity sports until 1972, and transfers had to sit out a year. As a transfer from Cincinnati to Miami, my option was to play freshman baseball as a sophomore and hope to make the varsity as a junior. Those were the rules and that was my plan.

I loved Miami from the first day. My good friend Mike Cohen had also transferred from UC to Miami, his sights on playing football. It turned out well for both of us, as our respective sports eventually provided a grant-in-aid to us both, and we were both named captains of our teams our senior year.

Also, on campus was one of my best friends, Sandy Schwartz. Sandy did not get into Miami initially and was a semester behind Mike and me in the fall of 1961. Thus, he was living in the newly built Anderson Hall, a freshman dormitory in what was called the South Quad.

In quick fashion, I was hanging out with Sandy (or *the Schvantz,* as we had long ago named him) as well as his Anderson Hall neighbor, Jim Cloughessy. Jim was a gangly, somewhat unsophisticated and highly pious Catholic boy from Lorraine Ohio. He had just the right mix of goodness, humor and naiveté to make him a perfect new college friend, who was, happily, and often, the butt of the joke.

Like the Schvantz, Jim was a second semester freshman rather than a first semester sophomore. In his case the reason was financial. He had worked on the Great Lakes as a deckhand to earn enough money to afford attending Miami, setting him a back a term.

I often chose to pay two bits at the Anderson dining hall in order to have dinner with the Schvantz and Jim. We were required to wear a tie at dinner. Each of us had opted for *clip-on* cravats, a popular choice for a late afternoon grab-and-go, readily available at Young's University Shop in uptown Oxford.

In addition to abundant and reasonably tasty dinners, the dining hall provided a copious number of attractive coeds for flirting purposes. We quickly befriended several of the choicest options. My favorites included Kathy Fitzgerald, who I would later date, Barbara Halle, who the Schvantz would date that semester and Gail Morris, who was so gorgeous no one had the nerve to ask her on a date.

Gail was blessed (or maybe cursed) with what could be described in the jargon of the day as *prestigious jugs* or as the Schvantz called them, *Quadraphonic Speakers*. Jim had speculated that her bust measurement had to be at least fifty-two, which, of course, was and extreme exaggeration.

But she sure could fill a sweater. Nonetheless, we ran with that and nicknamed her (behind her back), B-52. This secret moniker soon ran rampant around the South Quad.

In the realm of nicknames, Jim needed one; it was the law. Being a devout Catholic who spoke regularly of his pal Jesus Christ, and given that his initials matched up, he was quickly dubbed *J.C.* Never again was he called Jim.

We all had a raucously wonderful first semester. In fact, the Schvantz had such a good time he flunked out. J. C. and I managed to have tons of fun and still do the work, both earning a respectable 2.5 grade point average.

Sandy's poor performance also cost him his relationship with Barbara Halle, the daughter of Cleveland Department Store magnate Walter Halle. At the time, Halle's was one of the two preeminent department stores in Cleveland along with Higbee's. The Schvantz had already suggested to Barbara that after college they would marry and he could go to work for Walt. Though she was quite fond of the Schvantz, by the time he returned to Miami in the fall of 1962, Barbara had moved on and his retail career in Cleveland was gone with the wind.

An interesting side bar to Halle's is that the famous actress, Halle Berry, who was born in Cleveland, was given her name from her mother's love of the store.

In late January, with Sandy off working as the night manager at the new McDonalds in the Cincinnati suburb of Kenwood, J.C. and I grew closer. We shared one class that second semester. We had both chosen Physiology as the option of meeting our biological science requirement. Thus, on a dark snowy Saturday in mid-February, we had planned on cramming for our upcoming first test in that subject. Rather than trying to overcome the noise and Saturday night insanity at Anderson Hall, we chose the quiet calm of Mrs. McIntosh's farm house.

On this particular weekend, Mrs. Mac was off to Wisconsin to visit with one of her eleven off-spring, leaving J.C and me alone with our text books and notes.

By late afternoon, a heavy wet snow had started to blow up Spring Street from the west. By 6:30, it had turned to ice. And, just after 7:00, the electric went out with power lines succumbing to the weight of the persistent ice.

With J.C. due to arrive at 7:30, I sat in the dark in need of candles. I began to stumble about the farmhouse in a futile attempt to find some matches. Finally, after banging into chairs, tables and kitchen appliances, I made my way to Mrs. Mac's oven where, low and behold, I found a box of wooden matches.

Now with a good supply in hand, I went in search of candles. In the five plus months I had spent at the farm, I could not recall ever seeing a candle; not even a birthday candle. But there had to be some around somewhere, I reasoned. I started striking matches and opening drawers and cabinets in the kitchen, learning quickly the limited time I could get out of a match before singeing my fingers. In the wax torch department, the kitchen drew a blank.

I moved on to the dining room. Logic would have dictated that I begin my hunt with the huge sideboard just beyond the kitchen door. But logic wasn't necessarily my strong suit. I started with the bulky roll top desk across the room by the front door. The three drawers on the left side of the desk produced papers, envelopes, stamps, scissors, a stapler and extraneous junk. But as to candles, I got zilch.

I moved to the right-hand drawers. I opened the top one first to find more keys than Mrs. Mac could possibly need. She never locked any doors.

I moved on to the middle drawer. There was more junk plus a very fancy wooden box. I reasoned that it was too large for a ring, but I hoped some birthday candles could be hiding inside. Because the box was so pristine, with intricate carving, I took it from the drawer with great care. The current match signaled to my right hand its time was up. I set the box down and drew a new wooden stick with its phosphorus and sulfur red and white tip.

Mentally crossing my fingers, I gently lifted the burly polished top. Then I lit the new match. Before it had even fully ignited, I jumped back and let out a very guttural scream, almost falling to the floor. Staring back at me was an eyeball. Yes, an eyeball, resplendent with a dark black pupil, a bright blue iris and delicate very fine red blood vessels in the sclera (remember, I was studying physiology and I knew my eye parts). That eyeball may have been the scariest damned thing I had ever laid eyes on (pun intended).

What the hell, I thought as the match burned my fingers badly enough that I threw it across the room. Thankfully the eye disappeared with the little digit-seeking torch. I hesitated to light up the area again, still shaken from my discovery. I finally found the courage to strike the next one. Even though I knew what to expect, the sight of that small yet monstrous thing scared me all over again. I quickly slammed the box shut, now well aware of the new burning little time bomb I held tightly between my thumb and forefinger. I blew it out.

As I stood in the dark dining room, a thought hit me. A while back, I had overheard Mrs. Mac's two friends Flo Sigfuss and Rachael Schenkel (yes, those were their real names) discussing an accident that Doc McIntosh had when he was a young man that had cost him his right eye. In that burled walnut box sat Doc's eye. Of course, when you lose an eye your choices are limited to a patch or a glass eye. Doc had clearly gone the glass route. He was gone but his eye remained.

As I thought about this, my nerves began to calm. And then the humor of the whole thing came into focus. With a wry smile, I realized that I was clearly obligated to share my terror with J.C. when he arrived. One more match permitted me time to replace Doc's eye where I had found it.

Yes, I must see how J.C. might react to the same delightful surprise package in that roll top desk. Giddy with anticipation, I decided it would be smart not to be standing behind him when I shared my little discovery, but first I needed more light. I now went to the sideboard where, predictably, I quickly found a passel of candlesticks. Had I gone to the sideboard first, Doc and I would never have seen eye to eye. But I had defied logic and would now carry the vision of that frightening piece of glass art in my mind's eye forever more.

To my good fortune, I also found three candle holders that held three white waxy sticks standing ten inches tall. I went quickly to work setting up what little artificial light I could get from my third discovery of the night.

I put two of the candles in the kitchen, leaving one strategically positioned on the top of the roll top desk.

The next thing I did was make my way to my room through the flickering shadows to retrieve my battery-operated portable radio which I carried into the kitchen. WSAI Radio disc jockey Ron Britain was on the air, just starting the 7:30 segment of his show with his famous opening, "Hello my tulus, chico buddies and ducky friends."

Don't ask me what the hell all of that nonsense meant, but Britain was hilarious. And, per usual, on this stormy night, he was spinning the day's top-forty tunes, when J.C burst through the front door shaking off ice and snow.

Stomping his feet on Mrs. Mac's welcome mat, J.C. said, "Believe you me, Stert, that's some nasty doggone weather out there. That darned ice was blowing right in my face all the way down Spring Street. Jesus, *Mary* and Joseph, it's cold."

I was fairly certain that it rarely got close to freezing in Bethlehem, so I wasn't clear as to how these three Jews, Jesus, Mary or Joseph would be of much help to J.C., but I passed on that discussion. I had something waiting for J.C. that might resurrect all three of them, with a *Holy Moses* thrown in for good measure.

"Wow, the power is out, huh?" J.C. queried.

"Yep. It took me a while to find some candles," I answered. "But we have three all-nighters burning now, and in the kitchen, we have Ron Britain spinning the hits my tulu buddy and ducky friend."

J.C., like us all, loved Britain and acknowledged our good luck with a big smile.

"I hope you don't mind if I spend the night? I sure don't want to go back out in that mess tonight," he pleaded.

"No need to beg, J.C. Old Sid's bed is permanently available. God, I miss that guy," I joked.

I was more than a little anxious to share the pure joy of shock and terror with my Catholic buddy. But I didn't want to create any suspicion that I was up to no good either, so I said to J.C., "I guess we will have to wait until tomorrow to study. I assume you will be going to church?"

"Yea, Sunday mass is a must, but I can be back here before 10 and we can get at it," he confirmed.

"Well, we have cold Cokes in the refrigerator and plenty of pretzels and chips in the kitchen. But first, I have something really cool to show you," I said trying to bait his curiosity.

"What's that?" he asked taking the bait.

Reel him in slowly, I told myself.

I began to set the bait, "Hey, J.C., you know how Mrs. Mac is always talking about how poor she is?"

"Well, Stert, outside of that nice piano in the living room, she doesn't seem to have much," he responded.

"True. But when I was looking for candles, I found something really valuable in that old roll top desk in the dining room," I said, pulling on the fishing line.

"Oh, yea. What was that?"

"Why don't I show you, and you can tell me what you think. In my judgment, its worth a small fortune," I continued, feeling the hook poke through his Irish cheek.

"Really? OK, let's take a look. Is it jewelry?" J.C. asked.

"Well, it is certainly something you would wear to make you look better," I said, continuing the tease.

I nodded toward the toward the dining room and said, C'mon, let me know what you think."

With one of the candlesticks in hand, I guided him to the desk where I slowly opened the second drawer on the right side of the big roll top. I then gently removed the dark wooden box.

Before handing it to him, I warned, "Now be very careful with this. It's really something special."

He gingerly took the box from me, as I lowered my candle close to his hand. He hesitated, just holding it as if there was a million dollars in his grasp.

Finally, he lifted the lid.

Just as I had done, J.C. recoiled, letting out a shriek, worthy of every movie Vincent Price, Bella Lugosi and Boris Karloff had made all lumped together. And I swear, Doc's eye had J.C.'s eyes popping out of his head like Tom the cat in a Tom and Jerry cartoon.

He screamed once again, falling to the floor and dropping the box. The eye bounced out and rolled across the oriental rug stopping right next to J.C. still prone by the dining room table. He scampered to his feet and quickly dashed in to the kitchen.

"Motherfucker," J.C. yelled at me. That was especially significant, as I had never once heard him use such language.

"You bastard. What was that?"

I couldn't answer because I was laughing so hard.

"Son-of a-bitch. What the hell was that?" he asked again. I finally contained myself sufficiently to answer.

"I think it is Doc McIntosh's glass eye," I explained, tears running from my two real eyes,

conveying to him that I had overheard Flo Sigfuss and Rachael Schinkel discussing the accident that had cost Doc his eye as a young man.

"Jesus, Mary and Joseph, Stert. You scared the holy shit out of me."

I was fascinated with this new vocabulary of expletives that J.C. was displaying. On the radio, Ron Britain introduced the next song, the Everly Brother's "Crying in the Rain." I was crying with laughter as J.C. continued to shake with terror.

Suddenly I realized that Doc's eye was still laying on the dining room floor. One more chance to spook my friend, I reasoned.

"Hey J.C., you dropped that eye on the floor. You better go put it back in the box."

Still shaking, he exclaimed, "I'm not going near that damned thing. You can put it back."

Realizing that I had no choice, I forced myself to sneak up on *that damned thing*, reaching out, feeling the smoothness of the very real looking eyeball in my hand. I carefully placed it back in its box trying to remember what blood vessels went where. Then I set the box back exactly where I had found it, and closed the drawer, never to lay eyes on it again.

J.C. and I sat in the kitchen for over an hour, eating pretzels and chips washed down with America's drink, Coca-Cola straight from the bottle, while listening to the top hits for February 1962.

The next morning provided one more small shock. As J.C. started to head off to church, we discovered how bad the storm had been. There were electric lines down everywhere, including a still sparking wire within inches of J.C.'s footprints in the icy snow. From the looks of things, he had a very close call before being introduced to the good doctor's eye.

By the time he returned from church, there was a crew busily repairing wire up and down Spring street, including the one in our yard. We did study most of the day with good reward. We both aced the Physiology test on Monday.

Mrs. Mac returned from Wisconsin never to learn of the entertainment her dead husband had provided in her absence.

The following year, J.C. moved into the farm with me along with Sandy Schwartz and Mike Cohen, providing a full year of more College Joe jovial nonsense. Who knew farm life could be so much fun?

From that point on, though, neither J.C. nor I could pass that desk without keeping a close eye on it.

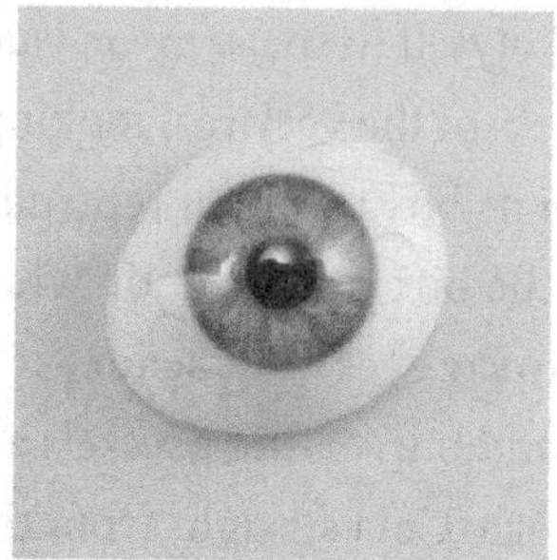
Not Unlike Doc's Eye

Not Unlike J.C.'s Eyes

Not Unlike the Scene at the Farmhouse

1962

Well I don't know, if I dreamed it. I don't know, might be real.
Lord, it's so strange, how one will find another,
But I keep on searchin,' cause I know you're out there,
And all I gotta do is open my eyes and see her - the mystery woman.
Cause I'm confused, but only sometimes.
Patiently waiting, baby just for you.
But I'll be leavin,' babe, I won't go under.
All I gotta do is open my eyes and see her - a mystery woman.

From *Mystery Woman*
By Daniel Toler, Gregory Allman

Pont Formation

The fall of 1962 was both historic and filled with personal drama and nonsense. It was a great time to be a junior at Miami University in Oxford, Ohio. The town and the campus were literally like something out of a Norman Rockwell painting. There are so many good memories and stories from that particular autumn.

I'm going to share a rather bizarre escapade from October of 1962, but I have chosen not to convey the names of two of the main characters. While I was a party to part of the adventure and my very trust-worthy friend and roommate Mike Cohen was an eyewitness, I still think it is best to protect the guilty.

The other major participant was Miami University football legend and head coach, Johnny Pont. If you were to pick a single word to describe Pont, you might call him *feisty*. He was small, even for a running back in the early 1950s when he played for the Miami University Redskins. And he was coached by two other Miami legends, Woody Hayes and Ara Parseghian.

As my tale unfolds here, I would suggest that it was his very spirited approach to life that has allowed Johnny Pont and this story to remain so vivid in my personal Miami football lore.

Pont was a starting halfback for the Redskins from 1949-1951. He led the entire nation in rushing in 1949, was named to the All-Mid-American Conference Team all three years and was honorable mention All-American twice. And, in 1951, his number 42 was the first to be retired at Miami. Only two others, Bob Hitchens (40) and Ben Roethlisberger (7) have been so honored.

After a short stint in professional football in Canada, Pont came back to Miami as an assistant coach under Parseghian, and then became the head coach in 1956. He moved on to the head job at Yale in 1963 and then at Indiana in 1965. He later coached at Northwestern and Mt. Saint Joseph College.

As stated, the other stars of this tale will remain anonymous. There are a few folks out there who will know their identities if they were to read this, but you will not learn the names from me. Let's just refer to them as *The Star* and *The Mystery Woman.*

One was, in fact, a star wide receiver and place kicker on the Miami football team that year. The other was a very attractive Jewish girl who had attended Woodward High School with my two roommates Mike Cohen and Sandy Schwartz and me, graduating a year ahead of us. In recent years, she had become quite notorious for pursuing well known professional and college athletes, the mission being to add names to her scorecard.

The fall semester started with great promise in 1962. I was back at Mrs. Ruth McIntosh's farm again after spending my first year at Miami there the previous year. My roommate from that first year was a guy named Sidney Bernstein from Chicago, whom I believe may have attended less than a half dozen classes the whole semester. It was quickly clear to me that he was majoring in beer and frat parties. He was a legacy at the Zeta Beta Tau Fraternity and planned to move into the fraternity house as soon as a room became available. That never happened as he quickly flunked out, leaving me solo at the farmhouse at the end of Spring Street for the second semester.

Mrs. McIntosh was the widow of Oxford's most famous farm animal veterinarian. Town folks also knew her as the former piano player for old silent movies many decades earlier. By the time I showed up, Doc McIntosh was long gone, movies had sound and Mrs. Mc needed the extra rent money. She had raised eleven kids on the big farm on the edge of town where they grew corn and hay on 20-plus acres of prime farmland next to the old Oxford Train Station.

The farmhouse had two large bedrooms on the second floor and I had convinced the widow lady to rent them to three friends and me for the 1962-63 school year. In mid-September, I moved in with high school pals, Sandy Schwartz and Mike Cohen. A new friend, Jim Cloughessy, from Loraine, Ohio rounded out our little fraternity. Mrs. Mc allowed us to use an extra bedroom on the first floor as a study room.

To show our appreciation, we helped her eldest son, Bob, put up a passel of hay the week before school started. That experience convinced all four of us that farming was not a vocation we would ever pursue.

Mike and I had both transferred to Miami in 1961. He was now a starting linebacker on the Redskin football team while I was competing for a starting position on the baseball team. By our senior year, we were captains of our respective teams.

Under Coach Johnny Pont, the Redskin football team would finish the regular season with eight wins, one loss and one tie, upset the number nine ranked Purdue Boilermakers and be selected to play in the Tangerine Bowl in late December.

After suffering through a week's worth of pitching hay, the *Four Musketeers,* as Mike Cohen referred to the Farmhouse Four, quickly settled into the fall semester. For Mike Cohen and me it was the start of our junior year, while for Sandy Schwartz and Jim Cloughessy it was the beginning of the second semester of their sophomore year. Sandy had flunked out the previous winter but was back for another try while Jim had started school a semester late, needing to earn tuition money before beginning school.

None of us were known by our real first names while residing at the two-story white farmhouse at 317 West Spring Street. Sandy had long ago been given the nickname *Schvantz,* a Yiddish word for, well how should I put this? Let's call a spade a spade... it meant penis. Mike and I had not called him Sandy for at least three years. He was now the Schvantz, period, end-of-story!

Mike had a new nickname I had given him the previous year. In high school, he was often called *Motto*. But he had proven to be such a vicious linebacker at Miami that I started referring to him as *Super Jew*. That name stuck and grew first on the football team and then around campus. Some of us quickly shortened it to *SJ*. And so, as we settled into life on the farm, he was now *SJ*, period end of that story.

My nickname was *Stert*. This dated way back to the post war years when my father was called Stert at the bank where he worked. When I moved to Bond Hill in 1953, my new friends, Fred Zigler, Wally Bohl and Carl Schiele, had quickly picked up on this. Thus, to most of my friends, *Stert* it was.

Now, poor Jim came to us without an appropriate moniker. We changed that quickly. He was clean-cut, naïve and very religious, the product of a good Catholic education. So, it didn't take me long to connect *Jim Cloughessy* and *Jesus Christ* into the obvious… *JC*. Welcome to our little fraternity, *JC*.

Autumn and Oxford, Ohio were made for each other. Founded in 1809, Miami University had a campus that might have been designed by Thomas Jefferson with Georgian architecture, consistently using red brick for most buildings, all settled into an environment of mature oak, maple, sycamore and chestnut trees that provided a constantly changing color palette as fall progressed toward winter.

And the campus emptied on its northwest side into a perfect downtown of college shops, restaurants, pubs, two drugstores, two movie theaters, a stately post office and a town square with a large water tower at its center. For me, it was too good to be true. Yet, there it sat, a mere thirty-five miles from my front doorstep in Cincinnati.

Of course, a big part of autumn in Oxford was football. In recent years, Miami had taken on a new identity. As it related to football, Miami was now known as *The Cradle of Coaches*. An inordinate number of successful coaches at major programs around the country had begun their college coaching careers in Oxford. The "A" list, if you will, consisted of Earl "Red" Blake (Army), Paul Brown (Ohio State and Cleveland Browns), Woody Hayes (Ohio State), George Little (Michigan, Cincinnati and Wisconsin), Weeb Eubank (Baltimore Colts), Paul Dietzel, (Louisiana State),

Sid Gillman (Cincinnati, Los Angeles Rams and San Diego Chargers) and Ara Parseghian (Northwestern and Notre Dame). Many more would follow in years to come building the brand with several NCAA and NFL Championships. You could add to this, Baseball Hall of Fame Manager, Walter "Smokey" Alston who took the Brooklyn Dodgers and later the Los Angeles Dodgers to several World Series, winning four times.

In the fall of 1962, Johnny Pont was hoping to become a part of this famous group. By October 6, the Redskins had a perfect 4 - 0 record with fairly easy wins over Xavier, Quantico Marines, Western Michigan and Kent State.

My roommate, Mike *SJ* Cohen had firmly established himself as the starting middle-linebacker.

As for me, I was finishing up five weeks of fall baseball practice under the guidance of assistant coach, Bud Middaugh, as our head coach, Woodrow "Woody" Wills, was busy coaching the offensive line on the football team. Middaugh would later become the University of Michigan baseball team head coach taking them to several College World Series. Fortunately, I had a great fall practice. As a *walk-on* transfer, I was competing against two scholarship boys in center field. As had occurred already with SJ, if I were to crack the starting lineup the following spring, it would likely come with a grant-in-aid scholarship. That would please my parents to no end.

From the moment the last bale of McIntosh hay was rolled and placed in the field, my junior year turned to near perfect. The four musketeers were settled in at the farmhouse. And all but JC were in hot pursuit of pretty coeds. Eeve Arkush, my girlfriend of the past two years, was off to Emory University in Atlanta for her freshman year. We had agreed to date around while she was away to prove the strength of our relationship... we did and it didn't. But that's another story.

SJ, Schvantz and I spent much time at street dances and open houses, checking out freshmen, sophomores, juniors and even seniors of the female persuasion. I zeroed in quickly on three in particular. I had met Chicago freshmen Lori Sundstrom and her friend Lynn Jenison at an open house at the Rez (short for Reservation), as the Student Union was known at Miami, on the first Saturday of the school year.

I liked them both and they both seemed to like me. I focused on Lori, as she was blonde and prettier and I was average and shallow. By the following weekend at a street dance, Harriett Cohen, a friend of Eeve's from Cincinnati, introduced me to her roommate, Donna Craig. Donna was petite, smart and gorgeous. She was both a good choice and a bad choice. It was bad because her roommate was Eeve's friend who was quite likely to report all of the details to the Emory campus but good because Donna had a boyfriend at the University of Kentucky, so we could make it seem so innocent. *We were just keeping each other company, don't ya know?*

Thus, my lips were alternately mingling with those of Lori and Donna most Friday and Saturday nights, with an occasional movie, study date or dance thrown in between. This, too, was a bit complicated as both girls lived on the same floor at Swing Hall, but it all worked out in September and October. While I was playing my little game of coed roulette, SJ and Schvantz were both enjoying the company of a much larger sampling.

As stated earlier, my fall baseball practices were going extremely well. I was hitting and fielding better than I ever had as my confidence grew.

I also loved my classes that semester and was turning in a bunch of As and an occasional B in the classroom.

At the farm, life was also good. Schvantz and I shared a room, as did SJ and JC on the abundant second floor. We had regular sing-a-longs with Mrs. McIntosh providing the instrumentals on her old upright piano. We also got to know her two spinster friends, Rachael Schenkel and Flo Sigfuss. Those three were a real hoot.

Then there was the hayloft. It was the perfect spot for coed exploration and experimentation. Donna Craig proved to be a big fan of the loft. Lori Sundstrom, not so much. SJ and Schvantz were using it at such a high volume that we decided we needed a system to assure a degree of privacy.

It was SJ who said, "Do you guys remember the movie *Stalag 17*? They would tie a dangling light fixture in a knot as a signal. Well, there's a dangling light hanging down in the barn when you come in. Let's do the same thing if one of us is using the loft."

That idea was passed unanimously although that fall JC never put it to use.

Yes, things were good at Miami in the fall of 1962. Then on Saturday, October 13, events really got interesting. SJ and the Redskin football team were off to Lafayette, Indiana to take on the number nine-ranked Purdue Boilermakers on a bright sunny autumn afternoon. Clearly, our boys didn't stand a prayer against the Big Ten team.

JC, Schvantz and I gathered around my little bedside radio at the farm anyway, tuned into WMOH to catch the action from Purdue. You never know. Right?

Miami did have two potential All-Americans in offensive tackle, Tom Nomina and, as mentioned earlier, our wide receiver/place kicker, *The Star*. Equally significant was sophomore left-handed quarterback, Ernie Kellerman. Ernie was a real phenomenon. He could throw the ball 60 yards in the air and was off to a spectacular first season for the Redskins. He later played safety in the NFL for the Cleveland Browns and the Cincinnati Bengals.

The three of us settled in, rooting for our team and our roommate against all hope. And wonder of wonders, our loyalty was rewarded mightily. Purdue couldn't do anything right. When the final gun sounded, the Redskins had upset the mighty ninth-ranked Boilermakers by a score of 10 - 7. Ernie Kellerman had hit *The Star* on a long sixty-five-yard pass along the Miami sideline for the Redskins sole touchdown. *The Star* kicked the extra point as well as the winning field goal from 35 yards out.

When the game ended the three of us headed the eight blocks up to downtown Oxford to find a huge crowd surrounding one of the goalposts from Cook Field. A picture of that was a centerpiece of the *Sports Section* of the *Miami Recensio,* the school Yearbook, the following spring. The celebration eventually moved from the street into several of the Oxford bars where the only thing available to enhance your mood was 3.2 beers. Oxford was a "dry" town, exempting full-throttled brew.

A little after 9:30 that night, we met our victorious roommate as he exited the team bus at Withrow Court. The team and the campus were enjoying what *Sports Illustrated* would later call the *biggest upset of 1962.*

The euphoria of that big win continued over the next few days. Then on Wednesday, October 18, things turned from unbelievable to bizarre.

It was just after eight-thirty that night when it all changed. As SJ, JC and I sat attentively studying around the dining room table while Mrs. McIntosh was in the living room watching *Hawaiian Eye*, there was a hard knock at the door.

Being closest to the door, I rose to see who was so anxious on the other side. When I opened it, I found an animated Johnny Pont staring at me.

He yelled, "Stert, where's Mickey?"

For some reason he decided that Mike Cohen should be called "Mickey." No one else did, but he was head coach, so who were we to argue?

Then looking over my shoulder he spotted SJ seated at the table. Pont brushed by me, rushing up to his star linebacker with a surprising celerity.

"Mickey," he screamed. "*The Star* is missing." (Remember, I am committed to not naming names).

Of course, Pont used *The Star's* last name with great emphasis.

"Whaddaya mean, Coach? He was at practice today," SJ countered.

Pont continued, "Listen to me, will ya? He's missing. Herb Street told me some Jewish girl from Cincinnati drove off with him about an hour ago"

Herb was the starting center on the football team and *The Star's* roommate.

Of course, JC was clueless as to what was happening. On the other hand, SJ and I looked at each other with an understanding glance. We knew, or at least suspected we knew, exactly what was up with this little development. This clearly fit the profile of the notorious *Mystery Woman.*

"How do you know she was Jewish?" Mike queried.

With a somewhat embarrassed look, but no less animated, Pont responded, "Well, Street said she looked Jewish, damn it. And, you're Jewish and you're from Cincinnati. So sue me. Do you have any idea who it might be?"

Fighting back laughter, SJ explained, "Well coach, there is a girl that Randy and I both know who might be the person involved. But I can't say for sure."

Pont looked from SJ to me and then back to SJ.

"Well, what the hell, son. This is all I got. Who is she?

SJ shrugged and named the *Mystery Woman*.

"OK, then," Pont screamed. "Do you know where she lives?"

As it turned out, both SJ and I knew that she lived in a very large, luxurious house in the Cincinnati suburb of Wyoming. We had attended a couple of parties there our senior year in high school.

"Hell, Coach, " SJ said. "They could be anywhere, if it's even her. But yes, I do know where she lives."

"Well, quit wasting time, Mickey, and get your damned coat. We need to get down there," Pont insisted.

SJ hesitated, and then ran upstairs to get his Miami letter sweater.

When he returned, Pont went ballistic.

"For fuck sake, Mickey, you can't wear that. Why not just run an ad in the paper that you're from Miami? Get a coat!"

This time SJ returned with a light jacket.

Pont grabbed him and guided him through the open door and threw him in the passenger side of his car. With that, we heard the squeal of gravel from the driveway and off they went.

At that point, I explained the legend of the *Mystery Woman* to JC. As he was processing this, Schvantz burst through the door.

I got him up to speed on *The Star* and the *Mystery Woman*, which, of course he found to be hilarious and believable.

This all was not conducive to studying, so we joined Mrs. McIntosh in the living room where *The Red Skelton Show* was just coming on the TV. Skelton entertained us for an hour. His Clem Kadiddlehopper sketch was particularly funny. While the three *Joe Colleges* in the room roared with laughter, the good Christian widow muffled a very subdued giggle.

Being a farm lady accustom to rising early, it was now Mrs. McIntosh's bedtime, so the three of us headed up to JC's room at the top of the stairs where the Schvantz and I filled JC in some more on the *Mystery Woman.*

At 10:50, we heard the door open and quietly close. SJ appeared with what could be fairly described as a legitimately *shit-eating* grin on his Jewish face.

If the night up to this point had been unbelievable, the story SJ now shared was simply preposterous.

First, the drive to the targeted Wyoming home of the *Mystery Lady* should have taken at least 45 minutes. Pont had cut that time by more than 10 minutes, scaring the beejeebies out of SJ several times as they flew down hilly US 27 along the way.

While I knew John Pont could be really intense, what SJ now described ran more along the lines of crazed.

Mike told his story with great flare.

"We pull into the drive way on two wheels. Coach hit the brakes so hard I thought I was going through the windshield. Now, listen to this. He jumps out of the car, sprints to the front door and starts pounding on it like crazy. The next thing I know, he tries the doorknob. The door is unlocked and he just barges right in."

After taking a deep breath, SJ continued, "I didn't know what the hell to do. First I thought about heading for the hills. But then I thought, what if Coach got shot? I knew the family. So, against my better judgment, I followed him into the house. He's yelling for Number 81 at the top of his lungs."

"I just knew we were going to get shot or wind up in jail," he continued.

Then SJ started laughing uncontrollably. He couldn't get the next words out.

Finally, the Schvantz demanded, "For Christ sake, SJ, what the hell happened?"

With tears running down his face, Mike finally contained his laughter enough to go on with his description.

"Well, he's running through the house like a banshee, opening doors and screaming. Finally, he heads upstairs. There's no sign of anybody. He's opening more doors. Nothing. Then finally he opens the last door, with me standing right behind him, and there they are, completely naked in her bed, with the covers over them."

Still laughing, SJ said, "I thought I was going to shit a brick. I don't even think she recognized me as she was so focused on Coach."

Mike continued, "For a second, Coach just stopped in his tracks. Then he walks calmly over to the bed and grabs our guy right out of bed. Then he walks to a chair and grabs his clothes and says to me, 'Mickey, get his shoes.'"

After another hard laugh, SJ said, "Man, at this point, I'm doing as I'm told. I got the shoes and socks. Then I notice a Miami letter sweater on the floor, so I picked that up."

"Did she see you then, " I asked.

"Hell no! She was buried under the covers still screaming to high heaven. I ran down the stairs behind our tiny coach and our big wide receiver dressed in his birthday suit. Pont forced him into the back seat and threw his clothes in behind him. Let me tell you, I wasted no time jumping in the front seat with the shoes, socks and sweater," SJ reported, still laughing.

"Then what?" the Schvantz asked.

SJ continued, "Well, my mother didn't raise no idiot. I kept my mouth shut. Coach calmly backed the car out of the drive and headed north. Once we were out of the neighborhood, he looked in the rear view mirror and said, 'Jesus fucking Christ. What were you thinking? Put your goddamned clothes on, you idiot.'"

SJ explained, finally getting his laughter under control, "Not another word was spoken until we got to the Sigma Chi House."

The Star was an initiated and committed member of the brotherhood and all that the rituals so implied at the Alpha Chapter of Sigma Chi. (Yes, sports fans, Sigma Chi was born at Miami University!).

SJ went on, "At that point all Coach said to the both of us was that he better never hear another word about this little episode ever and that he would see us at practice tomorrow. Then he dropped me off here. No *thank you*... no nothing... and off he went."

We all sat there in the upstairs bedroom totally dumbfounded.

Finally, Schvantz asked, "He was really in bed with her? No. Really?"

SJ answered, "I swear Schvantz, they were in bed naked as two Jaybirds. Pont scared that poor girl out of her mind. I know it's beyond belief. I couldn't imagine such a thing if I hadn't seen it with my own eyes."

JC finally chimed in, "What if she calls the police? And where were her parents?"

"Hell, if I know where her parents were. But I know we were damned lucky they weren't home. But think about it. Would she be schtupping him in her bedroom if her parents were home? Hell no. And that's exactly why she ain't going to be calling the police," SJ reasoned.

After digesting that logic, we all finally cashed in on this crazy Wednesday, just after midnight.

The next evening, we all gathered in our study room to hear SJ report that it was business as usual at football practice as the Redskins prepared for Ohio University on Saturday.

SJ explained, "I swear, it was like last night never happened. Coach was totally focused on the Bobcats. But I will tell ya this... *you know who* wasn't worth a shit all afternoon. He must have dropped a half dozen passes and Kellerman was getting pissed. But not coach. He just ignored it and went on with the practice."

Then looking at JC, he said, "No, the cops didn't show up. That's not going to happen."

As it turned out, *The Star* had only a fair game that following Saturday at Ohio University, and the Redskins lost their first game of the season 12 - 6. Then the next Saturday, we could only pull out a 24 - 24 tie at Bowling Green. The perfect season everyone had hoped for after the upset at Purdue was not to be, but the Redskins did get an invitation to play in the Tangerine Bowl, losing to Houston by a lopsided score of 49 - 21, finishing the 1962 season with a record of 8 - 2 - 1.

Of course, the main characters in this little tale all moved on. As stated earlier, Johnny Pont left Miami to coach at Yale the next season followed by stints at Indiana and Northwestern, taking Indiana to the Rose Bowl on January 1, 1968.

The Star was team co-MVP along with offensive tackle Tom Nomina in 1962. He was a second-round pick (25th overall) of the Chicago Bears the following spring. He was also selected by Buffalo in the third round of the new American Football League draft. At Chicago, he played mostly as a place kicker where he had a mediocre record of 14 field goals made out of 39 attempted. After three years, his professional career was over. But, hey, what the hell, he played in the NFL.

Then there was the *Mystery Lady*. She became a flight attendant (they were called stewardesses back then) with United Airlines and moved to, you guessed it, Chicago.

Sports Illustrated Cover – November 1962

Goal Post carried Downtown Celebrating Win over Purdue 1962

Johnny Pont on sidelines - 1962

My Roommate ***SJ*** (Mike Cohen)

1963

I'm an old hitchhiker, I wonder what's a waiting 'round the bend
I don't know what I might see and I don't need no guarantee
Just a ride from here to there...
Why don't you pull off to the side let the poor boy have a ride

From *Hitchhiker*
By John Denver

Tough Test

On January 28, 1963, I had two things on my mind. First, it was my cousin Rick's ninth birthday, but I would miss the party as I had one more exam to take and had to skedaddle back up to Oxford for my four o'clock Diplomatic History test.

I had come home for the weekend with the most difficult exams behind me. As it turned out, the toughest challenge would be the test of my will to actually get back to Miami University. For on this wintery Monday, Mother Nature decided to test my resolve.

The original plan was for my mother to drive me downtown to the bus station where I would catch the bus to Hamilton, Ohio. From there, I would grab a second bus that would take me up to Oxford. I planned to be on campus in time for lunch followed by an hour or so of further study for the upcoming exam.

But when I awoke at 6:00 AM, I gazed out of my bedroom window to see the beginning of a small blizzard. My good friend and college roommate, Sandy Schwartz, or Schvantz as we called him, had spent the night on our couch and was going to join me on my short trip north. But with the snow blowing sideways, any thought of my mother driving us into town was gone with the wind.

Of course, being the worrywart she was, she tried to talk us out of the trek that now faced us, but she didn't understand that my professor, Dr. Jellison, would not look sympathetically at my personal predicament. After a short debate, the Schvantz and I bundled up against the winter storm and headed down Grafton Avenue with hopes of catching a bus into town.

We waited and waited at the bus stop at Langdon Farm and Reading Roads. Not a hint of a bus came our way. Finally, we resorted to the thumb.

It seemed luck was in our favor, as the third car that drove past us stopped and offered us a ride. Driving a very slick brand-new powder blue Ford Fairlane 500 was a middle-aged gentleman who said he worked downtown at Procter and Gamble. We would crawl down Reading Road in heavy traffic. When he dropped us at Fountain Square, we had a short two-block walk to the bus station. Slipping and sliding through the slush, we arrived at the station just in time to buy a ticket to Hamilton and jump on a bus parked under the station's south side canopy. Things were looking good. It was nine o'clock and it seemed we had plenty of time.

The trip to Hamilton normally took about an hour and 15 minutes. But, with the Greyhound struggling through the storm, the trip took twice the normal time, and we didn't arrive in Hamilton until a few minutes after noon. There still seemed to be plenty of time. Just scratch the lunch plans. I could study on the bus.

Then our luck in trying to continue north went south. We were informed that all buses to Oxford had been canceled, and by this time a good ten inches of wet snow had fallen.

Schvantz and I looked at each other and shrugged. No big deal; we still had our thumbs. Thus, out we stepped into the blizzard onto High Street. Unfortunately, it appeared that Greyhound was not the only cancellation in Hamilton. There was not a single car in sight.

Every now and then a car would creep by in the eerie silence that comes with heavy snow, paying us, and our thumbs, not one bit of attention. After 15 minutes we began to walk north, more to stay warm than anything else.

At one o'clock, I started to worry. Sandy, on the other hand, was more interested in shelter than rides. He had finished his exams. He ducked into a Rexall Drug Store while I desperately looked south hoping to see a vehicle of some sort heading my way.

Finally, just as I was about to give up hope, I saw a beat up old pickup truck cross the High Street Bridge six blocks south of us. It slowly crept toward us. As it got closer, I noticed that only the windshield wiper on the driver's side seemed to be working.

No way this guy will stop, I thought to myself. But, sure enough, the damned beat-to-hell Chevy slid over to the curb. The passenger window was so crusted with snow I could not see in. I stumbled around to driver's side to find that I could not see in that window either. Then the door opened and I came face to face with the meanest looking German shepherd I had ever seen. The huge hound was all teeth, snarling, then barking, only restrained from removing my nose by the tight grip the driver had on the dog's leash.

As I recoiled, I got my first look at the driver. As impossible as it seemed, he was scarier looking than his dog. He was middle-aged, with a two or three day stubble and a long prominent scar running from his left ear down to his mouth. He was smiling a wicked smile, to prove that he only had a handful of teeth.

"Hi there, young'un. Where da hell you be headin' in this goddamned storm?"

I stammered back, "We need to get up to Oxford."

"Well, ain't this your lucky goddamned day. I live in Darrtown. But I need to be gettin' up to Oxfert to deliver dem bags of feed back der," he said gesturing to the truck bed.

"Get your goddamned ass in here before the cab fills with snow," he demanded.

Still stammering, I said, "Well I'm traveling with my friend in the drug store there. Do you have room for us both?"

"Shit fire. We'll make some goddamned room. Killer here will have to sit on your lap."

I didn't have to asked who Killer was as his goddamned dog was still snarling at me.

By this time, Sandy had figured that I had scored a ride and came running out of the Rexall. Before I could get back around to warn him, he grabbed the passenger door handle and quickly opened the rusty door. Killer announced his presence with more fervor than he had with me. The Schvantz recoiled stumbling half way back to the Rexall doorway.

"Holly shit!" he cried out.

Our limo driver widened his toothless grin and said, "Easy there young'un. Killer don't take kindly to strangers. He jest needs to git to know ya a bit."

Schvantz looked at me with deep concern and said, "Killer?"

I shrugged and reminded him that I really needed to get to Oxford lickkety split.

"Well, is you boozy comin' or ain't ya?"

"You first," said Sandy.

I gingerly lifted myself and my small satchel up into the truck waiting for Killer to live up to his name. Sandy climbed in behind me.

"Well, if we are gonna to ride all da way up ta Oxfert, we should git to know each utter," he said extending his gnarly right hand while holding Killer back with his other. "I'm Zeke. And you all done met Killer."

I took his hand noting that most of his forefinger was missing.

"Randy," I said.

Sandy then introduced himself as he closed the door.

"Well, I'll be a sonafabitch. Sandy and Randy. Ain't that just too goddamned cute. Ya all sound like an act at the County Fair. If ya'll gonna be runnin' 'round deez here parts together, one of ya might jest wanna change yer goddamned name," he stated, followed by a very wicked laugh.

I took a deep breath, not taking my eyes off of Killer, while Schvantz hugged the door.

Zeke looked at us and said, "These here are da rules. I'm gonna let Killer here climb on yer lap thar, Randy. But don't you darr touch him unless you want to lose that girly hand a yours, ya hear?"

"Yes sir," I said, my voice cracking and three octaves too high... like a girl.

I figured the circulation in Sandy's right arm must have stopped, as he pressed hard against the door trying to get a centimeter or two further from Killer.

The big shepherd snarled at Sandy as he climbed upon my lap, going nose to nose with the Schvantz. We both had our girly hands deep in our pockets.

With that, Zeke hit the gas fishtailing out onto High Street. Zeke was steering, and Killer was snarling. Zeke guided his poor excuse for a pickup truck north. We couldn't see where he was going because the passenger side wiper was not working. That was OK because we never took our eyes off Killer who must have weighed eighty ponds or more, stopping the blood flow to my legs.

We made our way through the northern part of Hamilton past Thompson Park slipping and sliding on the truck's bald tires.

As we came up into Darrtown, Zeke turn his attention from the truck's radio that was blasting the song *Hey Good Looking* by Hank Williams and said, "I gotta make a quick stop at the farm. It'll only take a minute. We'll be headed back ta Oxfert bafur ya can say 'zippity doo.'"

Sandy and I looked at each other with a blank gaze that said what we were thinking... *We're going to die.* I had visions of a violent attack by Zeke followed by Killer having us for lunch. After that, I feared Zeke would bury us somewhere in the back forty. Zeke showed us his diseased gums with another mischievous smile. He took a sharp right onto a road deeply covered with fresh snow.

We slid through the white powder as Zeke strained to keep the rusty heap, he called a truck on the road. Killer was becoming restless and sat up, allowing the blood to finally flow back to my feet. But his teeth came so close to my nose, the blood drained from my head.

After a mile or so, the toothpaste poster boy pulled the old Chevy pickup into a long driveway that led to a big ancient barn that looked like it might collapse at any minute. He guided the truck to a hard stop skidding to the right. With that, he jumped out of the cab, and Killer jumped up and growled. Sandy and I jumped out of our skin.

"Now you boyz just stay put, ya har?" Zeke demanded.

Yep, we're going to die, I thought. *Is he going for a knife or a gun?*

"C'mon, Killer," he yelled at the dog.

Killer snarled at me and then jumped out and followed Zeke into the barn. Before we could run for our lives, Zeke popped back out of the barn hauling a bale of hay, Killer close behind. He threw the ball onto the snow-covered bags of feed in the truck bed. Then he grabbed Killer's collar and hitched him to a post next to the barn.

With that, he jumped back into the truck and said, "Okee doke boyz, let's get yer young asses up to Oxfert."

The gasp of relief from both Schvantz and me had to be noticeable.

"I think Killer liked you boyz. Dats pritty unusual. He don't take ta strangers much" Zeke said giving off a hard hillbilly laugh.

"He's a nice dog," I lied. *Especially tied to that post,* I thought to myself.

The truck slid left and right back down the driveway and onto the street. It looked like we might live after all.

"You boyz wanta beer?" Zeke asked reaching behind the seat pulling out a Carling long neck. He cracked the cap off by banging it down hard on the steering wheel.

"No thanks," Sandy and I said in unison.

We turned right into Darrtown, skidding back and forth as Zeke took a long draw on the long neck in his mangled right hand. He started singing along to *Heartaches by the Number,* playing loudly on the radio. As bad as his singing was, it was music to my ears after 10 miles with Killer on my lap.

It was slow going in the snow, but we finally headed up the hill leading into Oxford. I suppose all the weight from the feed in the truck bed helped us navigate up the final steep slope.

"How 'bout I dump you boyz by dat der Student Union Buildin'?" Zeke asked. "I need to take dat shit back der to a farm out by da airport."

"That will be fine," Sandy screamed back over the blasting music.

Zeke took a hard right from US 27 onto Spring Street and skidded to the curb in front of the Student Union.

"You boyz study hard now and keep the Lord in your heart, ya hear," Zeke said.

We quickly thanked him and jumped out of the rattletrap into the piled-up snow at the curb, thanking the Lord that we had survived the blizzard, Zeke and Killer. He was off, and we were safe.

The Schvantz and I both broke into laughter, which was more to relieve stress than anything else. We both looked up Spring Street as Zeke and his version of Nellie Bell disappeared beyond a rise in the road.

Finally, Sandy said, "I need a goddamned toasted roll," with the emphasis on *goddamned*.

"Let's just get somewhere that's warm," I responded.

We dashed across Spring Street and into the front door of the Miami University Student Union.

As we shook off the snow, Sandy said, "The next time we hitch a ride with a toothless guy from Darrtown, let's introduce ourselves as Schvantz and Stert. Randy and Sandy sounds like an act at the County Fair."

"I'll tell you this, I will never get into a car again with a goddamned German shepherd," I responded.

Sandy then suggested, "Let's go downstairs to the cafeteria and get that toasted roll."

The toasted roll was an institution of sorts on the Miami campus. They were essentially a flat cinnamon roll sliced in half, slathered with butter, and then grilled to a toasty perfection. You could get them at either the Student Union cafeteria or at Tuffy's restaurant, another Miami institution.

I loved them, and they only cost a dime. But I looked at my watch, which informed me that I had exactly eight minutes to dash from the Student Union to Hughes Hall.

"Gotta go," I announced. "See you back at the farm."

Yes, the Schvantz and I lived on a farm at the other end of Spring Street with two more college characters, our roommates, Mike Cohen and Jim Cloughessy. But that, and our landlady, Mrs. McIntosh, is another story.

"Good deal and good luck," Sandy yelled to my back as I headed to the door. "Watch out for man-eating dogs!"

I took the steps at Hughes Hall two at a time and rushed into room 203 just ahead of Dr. Jellison. I reached into my satchel and pulled out a fresh Blue Book and a ballpoint pen. I had made it just in the nick of time.

My professor handed out a one-page test with only four essay questions. I scanned the paper and smiled. The first question on the exam was: *America's success in the Revolutionary War was due to two things; the balance of power in Europe and the skills of American diplomats. Discuss both in detail.*

I smiled again. As I put pen to paper I thought, *this should be easy. The real test was getting here.*

Zeke's Chevy? Maybe.

Killer as I Remember Him

Miami Campus on a Snowy Day

1963

Has anybody here seen my old friend John,
Can you tell me where he's gone?
He freed lotta people, but it seems the good die young
I just looked around and he's gone.

From *Abraham, Martin and John....*
By Dick Holler

November Weekend

November 22, 1963 started for me with my annoying Big Ben alarm clock ringing me awake from an intense sleep at 6:30. I hated that clock. But being just a few weeks shy of my twenty-first birthday, I slept long and hard and needed help to assure that I didn't doze the day away.

I pounded the damned thing hard, extinguishing the loud ring and jumped out of bed, throwing on some workout shorts and a Miami Baseball tee shirt. After bundling up, I took the short walk next door to Withrow Court for my Friday workout on the steps of the basketball court gym.

It seemed like just another Friday. As it turned out, this day would prove to be anything but normal.

After a half an hour up and down the steps, I took a quick shower and scurried back to my room in the two-story World War II barracks that now acted as a men's dormitory. The sun was coming up, and it looked as though we were going to have a beautiful fall day in Oxford, Ohio.

I threw on some khakis, a powder blue button down oxford shirt, black socks, tan penny loafers and my red Miami letter sweater with the big white M above the left side pocket, and headed to breakfast on the first floor of Billings Hall which sat next to the tall red brick tower that housed the Beta Bells.

After wolfing down some scrambled eggs, bacon and rye toast washed down with orange juice and a cup of coffee, I rushed off to the second floor of Irvin Hall for my eight o'clock Government 201 class. While most of the leaves had found their way to the ground by mid-November, the two big pin oak trees outside the window next to my desk still reflected the bright sun on their remaining golden leaves.

Our normally bore-snore Professor Johnson started the class that morning with an interesting discussion of the recent Army coup in Viet Nam that had deposed their President Ngo Dinh Diem. Johnson explained in detail the effect of the recent Buddhist unrest in which Quang Duc, a Buddhist Monk, had set himself on fire in June on a busy Saigon street. This turbulence and the threat from North Viet Nam, had alarmed many senior Army officers in the Diem regime. The Kennedy Administration and the US Ambassador to Viet Nam, Henry Cabot Lodge, had become embroiled in the conflict.

On November 2nd, Diem and his brother, Ngo Ninh Nhu were assassinated by the Army leaders. Professor Johnson explained to the class the current conundrum the US government now faced in the far-off land. Johnson was on a roll, and the entire class listened with intent interest.

All of this was important for us to understand, Johnson explained, as the current subject matter for this class centered on the State Department and the importance of diplomacy to keeping peace in the world. Thus, he articulated the possibility of the US becoming embroiled in a mess similar to what the French had faced in Viet Nam a decade earlier. Viet Nam had been at the forefront of the news for the first three weeks of November.

When our professor got back to the normal subject matter, half the class fell immediately to sleep. While I remained awake, I turned my attention to the gorgeous, unusually warm and sunny autumn day on one of the most beautiful college campuses in the country.

When the Beta Bells tolled three-quarters past the hour, I noted that I only had to endure five more minutes of Johnson's droll word-weary tedium. Outside the window, the campus was alive with coeds and college Joes wandering the crisscrossing walkways as auburn and golden leaves gently floated to the ground.

Finally, the bell in Irvin Hall sounded, relieving us of the agony of State Department stratagem. Just three more classes and the weekend would be here.

I took the steps down to the first floor and walked outside to breathe in the Indian Summer's fresh air and to take in the view of leggy college girls as they scampered about. A quick walk deposited me inside Mac Cracken Hall where my 9:00 o'clock American Literature class was held.

The first thing Professor Jacobi did was hand back our papers on Ralph Waldo Emerson and the Transcendentalism movement. In bright red at the top of my paper I noted an "A-" and the margin note "sp". My spelling, or lack thereof, had done me in again. I owned a Webster College Dictionary. I also owned a misguided confidence in my spelling which often kept me from reaching for Webster when I should have. Oh well. I was tracking for an "A" in this course. Lesson learned.

After the class settled down from either euphoria or disappointment, Jacobi turned our attention to *Walden* by Henry David Thoreau. He explained that Thoreau urged resistance to the dictates of normal society, writing his important piece by the calming waters of Walden Pond in eastern Massachusetts.

The class went by much more quickly than my Government class had, due in large part to the eloquent outgoing style of Professor Jacobi. His love of literature was inspiring.

At 9:50, class was dismissed, and I headed to the Student Union to study for my American Diplomacy History class at 1:00. I was scheduled to meet my former farmhouse roommates Mike Cohen and Sandy Schwartz there for lunch at 11:45.

I was really enjoying Diplomatic History as the Professor for the class, Dr. Jellison, was the best teacher I had my senior year. His approach was both funny and intellectual... not an easy thing to accomplish. Before I knew it, it was time to get up from the big soft leather easy chair in which I had been studying and head down stairs to The Zebra Room for lunch with my pals.

The Zebra Room was the unofficial name for the cafeteria in a newly completed wing of the Student Union. Its red and white and black and white striped booths had quickly led to the restaurant's new moniker.

When I arrived, I found The Schvantz, as Sandy was known, and S.J., as we called Mike, seated in a window booth waiting. We quickly went through the cafeteria line where I ordered a grilled cheese, a toasted roll and an ice tea.

The main discussion at lunch was the upcoming football game scheduled for the next day against the University of Cincinnati Bearcats. As always, the game would be played at Cincinnati's Nippert Stadium. S.J. (short for Super Jew, a name I had given him the year before) was concerned about containing the Bearcats' talented quarterback, Brig Owens. Mike started at middle linebacker for our squad who had our own great junior phenom at quarterback, Ernie Kellerman.

Our team was having an unusually poor season under new head coach, Bo Schembechler, after going to the Tangerine Bowl the previous year under coach Johnny Pont who had moved on to Yale. The record stood at four wins, three losses and two ties going into the last game of the season against Cincinnati.

Sufficiently fed, we all agreed that we would kick the Bearcats' asses the following day, and we scampered in three different directions… The Schvantz back down Spring Street to his apartment and a nap, S.J. off to his Kinesiology class, and I back to Irvin Hall for my Diplomatic History test.

I walked into room 205 on the second floor of Irvin Hall five minutes early to find Dr. Jellison shuffling papers at his desk at the front of the room. As always, the bell rang promptly at 1:00. The Professor closed the door to the room and proceeded to hand out the test papers.

As I opened a blank Bluebook, I looked at the clock across the room. It was 1:03. Unknown to me, at that moment, President John Fitzgerald Kennedy was riding in his open top Presidential limousine with his wife Jacqueline, Texas Governor John Connally and his wife Nellie, somewhere between Love Field and downtown Dallas.

The test was not difficult, and I was well prepared. I was sitting next to an open window. As I completed the last question and was reviewing my answers, I noticed a bit of commotion outside Irvin Hall but went back to the business at hand. It was 1:45 Eastern Standard Time when I walked to the front of the room to hand in my test. Returning to my desk, it was clear that something was going on when I noticed two girls in tears below the window next to where I sat. *What the hell?* I thought.

The bell rang, and everyone headed for the door. In the hallway, students were mingling, and I noted that the commotion outside had found its way to the second floor corridor of Irvin Hall.

Then I heard it for the first time. A girl across the hall in the direction I was headed screamed loudly, "Kennedy has been shot." The fifty plus students moving to and from classes in the hallway were abuzz, and there was an obvious air of consternation.

As I tried to process what was going on around me, I walked into room 203 where my Ohio History class was scheduled to convene at 2:00. I walked over to the window to observe the commotion outside. I looked north toward the Beta Bells Tower and something struck me like a load of bricks.

Suddenly, I was back twenty-four hours, standing beneath the shadow of the tower talking to Lori Sundstrom, a very pretty petite blond from Chicago, whom I had dated for a brief time early in my junior year. The main reasons we had dated for just a short time were two-fold. First, Lori was ultra-conservative and a big fan of Barry Goldwater. Though I had grown up in a Republican home, college had led my sensibilities in a very liberal direction. I was a big Kennedy admirer.

The second and more important reason I had stopped dating Lori was the result of an incident that occurred at the beginning of the Cuban Missile Crisis in October 1962. I had made a date with Lori to go to a movie. When I went to pick her up at her dorm, her roommate and Pi Phi sorority sister, Lynn Jennison, met me in the dormitory lobby and told me that Lori had returned to her hometown of Chicago. I asked why she had picked up in the middle of the week to go back to Chicago. Lynn responded with a laugh and shake of her head, "Well, Randy, she said she wanted to die at home with her family. She is convinced that Kennedy is insane and will get us into a nuclear war with Russia over this Cuba thing."

After quickly processing this, I decided that perhaps it was Lori who was insane, so I did the only thing I could. I asked Lynn if she wanted to go to the movie. She did. As it turned out, Lynn and I enjoyed the movie and each other, not to mention surviving Kennedy, Khrushchev and Castro.

At any rate, Lori returned to Miami, and we remained friendly in a very non-romantic way, despite the fact that Lynn and I had become an item for a while.

On the afternoon of November 21, I ran into Lori under the Beta Bell Tower. As always, she tried to convince me that America needed Goldwater and that Kennedy had to go.

I told her once again that Goldwater wouldn't stand a prayer against Kennedy in 1964. She insisted that Goldwater could beat Kennedy.

My parting shot, as we headed our separate ways, now echoed in my brain. I had smiled at Lori and said, "The only way Goldwater can become president next year is if someone shoots Kennedy."

Now I was filled with some very spooky perverted guilt, as my own words hung in front of me, while I gazed at the spot where I had uttered them.

My classmate and fellow athlete, Bob Schul, walked up to me at the open window, snapping me out of the bizarre mind games I had been playing. I asked him, "Bob, have you heard the same thing I just heard?"

"Yes. This is nuts. It can't be," he replied.

Our teacher, Dr. Northwick, commanded us to take our seats, but the buzz continued. He then banged a book on his desk and said, "If you want to watch the news about this crazy rumor, you can do so when this class is over. Please take your seats and take out your text book."

Paying little attention to Northwick, Schul yelled out the window, "What's going on?"

I heard someone reply, "The President has been shot in Dallas."

Schul then asked, "Is he OK?"

The answer rang back through the window, "I don't know."

Northwick demanded, "Mr. Schul, please take your seat and open your book to page 106."

Bob looked directly at me and nodded toward the door. I signaled my agreement, pulled my books together and stood up and headed toward the exit right behind Bob.

"Where do you two think you're going?" Northwick asked.

Without answering, we exited the room.

Bob Schul was a very special guy. He had come to Miami in the fall to run track as he prepared for the Olympic trials in the summer of 1964. He was a world-class runner with the real possibility to contend for a medal at the 1964 Tokyo Olympics in the 5,000-meter run. I often ran the steps with Bob at Withrow Court after which I would shower and he would go outside and run five or ten miles. Most importantly, as my Jewish friends would say, Bob was a *Mench*... just a really nice guy. Not the least bit full of himself.

As we rushed down the steps, Bob said, "Let's head to the Rez and see what we can learn on TV."

The Rez was another name for the Student Union where I had earlier studied and had lunch. Long ago, it was called the *Res*... short for Indian Reservation (we were the *Miami Redskins*, after all). At some point the *Res* became the *Rez*. It was a great place to eat, bowl, play pool, buy books and supplies, socialize and study.

Bob and I double-timed it the short distance to the Rez and rushed into the large center room that housed a console television. There was almost a full room when we arrived. But the room was silent as the crowd listened to Walter Cronkite.

All that was being reported was that Kennedy had been taken to Parkland Hospital with a possible head wound.

Then at 2:38 Eastern Standard Time, Cronkite scratched under his nose and said, "The flash from Dallas, Texas, apparently official, President Kennedy died at 1 PM Central Standard Time."

There was a noticeable collective gasp in the room where I stood next to Bob Schul.

Cronkite continued, "2 PM Eastern Standard Time. Some 38 minutes ago."

Then a bit overcome, he paused and swallowed hard before continuing, "Vice President Lyndon Johnson has left the hospital in Dallas, but we do not know to where he has proceeded. Presumably, he will be taking the oath of office shortly and will become the thirty-sixth President of the United States."

The entire room was in shock. I did not know how to process this. Of course, we had heard of other Presidential assassinations, the most famous of which was that of Abraham Lincoln almost a hundred years earlier. But not Kennedy! He was so young, so vibrant.

My words of the day before came back to me again, "...if some shoots Kennedy."

Several of the ladies in the room were sobbing, and I found myself fighting back tears. Had I caused this?

Of course not, I reasoned. But, God, I wished that I had not run into Lori Sundstrom the previous day and that I had not uttered those words.

We remained transfixed on the television as new details slowly were reported. A little after 3:00, an official walked into the room and advised the crowd that now spilled out into the hall, that he was going to change the channel to NBC. With that, Frank McGee appeared on the screen with his left hand pressed to his ear. He was in communication with someone at Parkland Hospital in Dallas. He reported that Kennedy had been given last rites and that Vice President Johnson planned to be sworn into office aboard the Presidential plane at Dallas' Love Field. McGee had a grim look on his face as he repeated what he was hearing in his left ear.

I glanced at the clock over the television and realized I was due at Withrow Court. My scholarship job for the semester was running intermural sports at Miami. On autumn Fridays, this meant I had to assign the officiating crews for fraternity intramural football games and hand out whistles and footballs to them. Clearly, I reasoned, the games would be canceled. But this would not be my decision. I told Bob I had to go, and why. We shook hands and I left the Rez.

On my way to Withrow court, as I passed the Administration Building, I noted that the flag that normally flew high above green space out front was already at half-staff. Then I saw Diggy Reynolds, a sports photographer for *The Miami Student* newspaper, aiming his camera at the lowered flag.

I snapped at that point, yelling, "Hey, Diggy, make sure you get a good fucking picture!"

With that, I realized how angry I was. *C'mon Stert. Get a grip on yourself,* I thought.

I then walked quickly over to Diggy. He recoiled; fearful I was about to attack him.

"Diggy, I am so sorry. This thing has gotten the better of me. I know you are just doing your job. Please forgive me."

Diggy smiled back at me and said "Sure 13. We're all a little unglued right now."

The very unathletic Diggy Reynolds, who clearly lived vicariously through the exploits of Miami athletes, had the strange habit of addressing Miami team members by their number rather than their name. And I was... you guessed it... number 13 on the baseball team.

We shook hands, Diggy went back to his task, and I moved on toward Withrow Court. Diggy's picture of the flag appeared on page 42 of *The Recensio*, the *Miami University Year Book*, later that year.

When I arrived at Withrow, I walked into the office of Dr. Nelson, the head of the Physical Education Department. He confirmed what I had expected. All of the day's games were to be canceled.

He addressed me with directions, "I'll advise the guys scheduled to officiate. I need you to run over to Cook Field and let the teams know. I don't know yet when we will reschedule. Tell them to check here on Monday, and I will post something on the Intramural bulletin board."

I ran next door to my dorm to deposit my books and moved on to Cook Field. When I arrived, I was quickly surrounded by twelve teams of fraternity boys, most of who had no interest in football at the moment.

I waited until everyone had gathered around me and said, "All right guys, as you may have already guessed, today's games are canceled. Dr. Nelson has promised to post a memo on Monday about how he plans to reschedule the games."

There was some push back from a few of the guys who still wished to play.

I said, "Look fellas, this is one of those things that you just don't plan for. Dr. Nelson feels it would be most inappropriate to play the games in light of what has happened today. I will tell you that I agree with his decision. So that's it. Will the captains please check the board at Withrow on Monday? There will be no officials and no game balls appearing here today. What you do on your own is up to you. Thanks again."

I waded back through the crowd of frat boys and rushed back to my dorm. When I got back, I was surprised to see that the phone was available, so I called my girlfriend, Eeve Arkush. Eeve and I had dated for two years until she started as a freshman at Emory University in Atlanta the previous school year. The 500 miles between her campus and mine had ended our relationship.

But toward the end of my junior year, she called me one night to advise me she missed me and was transferring to Miami in the fall. She was my first true love, and, though I missed her, I had moved on. But we got back together upon her return to Cincinnati in the summer, and it was like she had never left. We were now deep in the throes of young love.

I asked the operator at her dorm to ring Eeve's room. When she came to the phone, she was sobbing to the point I could barely understand her.

Through her tears, she said, "Can you believe this Ran? It can't be. I'm sad and I'm angry and I don't know what to do. I don't want to wait until tomorrow to go to Cincinnati. Let's find a way to go home tonight. OK?"

I promised to pack some things and head over to her dorm. As I exited my room, I ran into S.J. who was carrying an overnight bag.

"Hey, Stert," he said to me, "we just had a team meeting with Bo. The game tomorrow has been canceled and he has given us the weekend off. We probably will play the game on Thanksgiving. I'm headed home and thought you might want to join me."

"Gee, Mike, I replied, "your timing is perfect. I just talked to Eeve and she wants to head home too. Can we pick her up?"

"Of course. I just need to get out of here."

"I'll second that motion," I said.

I then told S.J. about my run-in with Diggy.

"I bet you scared the hell out of that pussy," Mike laughed.

"Well, he looked like he was afraid I was going to kill him at first, but I apologized and all is cool. He's an OK guy."

"Yea, he is," Mike agreed. "I have to admit that little shit got a great action shot of me in the Marshall game. And he gave me a glossy copy. What the hell were you thinking, picking on my favorite photographer?" Mike joked.

We walked back to the Withrow Court parking lot and jumped into Mike's 1958 Chevy. He kept his car hidden off campus. I say *hidden* because to have a car was prohibited if you lived on campus. S.J. was very good at skirting inconvenient rules. That was one of the reasons why I called him Super Jew.

After the short drive across campus, I scampered out of the car and ran into Eeve's dorm. She was waiting in the lobby, red-eyed and clearly shaken. We hugged for a long time and then I gave her the good news that S.J. was out front waiting to drive us home. That news lifted her spirits.

The hour drive back to the suburb of Roselawn where Eeve lived was quiet except for the radio report that came over the car's speaker. We learned that Johnson had been sworn in aboard the Presidential jet and it was headed back to Washington with Jackie Kennedy and John Kennedy's body. We also heard once again that Texas Governor John Connolly who had been wounded was now fighting for his life in a Dallas hospital.

When Mike pulled in front of 1510 Corvallis Avenue, Eeve and I jumped out of the Chevy and thanked S.J. for the ride. It had gotten colder and I was still wearing only my letter sweater, realizing, that in my haste, I had forgotten to bring a jacket. We darted into her house, which seemed empty.

Eeve yelled hello, and her mother responded that we should come down to the rathskeller. The Arkushes had a finished basement that they referred to as the rathskeller. I found this particularly odd and ironic, as the devoutly Jewish Arkushes detested anything German, lecturing me for considering buying a Volkswagen. Yet, there they were in their *Rathskeller.* Go figure.

Mr. and Mrs. Arkush, along with Eeve's seventeen-year-old brother Allan, were seated in front of their television. On the screen was a live picture from Andrews Air Force Base near Washington of the big jet that served the President, known as Air Force One, with its rear exit door open. The words *The United States of America* were clearly visible across the side of the plane. Within a few seconds, a large box truck with a lift pulled up. Then a group of men, some in suits, others in military uniforms, appeared with a casket as a light-colored Naval ambulance backed up to the lift truck. The lift was quickly lowered to the level of the ambulance.

With that, the men on the lift handed the casket off to a military Honor Guard that slowly loaded it into the ambulance. We looked on in silence and disbelief as Jackie Kennedy appeared with her brother-in-law, Robert Kennedy. That is when the reality again kicked in, as we all saw the President's widow in a stylish suit clearly covered in blood.

Emotion overtook Mrs. Arkush and Eeve as tears began to run down their cheeks. As for me, I was still filled with a mix of deep sadness and even stronger anger. We all remained transfixed on the scene on the TV. The dead President's brother, Attorney General Bobby Kennedy, jumped down and then helped Jackie to the ground. Robert Abernathy, the NBC commentator, noted that Mrs. Kennedy had removed her pillbox hat and confirmed that her pink suit was, in fact, covered with her husband's blood. She and Bobby quickly disappeared into the ambulance.

It was later reported that Mrs. Kennedy had refused to change from the blood-soaked dress on the flight back to Washington saying, "Let them see what they have done to him."

After the ambulance had pulled away, headed for a military helicopter on the other side of the tarmac, our new President Lyndon Baines Johnson, accompanied by his wife Lady Bird, stepped up to a bank of microphones in front of Air Force One and addressed the crowd, and via television, the nation.

President Johnson began, "This is a sad time for all people. We have suffered a loss that cannot be weighed. For me, it is a deep personal tragedy. I know that the world shares the sorrow that Mrs. Kennedy and her family bare. I will do my best. That is all I can do. I ask for your help, and God's."

With that, Johnson walked from the microphones as yet another new reality set in. Vice President Lyndon Johnson, the weather-worn Texan with his thick southern drawl, was now President of the United States, while Jack Kennedy, the young, vivacious Boston sophisticate with a keen intellect and famous wit, was gone.

The NBC coverage then went back to Frank McGee who spoke a haunting truth, "It is safe enough to say, that this afternoon, wherever you were, and whatever you might have been doing when you received the word of the death of President Kennedy, that is a moment which will be emblazoned in your memory and that you will never forget as long as you live."

I did not yet realize how profoundly true McGee's words would prove to be. It is hard to explain how heavy the weight of such utter disbelief had on me that day. The dreadfulness of such a thing and the associated level of injustice left me with a deep weariness impossible to describe.

It was now 6:30 and dark outside, adding to the gloom of the day. The phone rang and Allan hurried into his father's office to answer. He came back and told me it was Mike Cohen for me. Eeve followed me to the phone.

"Hey S.J.," I spoke into the phone. "What's up?

"Stert, it's too depressing here. My dad's pissed and my mom and sister can't stop crying. Can you and Eeve meet a few of us at Howard Johnsons for dinner?"

"Hold on a minute," I instructed.

I told Eeve what was up, and she rushed back to ask her mom if she could go. She came back smiling for the first time since I had picked her up at her dorm. She could go even though Friday night dinner was a big deal in the Arkush house. As practicing Conservative Jews, the Shabbat dinner and saying the Kiddush blessing, was an important ritual to their family.

On many Friday nights I had been invited to the Arkush dinner table where the meal always started with the prayer, "Baruch ata Adonai, Eloheinu Melech ha-olam, boreh p'ri hagafen."

To appease Eeve, I had learned to say the prayer phonetically. But, after chanting along many, many times, I still had no clue what those Yiddish words meant. What I did know is that getting the prayer out of the way got me closer to Rose Arkush's out-of-this-world pot roast. And I can also say with great certainty that for Mrs. Arkush to excuse Eeve from this ceremonial custom clearly reflected on the somberness of the moment, when something seemed bigger than tradition.

"Yea, we can join you," I reported. "Who else is going?"

"I asked Charlotte. And Freddie is coming. I'll call the Schvantz too. Charlotte and I can pick you two up. Is fifteen minutes OK?"

Charlotte Rinsky was Mike's old high school girl friend who lived just three doors from him in the Cincinnati suburb of Bond Hill. They still got together regularly when he was in town, though, in Yiddish parlance, he was aggressively dating Shiksas at Miami. In other words, Mike was cheerfully enjoying the company of an ongoing list non-Jewish co-eds.

'Fifteen ticks is good, " I said.

I hung up and called home. My mother answered, and I advised her I had come back to Cincinnati and that a group of us were headed to Howard Johnsons for dinner. I told her I would probably be home before 11:00. Like the rest of us, she sounded desolate. Knowing how much I admired Kennedy, she asked if I was all right. I assured her I was fine.

The restaurant was more than half empty when we arrived. Mike, Charlotte, Eeve and I walked in to find Sandy Schwartz and his young girlfriend, Judi Cohen, a freshman at the University of Cincinnati, already seated. Thirty seconds later Freddie Zigler showed up with Ricki Abraham.

After the usual pleasantries, Ricki said, "Thank God Fred called. I was ready to kill my father. I know he didn't like Kennedy, but he just kept bitching that the coverage was going to cause him to miss *Burke's Law* and the goddamned *Fight of the Week*. What a prick."

That kind of broke the tension.

Eeve laughed and said, "Do you really feel that way about your dad?"

"Damn right I do. I couldn't get out of there fast enough. Look up prick in the dictionary and there's a picture of my dad," she said, followed by a hearty laugh.

Dinner turned out to be just what the doctor ordered. Everybody except Judi Cohen ordered Howard Johnson's famous fried clam dinners. She ordered a cheeseburger platter. When seven plates showed up piled high with the squiggly little clams, golden brown French fries and a big scoop of coleslaw, plus an eighth dish with a thick burger for Judi, everybody quickly dug in. The waitress brought a squirt bottle full of the best tartar sauce known to mankind along with a matching bottle of Heinz ketchup.

S.J. kept the conversation light with his imitation of Bo Schembechler. I threw in a few gems about my coach Woody Wills. Fred and Sandy got into the now postponed football game, debating who was better... the Miami Redskins or the Cincinnati Bearcats. Since there were four of us from each school at the table, that argument went nowhere.

After polishing off dinner, everyone ordered ice cream, the other Howard Johnsons specialty.

Then, after almost an hour of assassination relief, the gloom of the day fell down upon us all again when we overheard a man, at another table nearby, state that they had arrested somebody for the shooting in Dallas.

Fred jumped up and rushed to the table, hoping to get details. Quickly, the rest of us surrounded the little table where the man sat with his wife. Then for the first time all of us heard the name Lee Harvey Oswald. Really, all the guy knew was Oswald's name and that he was 25 years old and was a fairly small guy. He had been seen briefly on TV at the Dallas police station. The man did tell us Oswald looked like he had a black eye.

The night ended with everybody headed home. Mike dropped Eeve off where I kissed her goodnight on the porch and grabbed my bag just inside the door. Mike and Charlotte then deposited me in front of my house at 5426 Grafton Avenue. I got the sense that S.J. was likely to get more than a goodnight kiss before the night was over.

My mother was already in bed, but my father, now sober for over three years, sat in front of the TV watching the NBC coverage. A sober Harold Stertmeyer was much more fun to be around than the old drunken version of years of Friday nights past. I was both amazed and proud that he seemed to finally have licked his drinking problem.

He said to me, "Hey, kiddo. They've canceled the Tonight Show. They were supposed to have Kirk Douglas and Henny Youngman on. But they don't kill a President every day."

Old Harold was able to find comedy even in the bleakest of times. He had served in World War II. Humor is a great tool when you are trying to survive another day.

He loved Henny Youngman, but he was also a history buff, and he was deeply engaged with the coverage. We sat together in our small living room and watched with little conversation. Before going to bed after midnight, I saw footage of Lee Harvey Oswald for the first time. He was dressed in a tee shirt and did indeed have a shiner.

"He's a little squirt," my father said. "I guess a crazy little guy with a rifle can do a lot of damage. I wasn't a fan of Kennedy, but this just is not right. We can't have a nutty son-of-a-buck like that killing the President."

The last ten hours had been more than surreal. I was exhausted. Yet, when I climbed between the sheets it took me over an hour to finally fall into a restless sleep.

Over the next three days the insanity continued, filled with events and visions that burn themselves into your mind permanently.

It started the next morning when I turned the TV on to see someone carting Kennedy's famous rocking chair from the White House in a light rain and placing it into a moving van. *Jesus,* I thought, *they're not wasting any time.*

I learned early that morning that half of the Kennedy Cabinet had been on a flight to Japan headed to an annual meeting of the US and Japanese cabinets when they learned of the assassination. Among them were Secretary of State Dean Rusk, Labor Secretary Willard Wirtz, and Treasury Secretary Douglas Dillon.

I spent the morning engrossed in the television coverage as the assassination evolved into an event. Plans were being made. President Johnson issued his first proclamation, declaring Monday November 25 to be a day of national mourning for the slain president.

Former President Harry Truman was also on television making a short statement to reporters.

Truman said in his typical folksy style, "I was very much shocked and hurt when I heard. He was a good man, an able President, and he did a good job. And it's too bad these things have to happen particularly by some good-for-nothing fella who didn't have anything else to do than try take the head of state away from us."

When Truman had finished and moved on, a reporter reminded the TV audience that in November 1950, an assassination attempt was made on President Truman. It had been carried out by militant Puerto Rican pro-independence activists Ocar Collazo and Griselio Torresola while the President resided at Blair House during the renovation of the White House. Both men were stopped before gaining entry to the house. Torresola mortally wounded White House police officer Leslie Coffelt who killed Torresola in return fire. Secret Service agents wounded Collazo. President Harry S. Truman was upstairs in the house and not harmed.

There was also an update on Lee Harvey Oswald. I learned that he was born in New Orleans in 1939 and had joined the US Marines in 1956. He was discharged in 1959 and nine days later left for the Soviet Union, where he tried unsuccessfully to become a citizen. He worked in Minsk where he married a Soviet woman and, in 1962, was allowed to return to the United States with his wife and infant daughter. Had the Russians put him up to this? My father had joined me in front of the television by mid-morning. My mother, on the other hand, was too stressed by the "whole mess," so she had driven over two streets to Newfield Avenue to visit with her sister, my Aunt Win. Throughout the morning, we learned of how America was changing its weekend calendar. The Yale-Harvard football game that President Kennedy had loved so much, was canceled. The lights on Broadway had been dimmed. The regular programming on ABC, CBS and NBC had been replaced by full coverage of the aftermath of the assassination. And, of course the Miami vs. Cincinnati game had been rescheduled for Thanksgiving Day.

Just before noon, Freddie Zigler called. He had been watching all morning as well and had decided what was needed was a good game of touch football. I didn't hesitate to agree. Thus, Fred, Wally Bohl, Carl Shiele, Mike Fulton, Marv Feldman, Spike Spiegle, Jimmy Luken and I convened at Woodward High School at 1:00. It proved to be a great distraction. The team of Luken, Fulton, Feldman and Spiegle beat Zigler, Bohl, Shiele and me by the close score of 102 to 96. We had decided, with the score tied at 96 all, that the next score would win. My team did not score next. It was after 3:30 when we threw in the towel. The eight of us dragged our worn-out butts across the street to Swifton Shopping Center for pizza at Pasqualle's.

When I got home a little before 5:00, I called Eeve and we decided, rather than submit ourselves to more depressing news coverage, we would to go to a movie at the Valley Theater in Roselawn, where the new release *It's a Mad, Mad, Mad, Mad World* was playing. With that title, it seemed an appropriate flick to see the day after the President was assassinated. The film was the first comedy ever directed by Stanley Kramer and starred Spencer Tracy. It included a great ensemble cast that included, Edie Adams, Sid Caesar, Milton Berle, Ethel Merman, Buddy Hackett, Jonathan Winters, Mickey Rooney, Terry Thomas and the great Jimmy Durante. Mike "Super Jew" Cohen and Charlotte Rinsky joined us. We met at the Valley Theater a little before 7:00. There were only a handful of other moviegoers there that night and way more popcorn than needed.

There were two problems with the very funny madcap film. First, unlike the distraction of our touch football game earlier in the day, a comedy was just too antithetical to the glum mood. Every funny occurrence in the movie resulted in a feeling of guilt rather than what should have been gleeful laughter. It just seemed un-American to laugh at the moment.

Second, the damned movie ran for more than two and a half hours. It was torture. When the four of us finally escaped the comfortable confines of the Valley Theater, we all agreed we were left feeling more soiled than happy.

We decided to take our gloom to Frisch's for a Big Boy, fries and a coke. At first, the popular Cincinnati greasy cuisine did help to take a bit of the edge off. But ultimately, it also helped to illustrate that not all of America had been affected by Kennedy's death in the same way as I. We ran into many former Woodward High School classmates at Frisch's who seemed totally oblivious to the whole thing. The upbeat mood at Frisch's made it obvious that this was an understatement. The young crowd appeared to be behaving as if it were just another autumn weekend. This just served to anger me more. S.J, Charlotte, and Eeve were all in my camp, so we wolfed down our food and split. When Eeve and I finally pulled up in front of her house, we just sat in the quite darkness, holding hands while trying to describe to each other the depth of the grief we were both feeling. On a normal Saturday night, we would have been exploring the renewed physical and emotional passion that had been spurred by the recent resurrection of our relationship. But not on this night. Passion was now buried deep inside, well blockaded by a new inexplicable group of emotions. Though we sat with the engine running on my old 1949 Dodge, its heater was failing us on this cold November night. We finally gave up. Like the previous evening, I walked her to the door, gave her a quick kiss and headed home. We agreed that I would come back to her house the next morning. If Saturday had been a peculiar mix of, anger, fear, depression and deflection, Sunday, November 24 just amplified all of those emotions while adding a large dose of bizarre. Thankfully, I slept well. After a quick breakfast of fried eggs and my mother's homemade goetta, I headed toward Roselawn in the *Nose,* our nickname for my 1949 Dodge Coronet, so dubbed due to its huge elongated hood. When I arrived at Eeve's house I found her father immersed in the thick Sunday *Enquirer*. The rest of the family was in the *Rathskeller* watching the continuing weekend saga unfold on television. Rather than submit ourselves to more agony, Eeve and I decided to take a walk. It was a sunny, yet cold, Sunday. As we strolled through her neighborhood, we speculated what a Lyndon Johnson-lead America might look like. We were both concerned that the southern-bred

Texan might not support the civil rights progress that the country had been making under Kennedy's leadership. As it turned out, we were wrong about that.

When we returned at exactly 12:30, we discovered that the Dallas police were about to move Oswald to a new "safer" location. Tom Pettit of NBC was reporting from the basement garage of the Dallas Police Station, which ironically was within clear vision of the Texas School Book Depository from which Oswald had allegedly fired the fatal shots ending the President's life. In the echoic garage, we heard Pettit say, "Oswald is being led out by Captain Fritz," as a car horn blared in the background buzz. Then a group of men, several wearing something between a fedora and a cowboy hat, appeared, surrounding the diminutive Oswald. Suddenly, the outrageous turned into something way beyond bizarre. If words like unbelievable, impossible, incredible, unfeasible, implausible, preposterous, ludicrous, outlandish and absurd could be combined into a single expression of emotion, it would still fail to describe what we witnessed next on the television screen. For me, there was this vision of what I would later think of as John Belushi playing Jake Blues, in the 1980 movie *The Blues Brothers*.

Pettit described the action this way,

"There is Lee Oswald," said Pettit as the back of a stocky man in a dark suit and hat lunged at Oswald.

Then we heard the shot and the groan from Oswald as he bent in half in pain. The police officers guiding Oswald all recoiled.

Pettit, as cool as cucumber, as if he had trained his whole life for this moment, described what we could not believe we were seeing.

"He's been shot. He's been shot. Lee Oswald has been shot. There's a man with a gun. There's absolute panic. Absolute panic here in the basement of the Dallas Police headquarters. Detectives have their guns drawn. Oswald has been shot. There's no question about it. Oswald has been shot. Pandemonium has broken loose here in the basement of Dallas Police headquarters." And, indeed, it was pandemonium we watched in total astonishment.

"Now whether the bullet actually hit Oswald or not, we are not absolutely positive," Pettit continued. "But there has been a gun shot. Oswald reached for his stomach... Doubled up. It will be impossible to determine if he was hit or not. Did you see if he was hit?" Pettit asked a bystander. "He was hit, wasn't he?" the reporter inquired as the witness confirmed that Oswald clearly grabbed his side in pain.

The reaction in the Arkush basement was not unlike what we were watching in the Dallas Police station basement... panic, confusion, and incredulity. Mr. Arkush started to laugh, exposing his large upper teeth. I suppose it was a nervous laugh. But it seemed so out of place that I actually curbed the urge to smack him.

We watched as Oswald was loaded into an ambulance that quickly drove up the ramp into the Dallas sunshine. More irony revealed he was being taken to Parkland Memorial Hospital, the same place almost exactly 48 hours earlier the mortally wounded President had been taken. Suddenly NBC took us from sunny Dallas to sunny Washington DC. The President's body was being moved from the White House to the Capitol, where it would lie in state for the next 24 hours. Frankly, there was just too much going on for the TV networks and the viewers. Yet NBC, the station the Arkushs preferred, somehow managed to keep it all seamless as if they had rehearsed the whole thing in advance. The coverage switched back and forth between DC and Dallas. As if watching a very good television show, we gazed at the screen as the President's casket was moved from the White House and paraded down Pennsylvania Avenue to lie in state in the great Rotunda of the Capitol, on the same catafalque that had cradled Abraham Lincoln almost a century earlier. It was a solemn scene. A rider-less horse named Black Jack, with tall black riding boots anchored backwards in the stirrups, and a sabre holstered in the side of the saddle, added to the drama. The anger and dread stuck in my throat as I listened to the mournful echo of the muffled drums. Those gathered along the street seemed dazed and quiet as they watched the procession slowly move down the wide thoroughfare.

After watching for a while, with the sound of the drums and the strain of Chopin's Funeral March adding an eerie pall, I found myself wondering how Oswald was doing and who was this crazy character that had shot him. In the mist of all of this insanity, the coverage switched back to the Capitol Rotunda where we discovered that a ceremony was about to get under way. The camera zoomed in on Mrs. Kennedy as she followed the military pall bearers up the steps of the Capitol, leading young Caroline and John Jr., just 5 and 2 years old respectively, by the hand. Once in the rotunda, a crowd of dignitaries assembled in a tight semi-circle. Jackie stood in the center; her eyes fixed ahead on the flag-covered casket. Three eulogies were delivered. Those given by Earl Warren, Chief Justice of the Supreme Court, and John McCormack, the Speaker of the House of Representatives, were appropriate and forgettable.

However, the eloquence of Senate Majority Leader Mike Mansfield was delicately delivered and historical. He spoke softly, articulating the loss for us all through the loss of Jacqueline Kennedy. I perked up with Mansfield's first words. "There was a sound of laughter. In a moment, it was no more. And she took a ring from her finger and placed it his hands."

Eeve and I gave each other a glance, realizing this eulogy would be unlike the others, as Mansfield continued: " There was a wit in a man, neither young nor old, but a wit full of an old man's wisdom and of a child's wisdom, and then, in a moment, it was no more. And so, she took a ring from her finger and placed it in his hands."

"There was a man marked with scars of his love of country, a body active with the surge of a life far, far from spent, and in a moment, it was no more. And so, she took a ring from her finger and placed it in his hands."

"She really did that," Mrs. Arkush said in a quiet statement. "They reported that she had taken off her wedding ring and placed it in the President's hands before they closed the casket at the White House," Rose Arkush continued, tears now running down her face. Mansfield went on with his eulogy: "There was a father with a little boy, a little girl and a joy of each in the other. In a moment it was no more, and so she took a ring from her finger and placed it in his hands."

"There was a husband that asked much and gave much, and out of the giving and the asking wove with a woman what could not be broken in life. And in a moment, it was no more. And so, she took a ring from her finger and placed it in his hands, and kissed him and closed the lid of a coffin." "A piece of each of us died at that moment. Yet, in death he gave of himself to us. He gave us of a good heart from which the laughter came. He gave us a profound wit, from which a great leadership emerged. He gave us of a kindness and a strength fused into a human courage to seek peace without fear."

"He gave us of his love that we, too, in turn, might give. He gave that we might give of ourselves, that we might give to one another, until there would be no room, no room at all, for the bigotry, the hatred, prejudice, and the arrogance which converged in that moment of horror to strike him down."

"In leaving us – these gifts, John Fitzgerald Kennedy, President of the United States, leaves with us. Will we take them, Mr. President? Will we have, now, the sense and the responsibility and the courage to take them?"

"I pray to God that we shall, and under God, we will."

With that, Mike Mansfield walked slowly away from the microphone. And, with that, I felt the truth in his words. He was correct. A piece of me had died. And that piece came from a place where my naive innocence dwelled. At the same time. I was struck with a clear sense of purpose. I somehow knew that I must honor the President and, in so doing, honor and distinguish myself. As I mulled all of this, I watched as Jackie Kennedy led her young daughter Caroline up to the flag draped casket.

"Kneel down," the mother softly whispered to her daughter. Mrs. Kennedy kissed the coffin, lovingly, as Caroline groped beneath the flag to touch the hard-shiny wood.

Just as the ceremony was ending, the TV cameras turned outside to the crowd of thousands that had quietly formed itself into a long line waiting to climb the Capitol steps in order to pass through the Rotunda to view the President's funeral bier. The commentator stated that the autumn day in the nation's Capital had turned cold, as the sun began to fall in a "soft pinkish blue" behind the Capitol dome. All we could see was contrasting shades on the black, gray and white on the television screen. For the rest of that afternoon, we remained locked on the coverage as we watched the line of American mourners grow longer and longer. Within a half hour, it stretched twenty blocks, as if a single snake-like unit, moving slowly in silence, shivering in the cold but determined. The procession would continue throughout the night and into the morning of November 25th. Every once in a while, NBC would report some sort of update, most significantly that Lee Harvey Oswald had died at the same hospital where John Fitzgerald Kennedy had expired two days previous. Mr. Arkush observed that with Oswald dead, we might never know how and why he had killed the President.

Then we learned the name of the mutt-like shooter from the Dallas Police Department basement. His name was Jack Ruby. He was described as a small-time *hoodlum* or *thug,* who ran a strip club in Dallas. His real name was Jacob Rubenstien, and it was reported that he might have connections to organized crime. With that, the speculation began that someone wishing to silence Oswald had hired him.

As the Cincinnati afternoon began to turn to dusk, it was time for our return to our Miami University campus in Oxford. Mrs. Arkush did not want Eeve to go back to Oxford, arguing that it was Thanksgiving week and she would be better off... safer... at home. She could miss a class or two. As it turned out, this was part of the dynamic created by the murders of Kennedy and Oswald. Almost universally, people did not feel safe. There was this sense that evil now lurked at every turn. I knew my mother and her two sisters, Winifred and Lois, were feeling it, just like Rose Arkush. Eeve and I decided we were better off back at school with our peers. So, against the wishes of the women in our lives, Eeve, Mike Cohen and I reversed our Friday afternoon drive in Mike's Chevrolet, arriving back on campus around 6:30. We were too late for dinner at the dorm, so the three of us agreed to meet at the Rez at 7. S.J. knocked on the door to my room at 6:50, and we walked together the short distance to the Rez. We entered on the main floor, walked past the closed Student Union Book Store and found Eeve in the main sitting room where I had heard Walter Cronkite confirm the death of the President on Friday.

There was a great deal of commotion including some yelling and screaming. Eeve brought Mike and me up to speed on the uproar evolving in front of us. The University had not yet canceled classes for the next day, even though President Johnson had declared it a *Day of Mourning*. Several of the more vocal students in the debate were advocating for a march on the University President Dr. Millet's home on High Street. Others were demanding a sit-in at the Rez or the Administration Building. Others yet, just sat in silence, some crying, some with a clear look of fear at what they were witnessing. We were about 50 hours into this national tragedy. The mix of emotions that I had experienced over the weekend now started to come to the surface as it had with Diggy Reynolds on Friday afternoon as he photographed the flag.

With uncharacteristic determination, I pushed my way through the crowd until I stood in front of the television and next to the main rabble rouser. Now, let me say first that I was beyond a painfully shy child. I lived in fear of being at the center of anything, especially having to speak. This was true throughout high school, where I tried to remain invisible. Finally, in college I was beginning to find some personal confidence. But what I did at that moment in that room on that day was still way out of character. It seemed as if some outside force was pushing me on. I stepped in front of the male student who had been trying to whip up the crowd. I then held up my hand, and to my surprise the room went silent. Looking first at the repel rouser and then out at the crowd, I said slowly but forcefully, "What is wrong with you people? The President is dead. This isn't about you or whether some guy in a suit wants you to go to class tomorrow. This didn't just happen here at Miami. This has happened to all of America and all of the world." I continued, "We all need to mourn this in our own way. Why would anyone want to join a mob at a time like this? If you do not want to go to class tomorrow, then don't go. I will not be attending class. We have to get a grip on our anger. We need, for just a short time, to shut up and just mourn. We all need to be bigger than this," I said, pointing at the stunned organizer. Holding my glare on him, I calmly said, "Shame on you. This is how you want to honor President Kennedy?" Then, looking back at the assembled throng, I concluded by waiving my arm at them and stating, "And shame on any of you who listen to this crap. Shame on you." I dropped my head and walked back through the gathering to where Eeve and S.J. stood, taking her by the hand, and without a word the three of us headed downstairs to the Zebra Room. None of us spoke until we were seated, although Eeve did squeeze my hand several times.

"What the hell, man?" Mike finally said. "That was amazing. Did you see the look on that guy's face? He's still crawling around looking for his tongue."

Eeve agreed, expressing her pride in my words. But I was fried. Praise just seemed inappropriate. "Let's just eat. I don't want to talk about it. Let's just hang out with each other tomorrow. Maybe everyone can start to heal once they bury Kennedy. As we ate our dinner, a few people approached our table with kind words of thanks or admiration for what I had done.

S.J., Eeve and I went through the food line where she and I ordered a grilled cheese and a toasted roll and Mike went big, ordering meat loaf, mashed potatoes and two toasted rolls. He had to maintain his playing weight.

While we ate dinner, a few more people stopped by to comment positively about my little speech. All I could muster was a shy *thank you*.

We all walked back to Eeve's dorm where I planted a healthy kiss on her and told her having her back in my life had made the whole weekend ordeal easier. She smiled, kissed me softly and disappeared inside. Mike and I cut back across campus to my dorm, where we agreed to gather a group of jocks at Tuffy's the next morning at 9:00. I turned on my little radio next to my bed and set my Big Ben alarm for 7:00 AM. Sleep did not come easy, but I finally dozed off with the radio still playing. The next thing I knew, Big Ben was ringing a loud wake up call. As I shook myself awake, I had two thoughts. First, as my mind cleared, I realized that this was the day that John F. Kennedy, the 35th President of the United States, would be laid to rest at Arlington National Cemetery. After mulling that outrageous fact for a few seconds, the next thing that came to mind was my words to Eeve outside of her dorm the previous night. It was true; sharing the past few days with her had made them easier. But, as always, there was this little hiccup somewhere in my psyche that would interrupt thoughts of a long time, or lifetime, relationship with her. From the day we met, I had noticed a peculiar edge in her. There was just this pushy, abrasive tone in how she sometime expressed herself. While most of my friends supported my relationship with her, it was clear that it was not with great enthusiasm. There seemed to be more tolerance than there was zeal in how my closest friends Freddie Zigler, Sandy Schwartz, Eddie Wikas and Jerry Ivins related to her.

The one exception was Mike Cohen. S.J. seemed to like her a lot and was pleased to include her in all we did. But then, Mike also had a certain edge. As a middle linebacker on the Miami football team, he was more than happy to knock anybody on his or her ass either physically or metaphorically. You knew he was a great, well-liked friend, but he wouldn't hesitate to tell you what he thought. As I sat on the edge of my bed going through this self-analysis, it struck me as odd that these thoughts had interrupted the emotional explosion of the past weekend. What I did conclude before getting on with the day was that there was a pure sincerity in what I had told Eeve the previous night. For me, she was the person I needed at this time. And I knew that confronting this fact had solidified my feelings for her. Whether it was love, or just gratitude, in my mind, we were now a more serious couple. I could deal with the rest later.

I showered and selected my attire carefully. In a convoluted way, I was dressing for a funeral, so I selected my blue chinos, a white button-down Oxford shirt, and my powder blue V-neck sweater. Remembering the sunny, yet chilly day that was being reported on WSAI radio, I also grabbed my navy-blue pea jacket, something that was all the rage on the Miami campus in 1963. Having risen early, I started rounding up a little army for breakfast at Tuffy's, by going next door to Swing Hall where many scholarship athletes were housed. I quickly succeeded in recruiting my good friends and teammates, Jerry Ivins and Terry Morris as well as football players, Glenn Trout, Tom Long, and Herb Street. Herb, being the biggest and scariest guy in the group, agreed to run to Tuffy's to claim and hold a table for ten in the front and most desirable room, even though there was only seven of us so far. Tuffy's was an institution second to none at Miami. It sat in the basement of old Miami dorm at the corner of High and Withrow Streets. It was also the place where the famous toasted roll had been first introduced. And it was owned by a former Miami graduate known as, guess what? *Tuffy*!! Myron Timothy "Tuffy" Potter had opened his greasy spoon in 1929. By 1963, Tuffy's was a remnant of bygone college days. It was that old soda fountain hangout where kids gathered to have a burger, a Coke, a phosphate, an ice cream soda or especially a toasted roll, play some music on the juke box and carve their initials into the tabletops. Tuffy encouraged the carving and even went to the extreme of putting regular coats of lacquer on each table to preserve these little personal statements of love. The result was tables that shined like a piece of glass. Some of the carvings went back decades noting things like:

RH x JP '29
or,
Tom loves Sally 1942.

To add to the Joe College ambiance, Tuffy ran a string of framed photos of the star athletes da jour along the top of the walls. Proudly, my photo was perched above the mirror behind the soda fountain. For most Miamians, Tuffy's was a very special place.

By the time our little group of testosterone-filled jocks had all assembled at 9:00, our ranks had swelled to twelve brutes. We all managed to squeeze in around the three tables Herb had been holding for a half an hour. What would have normally been a rather raucous gathering was fairly subdued on this particular November 25th. Herb had assigned himself as chairman of the jock council assembled at Tuffy's.

When Nancy Berling, a pretty and petite junior, arrived to wait on us, Herb stood proudly and announced, "OK, Nancy. We're going easy on you today. We need 12 toasted rolls, and make sure they don't burn the little buggers. The football players will all have coffee and the wimp-assed baseball players will have milk." That broke the ice and resulted in the biggest laugh I had heard in three days. Nancy was up to the challenge. Her response was perfect. "All right. Sit down, big guy. I'll take your order last. I'll start over there with those manly baseball players. After they order, if we have any toasted rolls left, you might get one." That brought another laugh and a big cheer from our second baseman Terry Morris. After the orders were actually placed and Nancy had flown off to the kitchen, the conversation turned to the reality of the day. School had been canceled and the only real decision to be made was where to find a television to watch the last leg of the Kennedy tragedy. Various possibilities were discussed. Coach Schembechler had called a short workout for the football team from 11:00 until noon. The teams place kicker, Glenn Trout, addressed me.

"Hey, Stertmeyer, I heard you buried that trouble maker, Frank Bedrosian last night." Not realizing at first what he was talking about, I asked, "Who is Frank Bedrosian?" "Bedrosian? Yea, I know that prick," Tom Long chimed in. "He's a Beta. They all hate him at the Beta House. But he's a legacy. My friend Rod Elsner roomed with him at Anderson Hall our freshman year. Couldn't stand the SOB." It finally registered with me. They were talking about the guy who was trying to organize the protest the night before at the Rez. In typical fashion, I turned red in the face and had not a word to say. Mike Cohen piped in, "Yea, I was there with Stert. You should have seen the look on that guy's face. He didn't know if he should shit or go blind." "Well, it couldn't happen to a nicer guy. A pure prick," said Glenn Trout.

While I squirmed and looked for something to say, the door to Tuffy's opened and Rita Stein walked in. She was the cousin of my good friend Fred Zigler. Rita was from Cleveland and was a sophomore at Miami.

Mike Cohen and I had learned to tolerate Rita, only because she was Fred's cousin. Sadly, she was not attractive... some would say downright ugly. And she was a social imbecile. Rita had a special talent for saying the wrong thing in the wrong way. And, as Mike had pointed out to me on several occasions, the large gap between her top front teeth, made her appear cartoonish when she smiled. Rita walked right up to Mike and me who were seated next to each other. "Well hi there you two," she began, exposing the gap. "I guess you heard, some creep shot the President?" Mike couldn't help himself and said with incredulity, "What? They shot the President? Are you kidding? When?"

Poor naive Rita just went on, "On Friday. Isn't it terrible? And they caught the guy. But then someone killed him too." Biting his lip, S.J. responded, "Oh, at first I thought you were serious. That's a funny story. But, no one is going to believe that, Rita."

"No! I'm serious," she spit back at him through gapped teeth. "Go check the television. You'll see. It's all true."

With a satisfied wide grin, and the space between her teeth serving as a metaphor for the gap in her brain, she departed our company. S.J. calmly and seriously announced to the table full of jocks, "You know, if you turn her upside down, you have a great ash tray." That all too cruel teeth joke resulted in the heartiest laugh of the day.

Our little gathering at Tuffy's really provided the best distraction yet for me. We actually had some laughs and some fun as the conversation ping ponged from talk of the upcoming football game with the University of Cincinnati and the ever-present events tied to the President's burial at Arlington. Our group broke up around 10:30, and I headed to Eeve's dorm. She was clearly happy to see me. She told me that her sorority, Alpha Epsilon Phi, was setting up a couple of televisions in their suite at her dorm, and she would like to watch the various ceremonies there. That sounded fine to me, so down the hall we went. There was a campus phone on the wall just outside the suite. I called the Zeta Beta Tau Fraternity House and asked for Mike Cohen. S.J., who had just returned from his team meeting, came to phone and happily screamed a hello. Knowing S.J. had been eyeing Eeve's A E Phi sorority sister, Maxine Katz, I suggested he skedaddle across campus and join us. I didn't have to ask twice. He was on his way.

Based on input from Eeve, Max would not be disappointed when my friend and Miami All-Conference linebacker showed up. After saying hello to several of Eeve's sorority sisters, including Max, we found four chairs in front of the smaller of the two televisions. Max claimed one, and we held one for S. J.

As we settled in, NBC reporter Edwin Newman confirmed that the Capitol Rotunda had been closed to the public earlier in the morning. He then reported that a half million, and maybe as many as 800,000 people were lining the route of the funeral procession. It was also conveyed by NBC's Chet Huntley that Mrs. Kennedy, her brothers-in-law Bobby and Teddy Kennedy, along with many of the dignitaries would walk the length of Pennsylvania Avenue behind the President's flag-draped casket, much to the consternation of the Secret Service.

The caisson carrying Kennedy's casket, like the day before, was drawn by four horses, including the rider less horse named Black Jack, a magnificent black gelding which carried an empty saddle and saber with the boots reversed in the stirrups. "The rider less horse is one of the highest military honors bestowed upon the fallen," reported the third NBC correspondent David Brinkley. Chet Huntley explained that Mrs. Kennedy had requested that the procession be modeled after that which had carried Abraham Lincoln following his assassination in 1865. As they paraded toward the White House, Jacqueline Kennedy led the funeral procession as they headed first for the White House and then on to St. Matthews Cathedral. She appeared in a classic black dress and coat, black high heeled shoes, a black veil and the saddest, broken-hearted eyes imaginable. We watched her strong feminine gait as she moved ahead between her brothers-in-law followed by Charles De Gaul, the President of France, our new President, Lyndon Johnson, and his wife Lady Bird, the actor Peter Lawford and his wife Pat, the dead President's sister, and other world leaders including the President of West Germany, Heinrich Lubke, Queen Fredericka of Greece, King Baudouin of Belgium, Emperor of Ethiopia, Haile Selassie and President of South Korea, Chung Hee Park. Throughout the entire route, we heard the haunting sound of muffled drums and the occasional playing of Chopin's Funeral March. At just before 12:15, the procession arrived at St. Matthews Cathedral where the funeral mass would be held. Gathered at the church were former Presidents Harry Truman and Dwight Eisenhower along with 53 heads of state. As the Honor Guard carried the casket into the church, the military band played the Naval Hymn. Following the service, Mrs. Kennedy and all of the assembled dignitaries loaded into several long black limousines for the short drive past the Lincoln Memorial, across the Potomac River and into Arlington National Cemetery.

I realized as the assemblage arrived at the grave site, that there had been hardly a word spoken in the sorority suite over the past two hours. Like the rest of the proceedings, the grave site ceremony was somber and tasteful, as though it had been staged in Hollywood.

Chet Huntley explained that we were looking at a temporary grave. A suitable memorial would be developed. He also stated that an eternal flame would be lit by Mrs. Kennedy and would be a permanent part of the solemn site.

Robert Kennedy walked the President's 34-year-old widow up to the cauldron where she bent over and ignited the flame. At that point, there were audible sobs in the sorority suite. I, too, fought back tears. The anger I had been feeling all weekend was gone. What was left at that moment was only grief.

I will say, that once that flame flashed to life on the television screen, I did have a sense that a deep, thought provoking movie that I had been watching had come to an end. With many movies, you are left confused, or unfulfilled. But you know it's over and it is time to exit the theater. That's how I felt as I watched the Kennedy's walk from the grave site on the Arlington hillside beneath the historic Lee Mansion. I actually articulated all of this to Eeve, S.J. and Maxine. Eeve grasped it and agreed. Mike and Max looked at me as if to say, *you need some sleep.* What we did all agree on was that it was time to give up on NBC and TV. S.J. and I also agreed that we had spent an inordinate amount of money on food over the last four days, given we could eat for free at the dorm. I had also concluded that S.J. had deemed Maxine un-meal-worthy. He liked her, but not enough to feed her. He was still in pursuit of that perfect shiksa.

Fortunately for my meager funds, Eeve was more than just a student. She was a scholar, and she had to study. And so, just like that, the four days in November that started innocently with my regular run of the Withrow Court stairs, ended with the clear need to start over. It takes a great deal of reflection upon significant life events to fully appreciate the real consequence of the experience, the true impact a specific incident ultimately has on you. Two things became clear to me upon reflection over time. That weekend had seriously compromised my personal *Age of Innocence*. It also had significantly solidified my feelings for Eeve, at least in the short term. To paraphrase a modern day saying, Tuesday, November 26, 1963 was the first day of the rest of my life. And indeed, life did go on. Two days later, the Miami Redskins defeated the Cincinnati Bearcats in a very close and exciting Thanksgiving Day game by the score of 21 to 19. Thanks to that win, Miami had won all four games against Cincinnati of my college years. And, Freddie Zigler and had I started what became a life-long tradition of attending the game together, sitting on the visitor's side for the first half and on the home team side for the second half, each politely rooting for our alma mater. My healing started without me actually realizing it at the time. Two days after my birthday on December 10, I sat studying at my dorm room desk, while listening to Dusty Rhoades on WSAI radio. For a period of two hours, he kept promising a very special surprise. At 9:00 PM, he came back on the air after a brief news and weather report. "OK, rock and roll fans, here is the treat I have been promising to you all night on this, Frank Sinatra's forty-eighth birthday. I want to introduce you to a new group from England that is all the rage throughout Europe. I predict we will soon see a similar mania for these four young men from Liverpool here in America. So, listen up. Here are The Beatles and their new release *I want to Hold Your Hand*." I listened, and I liked the song, but I didn't sense a craze of any sort in the future. Man, was I wrong? Ask anyone who was in college in 1963 and 1964, and they will tell you that the Beetles became our antibiotic for the assassination of John Kennedy. Like Sinatra and Elvis before them, they totally captured young America with their sometimes silly and sometimes touching, thought provoking songs. But, in spite of the Beatles, our world had changed. What followed that terrible weekend were further assassinations, assassination attempts, conspiracy theories about Oswald, the Russians and the mob, a useless and costly war in Viet Nam, the rise and fall of Richard Nixon, and what I believe was a backlash, in part, from Kennedy's murder, the birth of the *Flower Child* and the neurotic conflict of being a Baby Boomer in a less innocent world.

On Friday November 20, 1964, I found myself at Harrison High School in a rural community outside of Cincinnati, teaching World History, American History and Socio-Economic Problems. I strayed from the normal curriculum on that day with all of my classes. With November 22 falling on a Sunday in 1964, this Friday, for me, was the day to remember John Kennedy and challenge my students to learn from the events of the previous November. I had mimeographed 200 copies of Mike Mansfield's eulogy. This single sheet of paper was handed to each of the more than 180 students I faced in six different classes that Friday.

I suggested that if they wanted to learn something from the President's assassination, they could find it at the end of the eulogy I had gifted to each of them. I then referred them to the bold italic print of the last three stanzas, which contained these important words from Mansfield:

He gave us of his love that we, too, in turn, might give.

He gave that we might give of ourselves, that we might give to one another
until there would be no room, no room at all,
for the bigotry, the hatred, prejudice, and the arrogance
which converged in that moment of horror to strike him down.

In leaving us — these gifts, John Fitzgerald Kennedy,
President of the United States, leaves with us.
Will we take them, Mr. President? Will we have, now, the sense
and the responsibility and the courage to take them?
I pray to God that we shall, and under God, we will.

The Beta Bells at Miami

The Washington Post

President Kennedy Shot Dead; Lyndon B. Johnson Is Sworn In

The Headline on November 23

Ruby Shoots Oswald

Jon-Jon Salutes

Black Jack in Funeral Procession

Jackie in Capitol Rotunda November 24, 1963

The Rez – Miami University Student Union

Tuffy Potter in Front of Tuffy's

1964

Hey! Can you hear me?
Are you listening? Is anyone there?
It's no use shouting, there's nobody there
NOBODY THERE, there's NOBODY THERE

From *Nobody There*
By Veronica Falls

Wrong Number

When I moved into Swing Hall as part of my recently awarded baseball scholarship in late January of 1964, you might say it was the icing on the cake for my senior year.

Our coach, Woody Wills finally decided to invest one of his available partial Grant and Aids with me the previous summer after five weeks of hard work convinced him that he could move me from center field to third base. This solved a problem for our coach who had a wealth of outfield talent and a Swiss cheese infield. To get the greatest mileage from the Athletic Scholarship Program, Woody split his five full Grant and Aids into five tuition scholarships and five room and board scholarships.

By the time the room and board grant came my way, the only option available to me at the start of the new school year was a small single room in an old, World War II two-story barracks that sat between the upper-class dormitory, Swing Hall, and the Miami Gymnasium, Withrow Court. After suffering through the heat, then the cold and ever-present noise of the leaky old clapboard structure, the call came in the mist of first semester final exams that a two person room had become available to me on the second floor of Swing Hall.

I could not get there fast enough. Ironically, and perhaps, conveniently, my good friend Jim Cloughessy, or JC as we called him, was back to school after taking a semester off to sail the Great Lakes on a merchant ship, hoping to earn enough money to finish his education.

Contrast the harshness of sailing a large tanker on Lake Ontario and Lake Erie versus sledding through one of the most beautiful college campuses ever devised by man; and, needless to say, JC was a happy camper when he returned to Miami.

Coach Wills was willing to pull a few strings with campus housing; and, the next thing we knew, JC and I were securely ensconced in room 214 of Swing Hall affording us a great view of Tuffy's Restaurant to the right, the Sigma Chi and Delta Kappa Epsilon fraternity houses to the left and the towering Beta Bells and the Administration Building straight ahead, all framed by the beauty of sprawling pin oaks and delicate dogwoods.

After two and half years at Miami, I was finally going to enjoy the full college experience as provided by dorm life. I was surrounded by a menagerie of scholarship athletes along with the greatest cast of *College Joe* characters you could hope to assemble beneath one roof.

Among my neighbors were basketball stars Charlie Cole, Charlie Dinkins, John Swann, Skip Snow, and Jerry Pierson, football standouts Tom Longsworth, Glenn Trout, the faster-than-blazes running back Scotty Tyler, and quarterback and future NFL player, Ernie Kellerman, along with my baseball teammates, Jerry Ivins, Terry Morris, Bob Richie and Steve Graf. Most of us were located on the second floor of the south wing of Swing Hall. The exception was good friend Jerry Ivins, who was bunking on the third floor of the north wing.

Only the faint of heart locked their doors at Swing Hall. This honorable lack of judgment unlocked great opportunity for college boy tomfoolery. The typical short sheeting of beds, rearrangement of things like clothing and desk contents and taping Playboy centerfolds all over the rooms of the purer of heart inmates were just some of the regular pranks. Many of the guys who had framed photos of their girlfriends perched on their desk or dresser often returned to their rooms to find that the sweetheart had been replaced by a picture of a smiling Jimmy Durante. Who would do such a thing, I will never tell?

Living at Swing Hall also afforded me an opportunity to earn a few extra shekels. I had earned the reputation of being a pretty good writer, doing sports articles for the *Miami Student,* the school newspaper. Thus, the request for term papers and other lesser assignments started to roll in. At ten bucks a pop, I was earning some serious scratch each month. Not a bad deal for a little extra work. My customers gave me the nuts and bolts of the paper, and then I made it sound like it came from a person with a brain. I offered a money back guarantee for anything less than a B. I never had to refund the fee.

My renewed main squeeze was my old high school girlfriend, Eeve Arkush, who had transferred to Miami in the fall after a year at Emory University in Atlanta. She was a very smart cookie and started taking on some of the work as the demand increased. Between the two of us, we were able to go to a lot of movies and eat out on the weekends at one of the many uptown watering holes on our earnings.

My winter routine in early 1964 was aided by a very friendly second semester schedule. Most of the heavy lifting was behind me. What I had left were mostly courses that were easy and enjoyable, and all but one class was in the morning. On Monday, Wednesday and Friday I had American Literature at 8:00AM, Modern German History at 9:00 AM, Kinesiology (an easy A) at 10:00, and English Literature at 1:00 PM. Tuesdays and Thursdays were a cakewalk, with just one class, American Diplomatic History at 9:00 AM. This left plenty of studying time with intervals for my writing business. With the exception of Kinesiology, the course work did require a lot of reading. But Eeve and I typically spent two hours at the library after dinner each night, which was more than sufficient to keep up with the course load.

Being a member of the baseball team had its requirement of playing handball for an hour twice a week. I played at 10:30 on Tuesday and Thursday mornings, usually with teammates Jerry Ivins or Steve Graf. As part of my self-imposed conditioning program, I ran the steps for 30 minutes at Withrow Court each morning before breakfast. Often, my partner for this endeavor was Miami track star Bob Schul.

Bob was a great guy who was a world-class distance runner. At every track meet that spring, he was a threat to run a four-minute mile, though he never did. Thus, he always drew a crowd when he ran. Schul was five years my senior. At 6:30 in the morning, with his advanced level of maturity, he really pushed me up and down those Withrow Court steps.

In the fall of 1963, after serving four years in the Air Force, Bob returned to Miami, where he had started his college education. Though he was running track for the Miami Redskins, in reality, he was also training to qualify for the 5,000-meter run at the 1964 Tokyo Olympics. His main challenger would be a Frenchman named Michel Jazy.

Though he still had to qualify for the Olympics later that summer, Bob had told me with great confidence how he planned to beat Jazy, hoping to finish strong from behind. And sure enough, on October 18, 1964, I sat in front of my parents' television and watched a smiling Bob Schul come from fifth position to overtake three runners and then catch and blow by Jazy in the last 100 meters. My workout friend had won a gold medal at the Tokyo Olympics.

I never had been around such a dedicated athlete as Bob Shul. After we finished running up and down the steps of Withrow, I would shower and go to breakfast. Bob would, instead, bundle up against the Ohio winter's chill and go run five miles or more. A very special guy was he.

The fun never ceased over my last semester at Miami, thanks to the cast of characters at Swing Hall and the shenanigans of my old roommates from down on the farm, Sandy Schwartz and Mike Cohen. Sandy was still living off campus, while Mike, or *Super Jew (S.J.* for short), as we had dubbed him during our sophomore year, had moved into the Zeta Beta Tau fraternity house just a short walk from Swing Hall.

Mike and I had grown up together in the Bond Hill suburb of Cincinnati and had played high school sports together at Woodward, the oldest public-school west of the Allegany Mountains. Like me, he was a "walk on" when we both transferred to Miami in the fall of 1961. He quickly became a stand out linebacker on the football team. I felt that his nickname of *Super Jew* required a special cheer. So, when he took the field for the first time in each game an assembled group of *Super Jew* fans would loudly chant my creation, "Look out on the field. It's a jeep... it's a tank... It's Super Jew! Faster than a rolling bagel, stronger than a gefilte fish, able to leap tall synagogues in a single bound. S.J.'s on the way!"

I owed S.J. a big thanks for my smooth transition from center field to third base. He and I stayed at Miami for summer school in the summer of 1963, not so much for the course work, but rather because of athletics. While Woody Wills was anxious to turn me into a third baseman, the new Miami football coach and former Miami football player, Bo Schembechler, wanted to turn Mike into a center.

So, Mike and I took two morning courses, and then, in the afternoon got quickly to work to help each other aid our respective coaches fulfill their dreams for us. Schembechler gave Mike a football, while Woody gave me a bag of used baseballs and a fungo bat. I took hundreds of under-center snaps, short snaps and long snaps from S.J, after which he would slam ground balls to me at third. At the end of five weeks, we had both honed our skills to near perfection, and I was left seriously bruised.

As it turned out, I did wind up at third base, going the entire season without making an error. Mike, on the other hand was such a good middle linebacker, Schembechler had him back at that position well before the first game of the 1963 season. Mike was *All Conference* for the next two years.

As stated, the remaining member of the old *f*armhouse quartet of 1962, Jim Cloughessy, was doing his nightly snoring in the bunk above mine in room 214.

If we had done a highlights reel from that winter and spring of my senior year, it would have included a few really hilarious events.

For example, one unusually warm starlit February evening, word spread around the dorm that football tight end Bobby Stevens had pinned his girlfriend, meaning they were auditioning each other to get engaged. In the tradition of fraternity life at the time, Bobby's fraternity brothers were scheduled to serenade him from outside his dorm at 10 o'clock. I know... It sounds like a bad Ronald Regan - June Allison movie... but it's true. Such things were still part of the campus culture in 1964.

Stevens was living at Stoddard Hall, an old three-story Federalist building that sat next to its identical twin, Elliot Hall. Stoddard and Elliot Halls were two of the three oldest buildings at Miami, located smack in the center of campus. Someone from the football team decided it would be most appropriate for a small army of Miami athletes to hunker down in the Stoddard Hall attic with a cache of water balloons. I was recruited at dinner that evening based upon the strength of my throwing arm.

By 9:45, our small legion of hurlers was crouched down next to the two attic windows positioned right above Stevens' third floor room. Right on time, the brothers of Sigma Chi strolled up *Slant Walk,* which cut a long diagonal through the center of campus, singing like the Tabernacle Choir. They stopped just beneath us.

Mike Cohen (SJ) was acting as commander of the troops. At what he deemed to be the perfect time; Mike whispered "Commence fire!"

With that, the heavy bombing rained down on the unsuspecting frat boys neatly attired in sport coats with the Sigma Chi crest sewed on the breast pockets. The singing stopped and the cussing started. Sigma Chis were running amok in all directions.

Our little army scattered down the back steps of Stoddard as the Sigma Chis hurried up the front stairway. We quickly disappeared into the darkness, ironically passing by the Sigma Chi House before rushing back to the second floor of Swing Hall.

The evening had provided a good soaking of the brothers and a hardy laugh for the jock platoon. As it turned out, my teammate, Ed Kemp, who was one of the drenched Sigma Chis, confided in me the next morning at breakfast, that, while they didn't know who the culprits were, they strongly suspected the boys from Delta Kappa Epsilon (Dekes), the fraternity that sat next door to the Sigma Chi House. I am proud to say that I was able to contain myself while agreeing with Ed that the Dekes were known for their regular outlandish pranks. This information played very well on the second floor of Swing Hall later that day. As they say, *mum's the word,* or in this case—*Deke's* the word.

As funny as that was, the night Scotty Tyler was set up as the butt of the joke was even better. Scotty, a star running back on the football team, was the perfect selection for our next little monkeyshine. He could run like the wind. He also had a thing for naked coeds.

The scheme started at dinner when a couple of Scotty's teammates told him that there was this really hot girl who dressed for bed every night in front of her wide open third floor dorm room window. The room, Scotty was told, sat conveniently directly across from the top of the football stadium. The only question was whether or not he would take the bait. He did.

About twenty of us had positioned ourselves at the south end of the stadium, sufficiently out of site. Three of the culprits were Air Force ROTC members and had dressed in their uniforms making them look like Campus Security Police in the dark of night. They were armed with major league flashlights.

We all stood there waiting in the obscure stadium shadows, bundled against the early March wintry chill. I suppose that the groundhog had seen his shadow in Punxsutawney, Pennsylvania a month earlier.

Sure enough, here came Scotty looking from left to right as he tiptoed up the Miami Field stadium steps. When he reached the top, he moved back and forth searching for the alleged window.

The three ROTC boys, including my teammate, left-handed pitcher, Adam Polacek, jumped onto the track flashing their lights at Scotty and yelling at the top of their lungs, "Hey you. What are you doing up there?" Come down from there. You're under arrest!"

Tyler, after his eyes had ratcheted out of and then back into his head, took off across the top of the stadium like a scared rabbit. He then took a quick left going down the steps three at a time. When he reached the bottom, he leaped from the landing that was about eight feet high almost clearing the track and fell into a heap. For a second, I held my breath, certain that he had seriously injured himself. Had we caused the star running back to break his leg just weeks before spring football practice was scheduled to start? Well, if so, at least he may well have set a new long jump record.

Fortunately, Scotty gathered himself to his feet and limped across the field with the ROTC troop in fake pursuit. He either recovered or the adrenaline kicked in, as he found his well-documented speed and was gone into the dark.

Like Scotty Tyler, I had a close call that might have jeopardized my senior baseball season the night Mohammad Ali (still Cassius Clay at the time) won the World Heavy Weight Boxing Title. The buildup to the fight had a lot of hype by 1964 standards. This was due in part to the emergence of television coverage of sports and sports figures. But the real reason was the belligerent braggadocio of Clay, who had won the Light Heavy Weight Gold Medal at the 1960 Rome Olympics.

He turned pro almost immediately after his victory in Rome and started knocking off one contender after the other, often correctly predicting the round in which he would finish off his opponent. With each win he accelerated his bluster and was soon dubbed *The Louisville Lip*.

Thus, there was great excitement leading up to the February 5th match with the current champion, Sonny Liston. Liston was the total antithesis of Clay. He said little and had a scowl that was icy and mean. That glare clearly translated into, *I don't mean to beat you; I plan to kill you.* By all appearances, Clay was unfazed.

A group of us planned to listen to the fight in the room of Jerry Ivins and his roommate, Walt Kelsey, who occupied a larger than normal corner chamber on the third floor of Swing Hall. Walt was running a pool with an ante fee of a quarter. For two bits you could pick one of 30 small pieces of paper from Walt's hat each of which had a number and a letter on it. If, you picked the piece that said C-6, as I had, it meant you had Clay winning in the sixth round. Everybody wanted the scrap of paper that said L-1 believing Clay would be dead inside two minutes.

The Tuesday night fight was scheduled for 10:00 PM eastern standard time in Miami Florida. It wasn't broadcast on television, as the big moneymaker in 1964 was closed circuit bookings at large theaters, but it was aired on ABC radio with Les Keiter at the microphone. A not so well-known New York attorney named Howard Cosell was providing commentary, or what we today call *color*. He and the future Mohammad Ali became a perfect storm of personalities, each gaining great notoriety thanks to the other.

Also involved in the broadcast that night was Cleveland Brown running back Jim Brown, a mentor to Clay, and former undefeated Heavy weight champ, Rocky Marciano.

As described by Keiter, and to everyone's surprise, Clay controlled the first four rounds, using his superior quickness to avoid Liston's famed left hook while landing effective jabs to a frustrated Liston.

Then in the fifth round, Keiter and a squawking Howard Cosell both excitedly reported that Clay kept rubbing his eyes, and seemed to be having trouble seeing. It was later reported that Liston's gloves had some sort of substance on them that had gotten into Clay's eyes.

They reported that Clay seemed OK again in the sixth round (my round in the pool). The round came to an end with the surprise that, so far, Clay seemed to be winning. They advised us that Liston had a cut beneath his eye while Clay was dancing around in his corner waiting for the start of round seven.

Then we heard Keiter scream, "Wait a minute, wait a minute. Sonny Liston is not coming out. It's all over. Liston is not coming out for the seventh round!"

After that, it was all Cosell and Clay doing their shtick. Clay was exclaiming over and over "I am the greatest, I am the greatest, I told you. Give me justice. I am king of the world!"

Cosell asked, "Did you ever believe it?"

Clay came right back with, "I told you if you want to go to heaven, I'll take him in seven!"

I thought for a second that I had won the pool with Clay winning in the sixth. Then I heard Clay say, "seven."

As it turned out, it officially was a TKO in the seventh round, and Marv Lieterbeck, who didn't know a catcher's glove from a boxing glove had won the pool, not me.

Where the night really went wrong for me was when Walt Kelsey suggested a handstand contest. Five us entered to see who could do the longest handstand. My roommate, JC went first and was able to stay on his hands for a measly and wobbly six seconds. Jerry Ivins went next and lasted 52 seconds.

Then came my turn. I tipped myself up onto my hands and held on through 15 seconds, then 30 seconds, now being forced to walkabout in order to maintain my balance. At 45 seconds it really started to come apart and two seconds later I was through.

Now, totally disoriented, I came down a bit sideways crashing my left foot on the corner of Walt Kelsey's desk. No, I didn't see stars, but I do think I saw a couple of planets. The result was two broken toes on my left foot. This was not good with baseball practice scheduled to begin in six days.

I dared not allow Coach Wills to find out this piece of news. At the infirmary, they wrapped my toes tightly, gave me some crutches and advised me to wear hard sole shoes.

There was no way I would be able to log in for handball on Thursday. This would get Woody's attention by Friday. I would plead the need to study, hoping my coach would buy that excuse. I dare not let him see me tooling around campus on crutches, so I took to wearing a pair of really ugly brown wing tips that had not seen the light of day the entire school year. They were ugly but they helped. For the next five days, I was able to limp around without the crutches and fortunately never ran into my coach.

By the following Monday, my foot was much better. However, in spikes, running sprints was not fun. That damned foot still had a twinge of pain when the baseball season started in late March. Fortunately, I pushed off with my other foot when batting and throwing. Woody never knew, and I had a really great season at third base.

As to the litany of pranks at Swing Hall that spring, the one that remains the clearest in my mind's eye involved a Korean exchange student and a telephone.

The Korean was a very nice and confused young man form Seoul named "Tommy" Rhee. We were never sure where the name "Tommy" came from. However, we did know that it was not his real first name, but rather a selection he and his family had made to make his yearlong visit to the

United States less stressful, a common practice for visiting Asians.

Tommy was short, studious, and predictably gullible. Some of the nonsense he endured from self-involved white boys bordered on the edge of abuse. That said, it was very entertaining to hear Tommy talk. He had the predictable "R" "L" issue associated at the time with Chinese and other Asian folks. He also inserted a lot of "R's" where they didn't exist.

Tommy roomed two doors down from Jerry Ivins on the third floor of Swing Hall. His roommate was Marv Lieterbeck, who had won the Clay/Liston pool of $7.50. Marv was a perfect roommate, and American host, for the visiting Korean. Lieterbeck hailed from University Heights, Ohio a suburb of Cleveland. He was a well-dressed, shy but friendly milquetoast, who was at Miami on a full academic scholarship taking a pre-med curriculum. I immediately sensed upon meeting the roommates that Marv was dedicated to making Tommy's year at Miami as rewarding as possible. Marv was a surrogate ambassador to South Korea that year, and Tommy was a lucky guy to have landed Marv as a roommate.

As it were to evolve, Marv was dating a very smart and very studious, if somewhat frumpy, girl from Brooklyn. Her name was Abbie Wasserman. Being from Brooklyn, she was a lot edgier than Marv. She ruled the roost in the relationship. Abbie's roommate was another studious frumpster from Chicago named Elaine Goldman.

Before you could say lickety split, Marv, Tommy, Abbie and Elaine were getting educated, as a group, faster than any foursome on campus. The cumulative IQ within that band of brainiacs was off the charts. Tommy was so enchanted with Elaine, he may have been thinking of converting to Judaism though he was still expounding upon the assets of Buddhism around the dorm.

A noticeable routine had developed with Tommy by the Ides of March. Tommy and Elaine would study every night. All women at Miami had to live in a dormitory and had to be safely behind locked doors by 10:00 PM on Sunday through Thursday. After Tommy had deposited Elaine at McBride Hall in the East Quad, he would scamper back to the third floor of Swing Hall, deposit his books in his room and then go directly to the doorless phone booth that sat just outside the corner room of Jerry Ivins and Walt Kelsey.

Having taken note of this predictable behavior pattern, Walt Kelsey said to Jerry, Mike Cohen, Sandy Schwartz, Jim Cloughessy and me, who had all gathered into his room one night, "You know if we were to unscrew the mouth piece on that phone and take the little microphone out and then screw the mouth piece back on, the person at the other end of that phone wouldn't be able to hear a thing Tommy has to say."

We all processed this at our individual paces, with Sandy being the first to smile a reaction. We all eventually caught up with Walt and Sandy. Yep, we agreed, that could be pretty interesting.

There was no point in wasting time. At 9:55 that night, Walt walked to the phone and preformed the mic extraction. Then we all sat and waited. Like clockwork, Tommy burst through the third-floor stairway door down the hall at 10:08. Within seconds he had waived a quick hello at us and we then heard him deposit his nickel and dial the phone.

After a few more heartbeats we heard Tommy say, "Herro. May I spreak to Eraine Gorman prease?"

Silence… then, "Herro. Eraine Gorman prease. Herro Herro! Is anrybodry thele? Herro Herro Herro." More silence followed by a much louder and forceful Tommy now screaming, "Herro!! Herro!! Is anrybodry thele?

He slammed the phone down. We heard him drop in another nickel and dial again.

"Ah, herro, may I spreak with Eraine Gorman prease."

Silence followed by, "Herro."

A pause then, "Herro, Herro. All you thele? Is anrybodry thele? Can you heal me?"

This time he slammed the phone back on the hook and screamed "Ah fruck!!"

"What da fruck is long with dis phrone?"

At this point everybody in the room unraveled into uncontrollable laughter.

"What's so frucking frunny? I tlying to carr Eraine and da rady at McBlide dat answel da phrone just keep saying herro, den she hang up da phrone," Tommy yelled in our direction as he headed to his room and slammed the door.

The truth was that none of us had ever seen Tommy show any anger, much less hear him curse, since the day he showed up on campus.

I believe the only two people in the room that was feeling any sense of guilt or regret were J.C. and me. J.C. being Catholic could blow up his guilt with a quick trip to confession. I, on the other hand, would have to manage this curious pang of conscience that always invaded my psyche when I was around negative vibes. In this case, I was partly responsible, but even if I had not been, there was something in me that created an instant sense of remorse.

This same routine was repeated the next two nights, with Tommy getting more and more agitated. He threw out a lot of "frucks" throughout the three-night main event.

Finally, Walt Kelsey walked down to Tommy's room, with Jerry and me right behind, and handed our little Korean friend the mic, explaining what we had done. To his credit, Tommy took it like a real trooper and was willing to laugh at the prank and move on. I'm not sure any of us could have behaved with the same level of maturity.

After digesting the joke, he smiled and said, "Horry shrit. I courdn't undelstand why dat rady at McBlide Harr courdn't heal me. Velly frunny guys."

I don't know whatever happened to Tommy and have often wondered how his life back in Korea evolved. But I can tell you that often, when I get together with Jerry Ivins or Jim Cloughessy, those three nights come up in the conversation as a memory highlight of our semester together at Swing Hall. I'm pretty sure Tommy never became a Jew.

Swing Hall – Miami University

Stoddard Hall – Miami University

Old Miami Field

A Smiling Bob Schul Takes the Gold in Tokyo October 18, 1964

Sorry Tommy

1964

It isn't enough to hope
It isn't enough to dream
It isn't enough to plot & plan & scheme
It isn't enough to stand here
Saying that life is grand here
Waiting for something good to turn up
It isn't enough to sit here
Having a purple fit here
Worried to death the world will burn up
It isn't enough to hope
It isn't enough to dream
I've got a better answer
I've got a better scheme
Why not wish upon a wishbone
Pick a four leaved clover
Rub a rabbits foot & throw a horseshoe over
Your lucky shoulder
You'll find before you're very much older
A bit of luck will come your way
Now isn't that enough to make your day
From *It Isn't Enough*
By Anthony Newley

Looking Back

I have chosen to end my little sojourn to the past in the year, 1964. Why, one might ask? Well, I have always looked at the summer of that year as a clear line of demarcation of when my childhood ended and my adulthood officially began. So, it feels right.

My last term at Miami was my finest. I had my best semester in the classroom with a 3.8 grade point average while making the Dean's list. I was the Captain of the Miami baseball team, starting at third base while attracting interest from a couple of Major League scouts. At Tuffy's on campus, and uptown, at the dry cleaners, Jack's Corner Clothing Store, Minnis' Drugs and Al & Larry's Bar, a publicity photo of me hung, dressed in our home-team uniform, striking a pose of the confident batter ready to take the next pitch long.

Yes, I had chosen well… Miami University had given me all I could have hoped to find in the pursuit of growth, education and happiness.

The now famous Freedom Summer, was front and center in Oxford the week I graduated, especially at adjacent Western College, where young people were being trained to head to southern states to register African-American voters. Sadly, among those there that week included James Chaney, Michael Schwerner and Andrew Goodman, who were assassinated later that summer in Mississippi.

I was enjoying some of the best friendships of my young life. And the girl I thought I loved was in two of my classes and sported a diamond engagement ring I had offered to her on my twenty-first birthday.

I had accepted a teaching job at Harrison High School, twenty miles west of Cincinnati. In the fall I would be teaching American History, World History, Socio-economic Problems as well as being the Head Baseball Coach, the Freshman Basketball Coach and the faculty advisor to the school's only foreign exchange student. All of that would reward me with an astounding $5,350 for the school year, or just slightly more than my father was making at Fifth Third Bank after almost forty years of dedicated service.

In order to get my so-called adult life quickly out of the starting gate, my good friend and teammate Jerry Ivins and I had accepted jobs as counselors at a camp in the Catskills for the summer. We had received several job offers, choosing Camp Hillcroft in Lagrangeville, New York, where, ironically Andrew Goodman had once been a camper.

I graduated on June 7, 1964; a bright sunny Sunday afternoon. The ceremony took place at the football stadium, with author, Fletcher Knebel, giving the commencement address. He had recently published *Seven Days in May*, a wildly popular book about nuclear intrigue that was made into a movie starring Kirk Douglas, Ava Gardner and Burt Lancaster.

I remember that Knebel was a very good speaker. But frankly, I cannot tell you much of what he said to the Class of 1964 that day. What I can tell you is that I marched into that stadium with a deep joy and calm pride in becoming the first college graduate in my family. And I exited that same place less than two hours later with a sudden fear and realization that something very special had ended. The joyfulness had been replaced with the panicked thought, *Ok, hot shot, what the hell are you going to do now?*

To be honest, I still haven't figured that out. Like my youth, my adult life has been a series of mostly accidental events that I could never have envisioned. What I do know, is that whatever success and happiness I have enjoyed since that June day in 1964 has been born out of hard work and submitting to the better angels in me. And my many failures resulted when I reverted to laziness and losing my way at times.

For me, my youth was like a sweet gooey mix of events that my adulthood baked into a big delicious cake that has provided the luscious taste of those days every time I have taken a small bite of that memory-iced confection.

The route Jerry and I took to the Catskills took us through Washington, DC, New York City and finally up to Camp Hillcroft. Washington was exciting. Our teammate, Steve Graf was the son of the Chief of Staff of an Ohio Congressman. He got the three of us seats in the Senate gallery the day they voted on the 1964 Civil Rights Bill, where we heard Barry Goldwater give an impassioned speech against the bill. Afterwards we stood just feet away from Goldwater on the Capitol steps as he was interviewed by NBC's Edwin Newman.

We also visited the new grave of John F. Kennedy at Arlington Cemetery, where the eternal flame burned a sad reminder of the assassination the previous November.

In New York we attended the 1964 World's Fair for a dazing two and a half days. For me, the most impressive memory there was of the eloquently carved white Carrera marble *Pieta* by Michelangelo.

We also visited the famed Peppermint Lounge where we met three innocent girls from Grosse Isle Michigan. This led to a certain amount of mischief with the girls and a member of a rock group called the Rip Chords who had a hit record, *Hey Little Cobra,* at the time. They were scheduled to do a concert at Palisades Park across the Hudson from New York City. The night of the concert a fireworks barge blew up on the Hudson providing another deeply etched memory.

After all of that early excitement, a short drive up the Taconic State Parkway delivered Jerry and me at the front gate to Camp Hillcroft. In simple terms, the next eight weeks were exhilarating, educational and a major boost to opening the world to me.

The camp had been started in 1950 by Louis and Frieda Buttinger, who had fled the Nazis in their homeland of Austria early in World War II. Their story was not unlike that of the famous Von Trapp Family of the *Sound of Music,* in that they had narrowly escaped across the Alps into Switzerland and eventually immigrated to America.

Most of the campers were from ultra-rich families from New York City. For example, one lad in my bunkhouse that summer was John Mankiewicz, nephew of Joseph Mankiewicz, who had directed the 1964 movie *Cleopatra.*

John went on to become a

television and film executive producer and screenwriter. He was co-executive producer for *House of Cards* and *Bosch,* he co-created the television series *The Street* and has written and produced episodes for *House M.D.* and occasionally writes for *The New Yorker.* He was a special young man in 1964.

The staff was interesting and diverse, with seventeen countries represented, allowing me to learn about South Africa, Turkey, Italy, Spain, Australia, The Netherlands and North Korea, to name a few. Among the American counselors on staff were two very interesting Jewish girls from New York City, who were both former campers.

Addie Reed, was a University of Wisconsin student who had a small role in the film *David and Lisa* the previous year. She became Jerry's main squeeze for that summer. The second young lady of particular interest was Karen Streisand, cousin of the newly famous singer and Tony winner, Barbra Streisand.

Karen came to the University of Cincinnati in the fall of 1964. She was anxious to meet a nice Cincinnati-bred Jewish boy. So, I fixed her up with my old pal Sandy "The Schvantz" Schwartz. That did not go well, but the Schvantz bragged for years about his one failed date with Barbra Streisand's cousin.

That summer at Hillcroft provided everything, and more, that I had hoped it might. While I might have been honing my baseball skills with the Bismarck (North Dakota) Class A affiliate of the Minnesota Twins, I have no regrets in choosing, rather, to hone my interpersonal skills near Billings (New York) with the Buttingers and their special summer place.

I have only one regret from that summer. My old friend, Pete Rose, then playing second base for the Cincinnati Reds, had secured for me four tickets for a New York Mets double-header against the Philadelphia Phillies on June 21 (Father's Day). With two extra tickets, Jerry and I asked the afore-mentioned Michigan coeds to join us. To lure them to come along, we agreed to go to the World's Fair, just across from Shea Stadium, first and then head to the ballpark for the second game.

Big, big mistake. Philadelphia's Jim Bunning, pitched a perfect game in game one, while we played footsies in a boat ride called "It's a Small World." And, indeed, it seemed small that day. Just a half mile away in Flushing Meadows, Bunning pitched only the eighth perfect game in baseball history. And, I had four tickets to see it, neatly tucked away in my back pocket. That was a "live and learn" moment that is still a bit painful to this day. Oh well.

At the end of the summer, Jerry and I were prepared to leave Hillcroft in the late afternoon of Wednesday August 26th, after helping to pack campers into their parents' cars or one of two chartered buses that would take some back to New York City. There were lots of hugs and handshakes exchanged between the departing counselors.

I sought out Louis and Frieda Buttinger to thank them for a wonderful experience. Louie surprised me by thanking me for organizing a mock Republican Convention in mid-July. He had been against the idea when I first suggested it, pointing out that most of the campers came from rather liberal New York homes.

I had argued that the Republican race that year provided more interesting lessons than did the uncontested Democratic Convention. So, to assure diversity, I recommended that we include a slate of Barry Goldwater (who became the ultimate nominee), New York Governor Nelson Rockefeller, Pennsylvania Governor William Scranton and Maine Senator Margaret Chase Smith. Smith was a major stretch in 1964, as the thought of a woman President then was way outside the realm of reality.

Finally, with the enthusiastic urging of Frieda and their son Dennis, who was the head counselor in my bunkhouse, Louis capitulated.

After choosing four campers to assume the roles of the candidates, there was campaigning, signs, and speeches. Each camper was a delegate with credentials produced in the camp printshop. After a week of campaigning the stage was set. We held the convention in the camp's small gym.

On the evening of July 16th, while Barry Goldwater was being nominated at the Cow Palace in San Francisco, William Scranton took the prize in the Catskills. The whole process turned out to be an enthusiastic success.

To have Louis Buttinger, a brave soul who had escaped the Nazis, found his way to America and started his special camp, grasp my hand and thank me for teaching him the importance of maintaining an open mind, provided the perfect ending to my special summer.

Jerry and I drove through the night, twice stopping to nap in the car. I finally pulled up in front of our home on Grafton Avenue at 5:30 to find My father putting out his famous "NO PARKING" signs at the curb. As it turned out the Beatles were appearing at the Cincinnati Gardens that evening. Big events at the Gardens frequently found some folks, looking to save fifty-cents for parking, using Grafton Avenue as a convenient two block, money saving walk alternative. Dad's signs never worked, but he always tried. A long day's night, you might say.

And with that I had bookended my youth. Teachers were adults. And on Tuesday September 8th, I became both, when I walked into room 110 at Harrison High School, looked at the 28 Juniors in my homeroom, picked up a fresh piece of chalk and wrote on the blackboard behind my desk in bold caps, MR. STERTMEYER, I officially becoming a teacher.

Memories are a curious thing. Scientist suggest that recording a memory requires adjusting the connections between billions of neurons. Each new event tweaks some small subset of those neurons.

Psychologist, Sir Fredric Bartlett submits that remembering, "is more like making up a story than reading one. Each memory is a blend of knowledge and inference."

There is no doubt that memory is malleable. But this I can say with great conviction; there are certain stimuli to my senses, whether it is sound, smell, taste, feel or visual, that spark the most live, real recollections from my youth.

For example, I can still smell my mother's beef tongue or hassenpfeffer cooking on the stovetop. And there is her matzo pudding, beignets, egg dumplings, banana cream pie and homemade goetta, all gone with her, but still lingering on my well-trained taste buds. To this day, I can hear the flapping of freshly washed sheets blowing in the breeze on the backyard clothesline; or the sound of the garage door opening in our basement garage; or the squeaky hum of the "test pattern" on our 13" Philco TV after the 11:00 news; or the irresistible aroma of my Grandma Emma's baking, luring us up to her second floor Newport apartment on Friday afternoons.

And, there is the click and crack of the record changer on Aunt Lois' Victrola as it dropped a new 78 RPM single onto the turntable. Though the Cincinnati Reds haven't used the tune for over 50 years, the strains of *El Capitan* introducing an afternoon ballgame as described my Waite Hoyt, still rings true in my ear.

Then there is the feel of making contact with a Rawlings baseball as I swung a Louisville Slugger on Miami Field and the sound of that same ball slapping into the well-oiled pocket of my glove down at third base.

How is it possible that I can still recall the exact slushy sound of the engine on my 1949 Dodge Coronet as it turned over with the push of the dashboard starter button?

I still can easily pull up from the memory bank the unique giggle of my Father the banker. Equally available is the deep voice of my surrogate father, Bip Bohl chatting us up from the third base coach's box with his one-of-a-kind "Herp berp sha berp, 'mon babe."

Of course, the sounds from the movies still live on, so close to the surface, including my two favorite pieces of music, *Moonlight Serenade* from that old Victrola in the '40s and again in *The Glenn Miller Story* in the '50s as well as *Chopin's Nocturne in E-Flat Major* that I first heard my mother play on her baby grand and again when featured in *The Eddy Duchin Story,* both movies seen at the Twentieth Century Theater in Oakley. The smell and taste of the "world's best ever" popcorn at that theater is something I still reminisce about with Fred Zigler. Yes, I can still taste that as well.

And while you no longer see wood-framed screen doors like the one my Grandpa Lou built on the side entrance at 3315 Spokane Avenue from my youth, the sound of its spring stretching each time I pushed through it and the corresponding bang the door made as it closed itself, lives on. Of course, Aunt Win's tardy command when she heard the spring stretch, "Don't let that door slam, young man," quickly followed by the predictable whack of door meeting the frame still brings a smile... Sorry Aunt Win.

I last helped my grandfather shovel coal in the winter of 1953. Yet the sound of that coal sliding down the shoot into the basement bin hasn't left me.

So many other things continue to tumble around in my head just waiting for the right stimulus to pry them loose.

The echoey click of women's high-heel shoes on the travertine floor of the second-floor lobby of the Fifth Third Bank at 4th and Walnut Streets is readily available.

The voices of Gabby Hayes, Andy Devine, Jimmy Dodd, Ozzie Nelson, Peter Lorre, Clark Gable, Donna Reed, Martha Rae, Waite Hoyt, Mell Allen and so many more still ring true in my ear.

Some events seem to reside near the surface and come back so easily, including, Nick's ice cream wagon and his lack of tuttie-fruity; or bringing my new-born cousin Paul home from the hospital in 1948; or the day we moved to Bond Hill in 1953; or my first homerun at Miami in 1963.

Yes, I can still conjure up the aroma of the Maxwell House daily perk in Aunt Win's kitchen, the distinct difference between the smell of corned beef and pastrami at the Temple Deli and Big Boys and fries at Frisch's, the fragrances of Eua de Joy, so popular among the girls I dated and English Leather, Canoe and Old Spice, so popular with us manly men of the day, not to mention the less-than-pleasant, yet inspiring, stench of the Miami team locker room.

Perhaps, it is the memory-bank foundation built out of great youthful friendships that I cherish the most.

Like me, all of my supporting cast, grew up and moved on. Some have remained very close while others have disappeared.

From the Spokane years Chris Goebbel moved in the mid 50s to Ft. Worth and evaporated into that famous Texas thin air.

However, Neil Van Outer, after moving from Spokane Avenue in 1952, reappeared in my life ten years later at Miami University, where we quickly renewed our friendship. Neil married Jan Bertram, one of the sweetest young ladies from my Woodward class of '60. They built their life together in Lexington Kentucky.

My very first pal, my cousin Jay Pittroff, had a very successful business career in Columbus Ohio. He is retired living with his wife Michelle in the Columbus suburb of Dublin. We remain close after all these years.

The Grafton years list is larger. That guy I met the first day I moved to Bond Hill in 1953 remains my best friend. Fred Zigler graduated from the University of Cincinnati and went on to a very successful career as a Senior Investment Officer at banks, large investment firms and the Ohio Department of Workman's Compensation. Always an entrepreneur, he operates *Ski Cincinnati* that sells Cincinnati-related shirts, hats and pins. Taking a page from his father, Fred is also an accomplished artist. Several of his works hang in my home.

My other true brother, Sandy Schwartz, graduated from Miami in 1965 and became a teacher and coach. While I was coaching the boys' soccer team at Indian Hill High School, Sandy was the girls' soccer coach there. He spent his career in building materials sales, including a stint working with me in the 1970s. Sadly, he passed away in 2018. I should point out that living the dream of most of my Jewish friends, Sandy married two *Shiksas.*

Eddie Wikas studied pharmacy at the University of Cincinnati and has practiced the profession ever since. We remain in regular contact and I have visited him often in Scottsdale when there on business. Of course, Ed married a *Shiksa*.

Wally Bohl graduated near the top of our class at Woodward and went on the University of Cincinnati to study engineering. He spent many years working at the Kenner Toy Company in Cincinnati. Wally, Fred, old friend Sid Lieberman and I still share a chili three-way at Skyline, a Cincinnati institution, on a regular basis.

Carl Schiele graduated from Purdue University. Our mothers communicated regularly into the late 1980s. Since then, Carl has gone missing. But I believe he lives in Michigan.

The gentle giant, Mike Cohen (Super Jew) left us way too soon. After graduating from Miami in 1965, Mike married (you guessed it) a *Shiksa* and moved to California where he became a teacher and coach. I am sad to report that he had a heart attack and passed away at the age of 50. What a great guy to lose so early? Fortunately, we did connect the year before he died, talking at length about our days at Miami.

Jim (JC) Cloughessy graduated from Miami in 1965, served in the U.S. Army and moved early in his life to Phoenix where he had a very successful distribution business. After retiring he moved to Prescott. As with Ed, I was often able to visit with JC when business took me his way. I am sad to report that after a valiant four-year battle with cancer, JC passed away in June 2020. A special friend was he.

Jerry Ivins, like Sandy, Mike and JC, graduated from Miami in 1965. Without a degree in Education, he became a teacher. And before you could say *McGuffey Reader*, Jerry had a Ph. D. in Education and was the head of curriculum for the Northwest School District in Cincinnati and teaching at the University of Cincinnati. I introduced Jerry to his wife Joyce, a coworker of mine at the Hamilton County Welfare Department. They are two of the finest people I know.

And what happened to me? Well, as the old saying goes, "that is another story."

In the mid 60s we all scattered, no longer connected by school and suddenly separated by work, marriage and raising children of our own.

On a recent trip back to Cincinnati, I visited my old Walnut Hills neighborhood. As I drove past the Spokane Avenue house that, in my memory, represented the start for me, I was filled with a clear vision of the place from where I had come, as well as who I had become.

Looking at the dilapidated three-story, two-family white frame house of my early youth I was thankful that I had faired far better than it had. I had once heard that in the 1970's it had housed six families, not two. Though it appeared as though it might crumble at any second, I was filled with gratitude for the warmth, security, and happiness that this tired old abode had provided so long ago. It seemed more like home than ever. The same was true of the house in which my mother and her sisters were raised just eight doors down the one block street in Walnut Hills.

Both had been beat to hell over the sixty years since I had left, for what my family thought would be a better life in a new, more modern neighborhood.

I have often wondered about the many folks my old house has sheltered since my departure in 1953. I suspect that the place had not blessed them with the same wonderful start it had provided to me. Were there others out there that held sweet memories of the place that could match mine? Not likely.

And, ironically, within clear view of our dining room window of that old hose sits the United Jewish Cemetery where my Great Grandmother five times removed, Yetta Gross, is interred. I first discovered her grave just a few years ago. Her marker informs that she was born in Germany on March 16, 1814 and passed away on April 22, 1881. That is the sum total of what I know about her. How I wish some of her life stories were available.

But I have immodestly herein attempted to record some of my tales of youth. They are written primarily for the purpose of leaving to future generations a snap shot of what I believe was a special time, recognizing that it was anything but special for many. Fear, anger and hate are very prominent human traits. And, I am not particularly proud that my generation has not done more to eradicate the human scourge attached to those natural emotions.

What I can say is that I know how lucky I was. For that, I am most grateful. Looking back, as a student of history, I believe the creative arts are our greatest weapon.

As Friedrich Nietzsche said, "The man who is responsive to artistic stimuli reacts to the reality of dreams as does the philosopher to the reality of existence; he observes closely, and he enjoys his observation: for it is out of these images that he interprets life, out of these processes that he trains himself for life."

And as Anthony Newley wrote in his Broadway musical, *The Roar of the Greasepaint-The Smell of the Crowd:*

Fresh as an April morning,
Soft as a tulip's tongue,

Clear as the gleam of a mountain stream;
Warm as a summer sunrise,
Sweet as an evening breeze,
Pure as a note from a songbird's throat,
Rich as the green of the trees,
Strong as the bite of a frosty night,
Bold as a big bass band,
Keen as a bean or a young sardine—
Not very keen to be canned,
Bright as a newborn bluebell,
New as a song unsung,
Free as the breeze on the seven seas;
That's what it is to be young!!

And now, to quote my lifelong buddy, Bugs Bunny, *THAT'S ALL FOLKS!!*

About the Author

Randy Stertmeyer was born and raised in Cincinnati, Ohio. He is a graduate of Miami University, Oxford, Ohio with a Bachelor of Science degree in Education and of Xavier University, Cincinnati, Ohio with a Masters of Arts degree in History.

Randy spent a long career with several executive positions in the building materials industry including serving as President and CEO of both Green River American Hardwood and SureLock Industries. After retiring in 2012, he joined Communicators International, Inc., an advertising/public relations firm, as their COO.

Randy has two children, Scott and Allison, two step-sons, Lee and Gene, and nine grandchildren.

He resides in The Villages, Florida with his wife, Peggy.

Made in the USA
Columbia, SC
15 March 2024